INTERNATIONAL SERIES IN PHYSICS

LEE A. DuBRIDGE, Consulting Editor

MICROWAVE TRANSMISSION

This book is produced in full compliance with the government's regulations for conserving paper and other essential materials.

INTERNATIONAL SERIES IN PHYSICS

LEE A. DuBRIDGE, *Consulting Editor*

Dr. F. K. Richtmyer was consulting editor of the series from its
inception in 1929 until his death in 1939.

MICROWAVE TRANSMISSION

BY

J. C. SLATER

Professor of Physics, Massachusetts Institute of Technology

FIRST EDITION
EIGHTH IMPRESSION

McGRAW-HILL BOOK COMPANY, INC.
NEW YORK AND LONDON
1942

MICROWAVE TRANSMISSION

COPYRIGHT, 1942, BY THE
McGRAW-HILL BOOK COMPANY, INC.

PRINTED IN THE UNITED STATES OF AMERICA

PREFACE

Microwaves are electromagnetic waves of wave lengths that we may take, for definiteness, to be between 1 centimeter and 1 meter. They are unique in the whole range of electromagnetic waves, a range that extends from the longest radio waves to the shortest x-rays and gamma rays: they are the only electromagnetic waves whose wave length is of the order of magnitude of ordinary laboratory apparatus. This feature makes possible experimental methods that are completely different from those used for any other type of electromagnetic wave; only sound waves, which likewise have wave lengths comparable with ordinary apparatus, present a close analogy. This book describes the general theory underlying the methods actually used for transmitting microwaves from point to point, from the generator in which they are produced to the receiver in which they are detected, with the intermediate stage of radiation from one antenna and absorption by another antenna. This transmission generally takes place in the interior of a hollow conductor, either in a hollow pipe or in a coaxial line, which is the hollow space between two concentric cylindrical conductors. It is the short wave length of the microwaves that makes such transmission possible; in a hollow pipe, in particular, only those waves can be transmitted effectively whose wave lengths are comparable with the diameter of the pipe. Not only is transmission through a hollow line possible for microwaves; it is practically imperative. The reason is that waves transmitted along ordinary, nonenclosed transmission lines, such as parallel wires, radiate more and more vigorously as their lengths become smaller, until in the microwave range the radiation would be intolerably large. In an enclosed transmission line, on the contrary, radiation is impossible, except from antennas, horns, or other devices open to empty space and designed expressly as radiators.

An extensive theory of transmission lines has been built up, based on the ordinary ideas of electric circuits. Much of this theory can be carried over to the theory of microwave transmission, which is outlined in the first chapter.   Microwave problems differ from ordinary circuit problems, however, in that much more attention must be focused on the electromagnetic field. Maxwell's equations underlie the study of electromagnetic fields and are the basis of the treatment in this book.   Much of the work is devoted to finding out how far the simple circuit methods are really justified by the more correct methods of Maxwell's equations and how these simple methods must be supplemented. In this book the emphasis has been more on the fundamental theory than on practical applications.   Enough description of practical methods has been given, however, so that the experimental worker in the field will find that he can tie theory and experiment together without great difficulty.

No other text dealing exclusively with microwaves is at present available, and the author has tried to write a book of an intermediate range of difficulty.   No previous knowledge of microwaves is assumed, but some acquaintance with classical electromagnetic theory and Maxwell's equations is necessary.   These are familiar to the physicist and to the electrical engineer trained in communications, and they are treated in many well-known texts.   For the sake of those whose knowledge of electromagnetic theory is small, however, Maxwell's equations and the small amount of vector analysis used are introduced in a fairly elementary manner.   The first-year graduate student or the senior with good training in electricity should be able to handle the work, and an extensive mathematical knowledge is not assumed. On the other hand, the book is definitely not a simple descriptive treatment of microwaves, such as would appeal to the ordinary undergraduate.   Microwave transmission is such a new subject that the workers in the field, as well as students, should be interested in a book like the present one, bringing together considerable material that has been developed largely during the last 10 years and is now available only in the periodical literature, such as the *Proceedings of the Institute of Radio Engineers*, the *Bell System Technical Journal*, the *Journal of Applied Physics*, and one or two other journals.   The development of microwave technique may be said to date from the adaptation of hollow pipes and horns to microwaves, carried out independently by the author's colleagues Barrow, Chu, and others at the Massachusetts Institute of Technology, and by Southworth, Schel-kunoff, and others at the Bell Telephone Laboratories. This was followed by the development of cavity resonators by Hansen, Condon, and others. The author is indebted to various colleagues and friends, including those just named, and particularly to Prof. J. A. Stratton, for valuable advice and suggestions.

J. C. SLATER.

CAMBRIDGE, MASS.,
July, 1942

CONTENTS

ix

CHAPTER V

RADIATION FROM ANTENNAS

CHAPTER VI

DIRECTIVE DEVICES FOR ANTENNAS

CHAPTER VII

COUPLING OF COAXIAL LINES AND WAVE GUIDES

MICROWAVE TRANSMISSION

INTRODUCTION

Electrical communication has been carried on at ever-increasing frequencies. The progress has been from audio frequencies to radio frequencies, to short waves, and now to the range of waves called microwaves: wave lengths perhaps in the range from a half meter to a few centimeters. The progress has been an orderly one, with few new principles needed for its understanding, until the latest step; but microwaves are so different in many ways from longer waves that a new technique is needed, a technique that comes more naturally to the physicist trained in Maxwell's equations than to the electrical engineer trained in electric circuits. Microwaves are of the same order of magnitude as the dimensions of the apparatus used. We can no longer think of lumped resistances, inductances, capacities. If we think of conventional circuits at all, we must think of distributed inductances and capacities. But the differences are really much greater than this. The conventional conductor in the ordinary range of wave lengths is a wire, carrying current throughout its volume. Conductors in the microwave region are very different things: coaxial lines, consisting of a rod carried concentrically within a hollow pipe, or even simply a hollow pipe alone. The coaxial line is at first sight like an ordinary transmission line; current flows down the wire, back along the pipe. But the hollow pipe is very completely different from a conventional transmission line. Current flows in one direction in one wall of the pipe, in the other direction through the other wall. Though the two walls are connected electrically to each other, this condition does not lead to a short circuit. In many cases, it is not even practicable to define the current at all, in any unique way. Our attention rather must be focused on the electromagnetic field within the pipe. We must consider Poynting's theorem, and remember that it is best to consider the energy as flowing in

1

the field anyway. Maxwell's equations, and the electromagnetic field, must be our constant guide.

Nevertheless, the ideas of conventional transmission lines are of constant help. The theory of lines of continuously distributed parameters furnishes an analogy to actual lines which is very far-reaching and powerful. No actual line behaves like the theoretical line, for any actual line has many possible modes for the transmission of energy. These different modes are unimportant in work at longer wave lengths, for they have cutoff frequencies below which they cannot transmit power, and for long wave work only one mode is possible. But in the microwave region several or many modes are often important, and only by use of electromagnetic field theory can we understand them. In spite of this, each mode by itself behaves like a conventional transmission line, and an understanding of such lines gives the best way of understanding the actual propagation. For this reason we shall start our survey by a chapter on conventional transmission lines, and the terminology and properties of lines will be constantly at the foundation of our work. In particular, the idea of impedance is one of the most important concepts in transmission-line theory, and this concept can be carried over into microwave work, exerting a great unifying effect and contributing greatly to effective understanding of the field.

A communication system naturally has three parts: a source of power, a transmission line, and a receiver. The present book deals almost exclusively with the transmission line. This is an electromagnetic problem, a problem that can be handled by Maxwell's equations and that can be formulated mathematically and treated completely, subject only to mathematical difficulties. The power sources and the receivers, on the contrary, are almost always electronic or other devices which depend on a great deal besides Maxwell's equations. They are diversified in their structure, often not well understood in their operation. In the present state of the art, hardly more than a descriptive discussion could be given of these parts of the problem, although the transmission can be handled fairly completely. For these reasons we have left out power sources and receivers almost completely. We may form a very simple picture of their essential operation, however. We shall find that the thing in microwave theory that corresponds to the resonant circuit of ordinary circuit theory is a resonant cavity, a region enclosed by a conducting wall, in which certain electromagnetic oscillations can take place with large intensity and comparatively small losses. A microwave generator always contains fundamentally such a resonant cavity, determining by its resonant frequency the frequency of the generated power. The generators in common use are almost invariably electronic generators: electrons are given power by a direct-current source, as a battery; they come into the field of the oscillating resonant cavity; this field alters their motion, so that they have a periodic component in their motion; this periodic component is acted on by the periodic field, in such a way that the electrons lose energy to the periodic field. If the net effect is that each electron loses energy to the alternating field, energy which in turn it has gained from the direct field, the net effect is to sustain the oscillations, at the expense of power supplied by the battery. Thus we have an oscillator, a power source for microwaves. We may, for practical purposes, regard this as a resonant cavity on which is impressed a voltage, the voltage representing the effect of the electrons.

Similarly receivers of power in the microwave region are complicated things, but again they can be simply described, for the present purposes. Again we have a resonant cavity of some form, in which an oscillation is set up by the incident power. The cavity contains some form of detecting device: an electronic device, a rectifying crystal, or some other scheme. In any case, the effect of the receiver is to abstract energy from the oscillation in the cavity. We may replace this by a simple load in the cavity, for instance a resistance, which would absorb energy in a similar way. We may find the power dissipated in the resistance and regard this as a simplified model for the actual receiver.

In other words, the expedients that we must use for describing generators and receivers are very similar to what must be used in conventional transmission line theory, where a generator is regarded as an applied voltage with a certain internal impedance, and a receiver is replaced by a terminal impedance, and the primary attention is focused on the transmission line. We shall find, here as there, that we can build a complete and usable theory, without further study of the properties of terminal equipment.

In our study of transmission lines themselves, we shall consider constantly the two most common types of lines, the coaxial line and the hollow pipe.   In many cases we do not have a simple line, however; we have a composite line, consisting of sections of various types.   For instance, our generator may be represented by a resonant cavity, which is more like a closed hollow pipe than anything else.   From this cavity we may couple by a coupling loop into a coaxial line.   This may terminate in another loop or other coupling device, feeding its power into another pipe.   This pipe may terminate in a horn, feeding power into empty space.   We shall have to consider radiation in empty space and transmission from antennas and horns, with reception by similar antennas and horns.   The power after its radiation may be received by another horn or antenna, fed into another pipe, picked out of the pipe by another loop, led into a final cavity representing the receiver, and there received.   We shall have to consider all the elements of such a complicated composite line and how they join together.   In fact, one of our most important problems will be just this joining from one type of transmission line into another.   We shall find that the steady flow of power from generator to receiver can be interrupted in two ways.   In the first place, at every discontinuity, there can be reflection of power.   This sends some power back toward the generator, so that it does not reach the receiver, and yet it is not completely lost.   We shall learn how to avoid this reflection; a well-designed line, no matter how complicated, has no net reflection.   In the second place, there can be real power loss along the line.   This can come only by conversion of power into some other form, as in the heating of imperfectly conducting materials or in loss of power in radiation, in systems that are not closed.   We shall find where such losses occur and how to make them as small as possible.

Whenever reflections occur, standing waves can be set up and, if the dimensions of the system are properly chosen, we have the possibility of resonance.   We could focus our attention on this resonance, building up our theory by analogy with the mathematical theory of vibrating strings, for instance.   We prefer not to do this, however, regarding the resonance as an incident, rather than a fundamental thing.   Our main attention will be directed to the transmission of power. A resonant chamber from this point of view is just part of a transmission line, with power being fed in at one side, out the other, but exercising on account of the resonance a strong selective or filtering action. Even though we shall not make much use of the analogy of the vibrating string, this analogy and others are useful. Acoustics is obviously very similar to many problems in microwaves. The wave lengths are in the same range of magnitude, and many of the devices used for microwaves remind us strongly of similar acoustical devices. One can have electric horns, and they can even be tuned as trombones and cornets are tuned. There is one considerable difference: electromagnetic disturbances are transverse, sound in air is longitudinal, so that our electromagnetic horns have two modes of propagation, corresponding to the two directions of polarization, for each single mode of an acoustical horn. But this is a technical rather than a fundamental difference; fundamentally the analogy is close enough to be of great service both to microwaves and to acoustics.

Then there is an obvious analogy to optics. Light is a form of electromagnetic disturbance, and, if we were to reduce the wave length still farther from a few centimeters to a few hundred thousandths of a centimeter, we should go from microwaves to light directly. The analogy with light, however, is really not so close as it might seem, on account of the very small wave length of light in comparison to the size of our apparatus. Only with apparatus of the order of magnitude of the wave length do we get a good analogy. Sometimes we have such optical problems, as in diffraction of light through a slit of width comparable to a wave length, or in scattering of light by an obstacle comparable with the wave length. These cases are the exception, however. We must be very wary of optical analogies, when they deal for instance with reflection of light by mirrors very large compared to the wave length; we may not be sure that microwaves will behave in the same way.

With this preliminary understanding of our problem, we shall start with our most useful analogy, the theory of transmission lines. We shall develop this as a subject in itself, without particular reference to the actual type of line we shall take up later. After we have gained a thorough familiarity with the theory of lines, we shall go on to Maxwell's equations and the explanation of coaxial lines, hollow pipes, antennas, radiation, and methods of joining different kinds of lines, explanations which are given properly only by Maxwell's equations but in which the analogy with transmission line theory will be of constant help and will constantly add to the depth of our understanding.

CHAPTER I

TRANSMISSION LINES

In the theory of electrical networks, there is one particularly simple problem: the infinite transmission line, a succession of identical four-terminal networks connected together. In such a line, the electrical properties are very much like the mechanical properties of a stretched string: waves can be propagated down the line, in either direction. If the line has resistance, the waves are attenuated, otherwise not. If a line is terminated, rather than being infinitely long, the wave will be reflected at the termination, so that the disturbance in the line will consist of an incident and a reflected wave. If the terminal network absorbs no power, the reflected wave will have the same amplitude as the incident wave at the terminal, though it may have a different phase; if the terminal network absorbs power, the reflected wave will have smaller amplitude than the incident wave. The combination of the incident and reflected waves forms standing waves. If both ends of a line are terminated by reflecting networks, the line becomes a resonant system: only frequencies for which the length of the line is properly adjusted with respect to the wave length can be used to set up standing waves of large amplitude in the line. If other frequencies are impressed on the line, the amplitude will be small. The frequency difference between the frequencies at which the response of the resonant line has half its maximum value can be used to define a Q for the line, just as for the corresponding resonant circuit. Not only is a single transmission line, terminated or not, of interest; we must consider combinations of lines. Thus we can have two lines of different properties connected together in series. There will be reflection at the junction between the two lines, just as there would be at the junction between a line and a terminal impedance. Again, we may have one line in shunt across another line. This again will introduce reflections into the line and can be treated much as the corresponding problem in ordinary circuit theory would be handled, the prob-

7

lem of one impedance shunted across another. Problems of these types will be taken up in the present chapter. Later on, we shall see how actual coaxial lines or hollow pipes form analogues to transmission lines, how terminated lines form resonant cavities, and how coaxial lines and pipes can be connected together to form analogues to transmission lines in series or in shunt.

1. The Infinite Line.—By an infinite transmission line, one means an infinite set of identical four-terminal networks, connected together as shown in Fig. 1. Before understanding the nature of the transmission line, we must understand clearly the structure of the four-terminal networks that make it up. We shall assume that these are linear networks; that is, that the currents flowing to the various terminals are linear functions

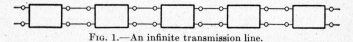

Fig. 1.—An infinite transmission line.

of the voltages of the terminals. This will be the case if the networks consist entirely of resistances, inductances not containing iron, and capacities, but will not be the case if they contain vacuum tubes, iron-core inductances, or other nonlinear devices. In a general four-terminal network, there are four separate currents, the currents flowing into each terminal; and four voltages, the voltage of each terminal with respect to ground. On account of the linear nature of the network, each voltage will be a linear function of the four currents, and the four resulting equations will have 16 coefficients, of the dimensions of impedances. This case is much more general than we need, however. Our actual networks have two terminals at one side, for definiteness the left side, which we shall consider as input terminals, and two others at the right side which are output terminals. We shall consider only the case in which the current flowing into one of the input terminals equals the current flowing out from the other input terminal, and the current flowing out from one output terminal equals the current flowing into the other output terminal. This is the case analogous to the familiar, closed, two-wire circuit of low-frequency work, in which equal currents in opposite directions flow through the two wires. Thus there are only two currents which we must consider, which we shall denote by i_a and i_b. These currents are shown in Fig. 2. Simi-

larly there are only two potential differences of importance, the
one between the two input terminals, which we shall call V_a,
and the one between the output terminals,
V_b. V_a will be assumed positive if the
upper of the terminals a is at higher voltage,
and V_b is positive if the lower of the terminals b is at higher voltage; thus in each
case the current flows in the direction of
decreasing voltage. The linear equations
connecting the currents and potential differences will have four coefficients, and may be written

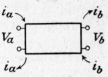

Fig. 2.—Currents
and potential differ-
ences in a single
network.

$$V_a = Z_{aa}i_a + Z_{ab}i_b$$
$$V_b = Z_{ba}i_a + Z_{bb}i_b \qquad (1.1)$$

It can be proved, however, that the coefficients Z_{ab} and Z_{ba} are
equal. This proof is similar to that of the reciprocity theorem,
which can be stated as follows: If we have any system of ironless
alternating-current circuits, however complicated, and if we
have in the system a sinusoidal impressed e.m.f. applied at any
point of the system and an impedanceless ammeter at any other
point of the system, the ammeter and e.m.f. are interchangeable
without changing the amplitude or phase of the steady-state
current through the ammeter. This theorem is proved by
setting up Kirchhoff's equations for an arbitrary network and is
true because a corresponding result holds for each element common to two circuits of the network. Thus if a resistance or
capacity or inductance is common to two circuits, or if there is a
mutual inductance between them, the e.m.f. induced in one
circuit by a given current in the other equals a mutual impedance
times the current in the other, and this mutual impedance is
the same for the e.m.f. induced in the first circuit by a current
in the second, or for the e.m.f. induced in the second by a current
in the first. It is an extension of this fact that leads to the
result

$$Z_{ab} = Z_{ba} \qquad (1.2)$$

in Eq. (1.1). Thus there are only three independent impedances
for a four-terminal network with currents and voltages as in
Fig. 2, and we may rewrite Eqs. (1.1) as

$$V_a = Z_{aa}i_a + Z_{ab}i_b$$
$$V_b = Z_{ab}i_a + Z_{bb}i_b \qquad (1.3)$$

As a result of Eq. (1.3), we see that the network has just three arbitrary parameters in it, and the suggestion is obvious that we can construct an equivalent network in a simple way out of three properly chosen impedances. We can at once show that this can be done in the form of a T network, as shown in Fig. 3. If we take the T structure of Fig. 3 and apply Kirchhoff's laws in

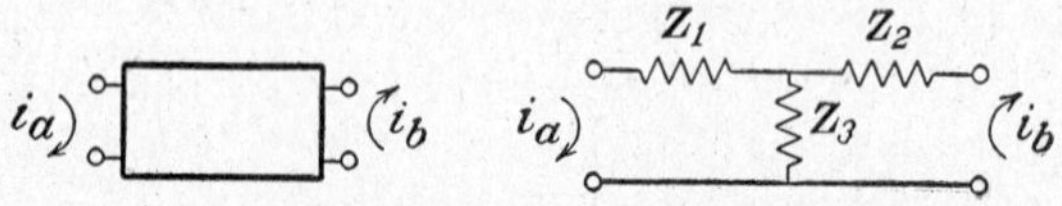

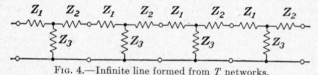

Fig. 3.—A T structure equivalent to a four-terminal network.

the usual way, taking account of the fact that the current in the shunt element Z_3 is $i_a - i_b$, we have at once

$$V_a = (Z_1 + Z_3)i_a - Z_3 i_b$$
$$V_b = -Z_3 i_a + (Z_2 + Z_3)i_b \qquad (1.4)$$

a pair of equations similar to (1.3). Comparing them, we see that

$$Z_{aa} = Z_1 + Z_3, \qquad Z_{ab} = -Z_3, \qquad Z_{bb} = Z_2 + Z_3$$
$$Z_1 = Z_{aa} + Z_{ab}, \qquad Z_2 = Z_{bb} + Z_{ab}, \qquad Z_3 = -Z_{ab} \quad (1.5)$$

The network of Fig. 3 furnishes a convenient way of visualizing the general network that we are considering. It should be

Fig. 4.—Infinite line formed from T networks.

understood that many other simple networks could also be set up equivalent to the general network, but the T structure is as simple as any. It should also be understood that, in order that Eqs. (1.5) should hold at all frequencies, the Z's, both of the set Z_{aa}, Z_{ab}, Z_{bb}, and of Z_1, Z_2, Z_3, may have to be complicated functions of the frequency, so that it is not to be assumed that in general the impedances Z_1, Z_2, Z_3 of the T section can be chosen as simple elements, such as simple series combinations of inductances and capacities.

Using the equivalent T section of Fig. 3, let us now set up the infinite transmission line. This is shown in Fig. 4. From the appearance of the network, it is obvious that the two series members Z_1 and Z_2 between two shunt impedances Z_3 are in series with each other. Now it is really arbitrary where we draw the terminals of our separate networks (shown by circles in Fig. 4). We have spoken, in Fig. 1, as if each network were definitely fixed, confined in a box so to speak. But this of course is not really so, and, with the impedances Z_1 and Z_2 in series, we may imagine terminals to be inserted anywhere in the series impedance $Z_1 + Z_2$. In particular, we may make our T networks symmetrical, by inserting the terminals halfway through the impedance $Z_1 + Z_2$, which amounts to replacing both Z_1 and Z_2 by $(Z_1 + Z_2)/2$. This will make no real change in the network. Since it involves no loss of generality, we shall from now on deal with such a symmetrical line, as shown in Fig. 5.

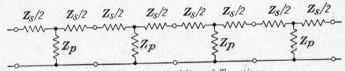

FIG. 5.—Symmetrical line of T sections.

In this figure, we have relabeled the series elements $Z_s/2$, so that two together form Z_s, and we have called the shunt, or parallel, elements Z_p. (We might have called the series elements by the subscript s for series and the shunt elements by s for shunt, but then we should be involved in the same difficulty as the old lady who labeled her mince pies TM for "'Tis mince," and her others TM for "'Tain't mince," and never did figure out why the pies got so mixed up.) As we have seen in the preceding paragraphs, this line of symmetrical T sections is really just as general as the most general line shown in Fig. 1. Using (1.5), we then have

$$Z_s = Z_1 + Z_2 = Z_{aa} + Z_{bb} + 2Z_{ab}$$
$$Z_p = Z_3 = -Z_{ab} \qquad\qquad (1.6)$$

Let us now set up our electrical network problem, to find the currents that can flow in the line. In Fig. 6 we show the line, indicating by i_n the current flowing into one of the networks of the type shown in Fig. 1, or the current flowing in one of the series elements of the line of the type of Fig. 5. The voltage V_n is measured across the terminals of the network in the first case or is measured from the mid-point of the series impedance to

the opposite side of the line in the second case.   In either case,
we shall take the current to be positive if it flows in a clockwise
direction, and the voltage to be positive if the upper terminal is
positive with respect to the lower.   If i_n and V_n are positive,
then, the current is flowing in the direction of decreasing voltage
to the right of the terminals, and in the direction of increasing
voltage to the left of the terminals.   We shall now set up the
problem by both methods illustrated in Fig. 6.

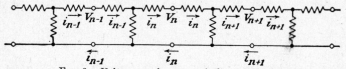

FIG. 6.—Voltages and currents in line of T sections.

Using the first method, we have Eqs. (1.3) for the voltage
in terms of the current.   Applying to the network to the right of
the terminals in which i_n is flowing, we have

$$V_n = Z_{aa}i_n + Z_{ab}i_{n+1} \qquad (1.7)$$

Applying to the network to the left of these terminals, we note
that our present convention of signs for the voltage is the opposite
of what was used before.   Thus we have

$$-V_n = Z_{ab}i_{n-1} + Z_{bb}i_n \qquad (1.8)$$

Adding (1.7) and (1.8), we find

$$(Z_{aa} + Z_{bb})i_n + Z_{ab}(i_{n-1} + i_{n+1}) = 0 \qquad (1.9)$$

Similarly using the second method, we note that the downward
current in the shunt element to the right of the terminals where
V_n is measured is $i_n - i_{n+1}$, and the downward current in the
shunt element to the left is $i_{n-1} - i_n$.   Applying Kirchhoff's law
to the circuit consisting of the series element Z_s and the two shunt
elements Z_p, we have

$$Z_s i_n + Z_p(i_n - i_{n+1} + i_n - i_{n-1}) = 0 \qquad (1.10)$$

or

$$(Z_s + 2Z_p)i_n - Z_p(i_{n-1} + i_{n+1}) = 0 \qquad (1.11)$$

Using Eqs. (1.6), we see that Eqs. (1.9) and (1.11) are identical,
as of course they must be.

It is now possible to solve Eq. (1.11) by a very simple device. We assume

$$i_n = A e^{-\gamma n} \qquad (1.12)$$

where A and γ are complex constants. Then we have

$$(Z_s + 2Z_p)A e^{-\gamma n} - Z_p(e^\gamma + e^{-\gamma})A e^{-\gamma n} = 0 \qquad (1.13)$$

Canceling $A e^{-\gamma n}$, we have an equation independent of n:

$$\frac{e^\gamma + e^{-\gamma}}{2} = \cosh \gamma = 1 + \frac{Z_s}{2Z_p} \qquad (1.14)$$

If γ is chosen to satisfy (1.14), the assumption (1.12) will furnish a solution of the infinite set of equations (1.11). We notice that, since the hyperbolic cosine is an even function of γ, each set of values of Z_s and Z_p will furnish two solutions for γ, one the negative of the other, so that we could equally well have written (1.12) in the form $A e^{\gamma n}$. We shall prefer to handle the two possible values in the following manner, whose significance will become plain shortly. We write the complex number γ in the form

$$\gamma = \alpha + j\beta \qquad (1.15)$$

where α and β are real and imaginary parts of γ, $j = \sqrt{-1}$. Of the two possible values of γ, one will have its real part α positive, the other will have α negative. Henceforth we shall denote by γ that root of (1.14) which has its real part positive, and shall call the other root $-\gamma$. We then have found two solutions of (1.11): $A e^{-\gamma n}$ and $B e^{\gamma n}$, where γ is defined as just described, and A and B are arbitrary complex constants. Since (1.11) forms a set of linear homogeneous equations, the sum of these two solutions is itself a solution. Inserting the factor $e^{j\omega t}$ representing the time variation of the current, our general solution of (1.11) is then

$$i_n = A e^{j\omega t - \gamma n} + B e^{j\omega t + \gamma n} \qquad (1.16)$$

This is the most general solution of (1.11) which is a sinusoidal function of time with angular frequency ω; of course the general solution would be a sum of such terms for all frequencies, with A and B arbitrary functions of frequency and γ determined as a function of frequency by (1.14), but as usual in circuit work we can deal with solutions sinusoidal in time and combine them at the end of our calculation.

The interpretation of our solution (1.16) is most easily found by using (1.15). We then have

$$i_n = A e^{-\alpha n} e^{j(\omega t - \beta n)} + B e^{\alpha n} e^{j(\omega t + \beta n)} \tag{1.17}$$

where we remember that α is positive. We can also arrange to have β positive. We remember that $\cosh \gamma = \cosh (a + j\beta)$ is periodic in β with period 2π, since it can be written in terms of trigonometric functions of β. Thus β is not uniquely determined by (1.14); an infinite set of β's is possible, differing by integral multiples of 2π. We shall for definiteness choose β to be between 0 and 2π. We shall now show that the two terms of (1.17) represent two waves propagated along the transmission line with definite velocity and wave length, attenuated as they go along, the first term being a wave propagated to the right, the second to the left. To see this, let us remind ourselves of a few simple facts regarding wave motion. An undamped sinusoidal wave propagated along the x axis in a continuous medium has a displacement as a function of x and t given by

$$u = A e^{j\omega\left(t - \frac{x}{v}\right)} = A e^{j(\omega t - kx)} \tag{1.18}$$

where v is the velocity of propagation, so that the disturbance will be in the same phase at points for which

$$t - \frac{x}{v} = \text{const.}, \qquad x = vt + \text{const.} \tag{1.19}$$

from which we verify at once that v is the velocity. The quantity k is given by

$$k = \frac{\omega}{v} \tag{1.20}$$

It is closely related to the wave length λ, the distance along the x axis in which the disturbance repeats itself, at constant time. This quantity is easily derived by rewriting (1.18) in the form

$$u = A e^{2\pi i (ft - x/\lambda)} \tag{1.21}$$

where

$$f = \frac{\omega}{2\pi} \tag{1.22}$$

is the frequency, or number of vibrations per second; for from (1.21) we see at once that increase of x by λ brings u back to its original value.   We then have

$$k = \frac{2\pi f}{v} = \frac{2\pi}{\lambda}, \qquad f\lambda = v \qquad (1.23)$$

Now let us consider the possibility that the constant k may be complex, writing

$$k = k_r + jk_i \qquad (1.24)$$

Then we have

$$u = A e^{k_i x} e^{j(\omega t - k_r x)} \qquad (1.25)$$

The factor $e^{k_i x}$ is a damping or attenuation term; if k_i is negative, as it normally would be, the amplitude is attenuated as we go along the x axis, falling to a factor $1/e$ of itself in a distance $1/k_i$. The remaining factor $e^{j(\omega t - k_r x)}$ represents a propagated wave, just as in (1.18), and k_r is to be substituted in (1.20) and (1.23) in place of k in finding the velocity and wave length of the wave.   The wave (1.25) is propagated along the positive x axis; for a wave along the negative x axis, we need merely change the sign of x, which amounts to the same thing as changing the sign of k.

Comparing (1.25) with the first term of (1.17), we see that they agree if we regard n as a distance equivalent to x (it is actually distance along the line measured in terms of the length of a single network as a unit) and if we place

$$\beta = k_r, \quad \alpha = -k_i, \quad (\alpha + j\beta) = \gamma = jk = j(k_r + jk_i) \qquad (1.26)$$

Thus we see, as we stated earlier, that the first term of (1.17) represents an attenuated wave traveling to the right, and the second term, which differs from it in a change of the sign preceding n, is an attenuated wave traveling to the left.   The constant α, which measures the attenuation, is often called the attenuation constant; β, which determines the wave length according to the equation

$$\lambda = \frac{2\pi}{\beta} \qquad (1.27)$$

which we derive from (1.23) and (1.26), is called the wave length constant.   The complex quantity γ is often called the propagation constant.   We note that, from (1.20) and (1.26), the velocity of propagation is given by

$$v = \frac{\omega}{\beta} \qquad (1.28)$$

This of course is in units of networks, or sections of line, per second.

Before leaving the infinite line, we shall derive several formulas that will be useful in our later work. In the first place, we may regard (1.14) as a quadratic for either e^γ or $e^{-\gamma}$ and solve for that quantity directly. We find

$$e^\gamma = 1 + \frac{Z_s}{2Z_p} \pm \sqrt{\left(1 + \frac{Z_s}{2Z_p}\right)^2 - 1}$$

$$= 1 + \frac{Z_s}{2Z_p} \pm \sqrt{\frac{Z_s}{Z_p} + \left(\frac{Z_s}{2Z_p}\right)^2} \tag{1.29}$$

The choice of the proper sign is to be made according to the principle discussed in connection with Eq. (1.15), so as to make the real part of γ positive; whether it is the $+$ or $-$ sign in (1.29) depends on the nature of Z_s and Z_p. In any case, one sign in (1.29) is to be chosen, in accordance with the principle just mentioned; when this has been done, the other sign in (1.29) will give $e^{-\gamma}$, as we can easily verify from the fact that the product of the two values in (1.29) is unity.

Another useful relation is found by considering the ratio of voltage to current in the nth network, in the case where the current is just given by the first term of (1.16), $i_n = A e^{j\omega t - \gamma n}$, representing a wave traveling to the right along the line. This ratio is called the characteristic impedance of the line and is a quantity of which we shall make constant use in our later work. It is denoted by Z_0. To find it, we may use the line in the form shown in Fig. 6. In that case, remembering that the current in the shunt element to the right of the terminals is $i_n - i_{n+1}$, we have

$$V_n = i_n \left(\frac{Z_s}{2}\right) + (i_n - i_{n+1})Z_p$$

$$= i_n \left(\frac{Z_s}{2} + Z_p - e^{-\gamma}Z_p\right) \tag{1.30}$$

where we have used the fact that

$$i_{n+1} = e^{-\gamma}i_n \tag{1.31}$$

which follows directly from the assumed current. From (1.29) we substitute for $e^{-\gamma}$, using the $\mp$ sign in front of the radical, in place of the $\pm$ which appears in e^γ.   Then we find

$$V_n = i_n Z_0 \tag{1.32}$$

where

$$Z_0 = \pm \sqrt{Z_s Z_p + \left(\frac{Z_s}{2}\right)^2} \tag{1.33}$$

As in the formula for e^γ, (1.29), the sign in (1.33) is to be determined uniquely.   The positive signs in (1.29) and (1.33) go together, as do the negative signs, so that when the sign of (1.29) is determined, that of (1.33) is known as well.

Finally, we can get an interesting relation between Z_0 and γ by computing $\sinh \gamma$.   To do this, we use (1.29), finding at once

$$\sinh \gamma = \frac{e^\gamma - e^{-\gamma}}{2}$$

$$= \pm \sqrt{\frac{Z_s}{Z_p} + \left(\frac{Z_s}{2Z_p}\right)^2}$$

$$\sinh \gamma = \frac{Z_0}{Z_p} \tag{1.34}$$

We observe that the $\pm$ sign has disappeared from (1.34); this forms, then, a convenient way for finding Z_0 uniquely from γ.

2. The Infinite Line with Distributed Parameters.—The lines we have considered in Sec. 1 consist of finite lumped networks. A much closer analogy to the transmission lines of microwave theory is found in continuous lines with distributed parameters. We can conveniently consider such lines by passing to the limit as the size of the network elements becomes smaller and smaller. Let us think of such a line as that of Fig. 1, in which each network represents a length dx of the line.   Let us assume that the distributed series impedance per unit length of the line is Z and that the distributed shunt admittance per unit length is Y. Then the series impedance of the element of length dx is

$$Z_s = Z \, dx \tag{2.1}$$

Similarly the shunt admittance of the length dx is $Y \, dx$, so that the shunt impedance of this length is

$$Z_p = \frac{1}{Y \, dx} \tag{2.2}$$

Since we are interested in the limit as dx goes to zero, we see that the series impedance per element will become small in this limit, but the shunt impedance will become infinite.   This allows us to neglect certain terms in the formulas of the preceding section.

First let us find the current $i(x,t)$ at a point with coordinate x along the line, at time t.   We must here adopt a convention slightly different from that made in the preceding section.   There we assumed, for instance in (1.31), that the ratio of the current in the $(n + 1)$st network to that in the nth element was $e^{-\gamma}$. If we did that in this case, since the $(n + 1)$st and nth elements are infinitesimally separated from each other, $e^{-\gamma}$ would be arbitrarily close to unity, and γ infinitesimal.   We prefer rather to define γ so that $e^{-\gamma}$ is the ratio of the current at coordinate $(x + 1)$ to that at coordinate x.   That is, in place of (1.16), we assume for the continuous line

$$i(x,t) = Ae^{j\omega t-\gamma x} + Be^{j\omega t+\gamma x} \tag{2.3}$$

This would agree with (1.16) only if x were a coordinate measured along the lumped constant transmission line, increasing by unity in going from one network to the next.   Now, taking only the first term representing the wave propagated to the right, we have

$$\begin{aligned} i(x + dx,t) &= e^{-\gamma dx}i(x,t) \\ &= (1 - \gamma \, dx \cdots)i(x,t) \end{aligned} \tag{2.4}$$

We may compare this formula with (1.29).   As we pass to the limit in that formula, we note that

$$\frac{Z_s}{Z_p} = ZY \, dx^2 \tag{2.5}$$

We need retain only the term of (1.29) in dx; this is the first term under the square root.   Thus we have

$$e^{-\gamma} = 1 \mp \sqrt{ZY} \, dx \cdots \tag{2.6}$$

By comparison with (2.4), we see that

$$\gamma = \pm \sqrt{ZY} \tag{2.7}$$

As usual, the sign is to be chosen so as to make the real part of γ positive.   Next let us find the characteristic impedance of the line.

In formula (1.33), the second term under the radical is negligible compared to the first, for the continuous line.   Thus, using (2.1) and (2.2), we have

$$Z_0 = \pm \sqrt{\frac{Z}{Y}} \qquad (2.8)$$

Combining (2.7) and (2.8), we have

$$\gamma = Z_0 Y \qquad (2.9)$$

The close relationship between (2.9) and (1.34) is obvious, if we replace sinh γ by the value which it would have for small γ and remember that Z_p is inversely proportional to Y.   As in (1.34), the sign in (2.9) is unique and serves conveniently to define the relation between γ and Z_0.

It is often convenient to have a specific case of continuous transmission lines in mind.   In either a parallel-wire transmission line, or a coaxial line, the series impedance Z per unit length consists of resistance and inductive impedance in series, and the shunt admittance Y per unit length consists of conductance and capacitive admittance in shunt.   Thus we may write

$$Z = R + j\omega L \qquad (2.10)$$

where R is the series resistance per unit length, L the series inductance per unit length, and

$$Y = G + j\omega C \qquad (2.11)$$

where G is the shunt conductance per unit length and C the shunt capacitance per unit length.   Then we have

$$\gamma = \pm \sqrt{(R + j\omega L)(G + j\omega C)} \qquad (2.12)$$

For a nondissipative line, the series resistance and shunt conductance R and G would be zero.   Thus in this case we should have

$$\gamma = \pm j\omega \sqrt{LC} = \alpha + j\beta \qquad (2.13)$$
$$\alpha = 0, \qquad \beta = \omega \sqrt{LC} \qquad (2.14)$$

In (2.14), we have chosen the positive sign for β, to agree with our assumption that β is positive.   Using (1.28), we have in this case

$$v = \frac{\omega}{\beta} = \frac{1}{\sqrt{LC}} \qquad (2.15)$$

for the velocity of propagation. Actual lines have some dissipation, but it is generally small. In case R is small compared to ωL, and G is small compared to ωC, we can expand the square root in (2.12) in powers of $R/\omega L$ and $G/\omega C$, and the leading terms become

$$\gamma = \alpha + j\beta = \pm \omega \sqrt{LC} \left(j + \frac{R}{2\omega L} + \frac{G}{2\omega C} \cdots \right) \quad (2.16)$$

$$\alpha = \frac{R}{2} \sqrt{\frac{C}{L}} + \frac{G}{2} \sqrt{\frac{L}{C}}, \qquad \beta = \omega \sqrt{LC} \quad (2.17)$$

$$\frac{\alpha}{\beta} = \frac{R}{2\omega L} + \frac{G}{2\omega C} \quad (2.18)$$

where we have again chosen the positive sign, making both α and β positive.

We may find the characteristic impedance of our specialized line from (2.8), using again the positive sign before the square root. It is

$$Z_0 = \sqrt{\frac{R + j\omega L}{G + j\omega C}} \quad (2.19)$$

For the dissipationless line, this becomes

$$Z_0 = \sqrt{\frac{L}{C}} \quad (2.20)$$

a real quantity, and therefore a pure resistance. For the line with slight dissipation, expanding as in the preceding paragraph, we have

$$Z_0 = \sqrt{\frac{L}{C}} \left[1 + j \left(-\frac{R}{2\omega L} + \frac{G}{2\omega C} \right) \cdots \right] \quad (2.21)$$

We see that losses in the line introduce a reactive component into the characteristic impedance of the line, just as they introduced an attenuation, as we saw in (2.17). It is possible, however, for the series and shunt losses to cancel in their effect on characteristic impedance, though not on attenuation. Thus if $R + j\omega L$ and $G + j\omega C$ are chosen to have the same phase angle, it is plain from (2.19) that Z_0 will be real. As we see from (2.21), this is accomplished if

$$\frac{R}{L} = \frac{G}{C} \quad (2.22)$$

For some purposes, it is desired to have attenuating lines which nevertheless have real characteristic impedances. This can be done, as we see from (2.22), by using properly chosen series resistances and shunt conductances.

3. The Terminated Line and Reflection.—We have seen in (1.16) and (2.3) that the current in an infinite line consists of two waves, one propagated to the right, the other to the left, with arbitrary amplitudes and phases. We shall now show that if the line is cut at an arbitrary point and terminated by a terminal impedance Z_R, the ratio B/A between the complex amplitudes of reflected and incident waves, which is called the reflection coefficient, is uniquely determined. In particular, we shall find that if the terminal impedance equals the characteristic impedance Z_0, the reflection coefficient is zero; the greater the difference between Z_0 and Z_R, the greater the reflection.

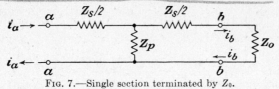

Fig. 7.—Single section terminated by Z_0.

As a preliminary, let us consider a line terminated by the characteristic impedance Z_0. When we first defined this quantity, in deriving Eq. (1.33), we stated that it was the ratio of voltage to current in the nth section of the line, when the current consisted only of a wave propagated to the right. Now if we have a terminal impedance Z_R, the ratio of voltage across Z_R to the current flowing in it must be Z_R, by definition. If the terminal impedance equals Z_0, the ratio of voltage across the line at the terminals of Z_0 to current flowing in the line, and therefore flowing into Z_0, must be Z_0. But this is just the ratio that we should find if the disturbance in the line consisted only of a wave flowing to the right. This single wave, then, satisfies the boundary conditions at a terminal impedance Z_0, showing that when a line is terminated by this impedance only the incident wave is necessary, and there is no reflection.

A line terminated by the characteristic impedance Z_0 acts like an infinite line, in that it can sustain a single wave traveling to the right; any other type of line must have simultaneously a reflected wave. It follows that any length of line, terminated by Z_0, will itself have an input impedance Z_0. This will be made clearer by Fig. 7, which shows a single section of lumped constant line, terminated by Z_0. Since the current in this line will be simply a wave traveling to the right, it follows as in (1.32) that the ratio of voltage to current at the terminals aa will be the same as at bb, equaling in each case Z_0. Thus the input impedance of the network whose terminals are aa is Z_0. From this fact, we can find Z_0 by elementary circuit theory, verifying the result of (1.33), which was found by considering the waves propagated down the line. The whole network between aa is a combination of an impedance $\frac{1}{2}Z_s$ in series with a parallel circuit containing Z_p in one branch, $\frac{1}{2}Z_s + Z_0$ in the other. Thus we have

$$Z_0 = \tfrac{1}{2}Z_s + \cfrac{1}{\cfrac{1}{Z_p} + \cfrac{1}{\frac{1}{2}Z_s + Z_0}} \qquad (3.1)$$

$$(Z_0 - \tfrac{1}{2}Z_s)(Z_0 + \tfrac{1}{2}Z_s + Z_p) = Z_p(Z_0 + \tfrac{1}{2}Z_s)$$
$$Z_0^2 = Z_pZ_s + (\tfrac{1}{2}Z_s)^2$$
$$Z_0 = \pm\sqrt{Z_sZ_p + (\tfrac{1}{2}Z_s)^2} \qquad (3.2)$$

agreeing with (1.33). Now having shown that one network element terminated by Z_0 has the impedance Z_0, we can consider the second network and show in an obvious manner that its impedance, terminated by the first element and Z_0, is again Z_0, and so on indefinitely. We could use the same method to find the impedance of any number of network elements terminated by an impedance Z_R different from Z_0; but in this case we should find that the impedance of n elements terminated by Z_R depended on n, and the calculation would be very involved. The line terminated by Z_0 is the only one that has the same impedance, no matter where we cut it. One of our next problems will be to find the impedance of a line of arbitrary length terminated by an arbitrary Z_R. We shall find that this problem is much more easily solved by considering direct and reflected waves than by the type of network theory just described.

Let us now assume a line terminated by a general impedance Z_R. At the terminals of Z_R, the ratio of voltage across the line, to current flowing in the line, must be Z_R. Since this is in general different from Z_0, it is plain that the current in the line cannot be simply a wave traveling to the right. By combining such a

wave with a wave traveling to the left, however, we can give the
ratio of voltage to current any desired value, and this must be
done to satisfy our general boundary condition. Let us then
ask what is the voltage across a line, when the current consists
of the sum of waves traveling to right and left. For simplicity,
we shall consider the continuous line, in which, following (2.3),
the current is

$$i(x,t) = (Ae^{-\gamma x} + Be^{\gamma x})e^{j\omega t} \tag{3.3}$$

We can adapt our result to the lumped constant line, where the
current is given by (1.16), by replacing the continuous variable x,
measuring distance along the line, by n, indicating the nth section
of line.

We now know, following (1.32), that if we have only the first
term of (3.3), so that $B = 0$, the voltage is given by Z_0 times the
current. We have not so far asked what is the voltage if we
have only the second term, so that $A = 0$. Looking back to the
derivation of (1.32) and taking $i_n = Be^{j\omega t + \gamma n}$, we see that the
derivation goes through in just the same way, except with a
changed sign; we have

$$V_n = i_n(-Z_0) \tag{3.4}$$

where Z_0 is defined as before. Let us try to understand why
there is this difference of sign between waves propagated to the
right and to the left. Suppose we have an infinite line, with a
wave propagated toward the right, attenuated as it goes. If
we imagine this line to be cut at terminals aa, then when the
upper of the terminals a is at positive voltage with respect to the
lower, the current i_a will be flowing into the upper terminal, out
of the lower one. That is, within the right half of the line, the
current is flowing in the direction of decreasing voltage. The
impedance of this half line is positive, and the current is delivering
power to the half line. The other half line, to the left of the
terminals aa, however, is in just the opposite situation. The
upper terminal is still at higher voltage than the lower one, but
current flows out of the upper terminal, into the lower one. The
current flows opposite to the voltage, so that the left-hand half line
is delivering power, or is acting as a generator. If we compute
its impedance, as the ratio of voltage difference between top and
bottom terminals. to the current flowing into the top terminal, in

the same direction as the voltage difference, we find the impedance to be negative, the negative of the impedance of the right half line.   In other words, we see that the impedance of a half line, looking in the direction of power flow, from generator to receiver, is positive, and that the impedance of the other half line, looking opposite to the power flow, is negative.   Next we may consider the case of two simultaneous flows of power, arising from two waves, one traveling to the right, the other to the left. We consider the impedance of our same half line, looking to the right.   This impedance will be different for the two waves: for the wave traveling to the right we shall be looking toward the receiver and the impedance will be positive; for that traveling to the left we shall be looking toward the generator and the impedance will be negative.   This is the meaning of the negative sign in (3.4).

We now see that, corresponding to the current (3.3), the voltage between the two conductors of the line, at x, is

$$V(x,t) = Z_0(Ae^{-\gamma x} - Be^{\gamma x})e^{j\omega t} \tag{3.5}$$

the sum of the voltages connected with the two waves.   The ratio of voltage to current at point x, which we may call the impedance at x, Z_x, is

$$
\begin{aligned}
Z_x &= \frac{V(x,t)}{i(x,t)} \\
&= Z_0 \frac{Ae^{-\gamma x} - Be^{\gamma x}}{Ae^{-\gamma x} + Be^{\gamma x}}
\end{aligned}
\tag{3.6}
$$

Suppose now that the line is cut at a particular point l and terminated there by the impedance Z_R.   In this case, the ratio of voltage to current at l, which we have called Z_l, must equal Z_R. That is, we must have

$$Z_R = Z_0 \frac{Ae^{-\gamma l} - Be^{\gamma l}}{Ae^{-\gamma l} + Be^{\gamma l}} \tag{3.7}$$

Equation (3.7) provides the condition that we have been looking for, giving the reflection coefficient B/A.   We have

$$
\begin{aligned}
Ae^{-\gamma l}(Z_0 - Z_R) &= Be^{\gamma l}(Z_0 + Z_R) \\
\frac{Be^{\gamma l}}{Ae^{-\gamma l}} &= \frac{Z_0 - Z_R}{Z_0 + Z_R}
\end{aligned}
\tag{3.8}
$$

In the particular case where the terminal impedance is located at $x = 0$, this becomes

$$\frac{B}{A} = \frac{Z_0 - Z_R}{Z_0 + Z_R} \tag{3.9}$$

This important result verifies our earlier statement that if the terminal impedance equals Z_0 there is no reflected wave, and that the amplitude of the reflected wave is greater, the greater the difference between Z_0 and Z_R. Two limiting cases are of particular interest: the short-circuited and the open-circuited lines. For the short-circuited line, $Z_R = 0$, and B/A equals unity, so that the reflected and incident currents at $x = 0$, where the line is short-circuited, are equal, while the reflected and incident voltages are opposite and cancel. For the open-circuited line, Z_R is infinite, B/A equals -1, the reflected and incident currents cancel, while the voltages add. These results fit in with the obvious condition that the voltage across a short circuit and the current across an open circuit must be zero. They also show that the power carried to the termination by the incident wave must just equal the power carried back by the reflected wave, since it is obvious that no power can be lost in the short circuit or the open circuit.

4. Impedance of the Terminated Line.—Let us assume a line extending from $x = 0$ to $x = l$, terminated at $x = l$ by a terminal impedance Z_R. Our problem in this section will be to find the impedance of such a line. We have already seen that if Z_R equals the characteristic impedance Z_0 of the line, the input impedance will also be Z_0, independent of the length l of the line. In any other case, however, the input impedance will depend on l. We shall call the input impedance of the line of length l, terminated by Z_R, $Z(l)$. We can find it as follows. From (3.6), the impedance of the line at $x = 0$ is

$$Z(l) = Z_0 \frac{A - B}{A + B} \tag{4.1}$$

From (3.8) we have the value of $Be^{\gamma l}/Ae^{-\gamma l}$, given by

$$\frac{Be^{\gamma l}}{Ae^{-\gamma l}} = \frac{B}{A} e^{2\gamma l} = \frac{Z_0 - Z_R}{Z_0 + Z_R} \tag{4.2}$$

(4.2)

Combining with (4.1), we have

$$Z(l) = Z_0 \frac{A - B}{A + B}$$

$$= Z_0 \frac{1 - B/A}{1 + B/A}$$

$$= Z_0 \frac{1 - \dfrac{Z_0 - Z_R}{Z_0 + Z_R} e^{-2\gamma l}}{1 + \dfrac{Z_0 - Z_R}{Z_0 + Z_R} e^{-2\gamma l}}$$

$$= Z_0 \frac{(Z_0 + Z_R)e^{\gamma l} - (Z_0 - Z_R)e^{-\gamma l}}{(Z_0 + Z_R)e^{\gamma l} + (Z_0 - Z_R)e^{-\gamma l}}$$

$$Z(l) = Z_0 \frac{Z_0 \sinh \gamma l + Z_R \cosh \gamma l}{Z_0 \cosh \gamma l + Z_R \sinh \gamma l} \qquad (4.3)$$

Equation (4.3) is an important formula for the input impedance of a line of length l, and characteristic impedance Z_0, terminated by an impedance Z_R.

When the general formula (4.3) for the impedance of a terminated line has been found, it is often useful to consider the special cases of short-circuited and open-circuited lines. The first is the case where $Z_R = 0$, the second the case $Z_R = \infty$. Substituting these values in (4.3), we have at once

$$Z_{\text{cl}} = Z_0 \tanh \gamma l \qquad (4.4)$$

for the impedance of a closed or short-circuited line, and

$$Z_{\text{op}} = Z_0 \coth \gamma l \qquad (4.5)$$

for an open-circuited line. We note, since the hyperbolic tangent and hyperbolic cotangent are reciprocals of each other, that

$$Z_{\text{cl}} Z_{\text{op}} = Z_0^2 \qquad (4.6)$$

so that the characteristic impedance of a line is the geometric mean of its short-circuited and open-circuited impedances. This is a general relation for any line and can furnish a convenient method for determining the characteristic impedance experimentally from a finite length of line, by measuring short-circuited and open-circuited impedances, experimentally.

It is important to consider Eqs. (4.4) and (4.5) for the impedances of short-circuited and open-circuited lines, as a function of l, the length of the line. Let us start with (4.4) and first consider

a line without attenuation, for which $\alpha = 0$, $\gamma = j\beta$. In this
case we have

$$\sinh \gamma = \frac{e^{\gamma} - e^{-\gamma}}{2} = \frac{e^{j\beta} - e^{-j\beta}}{2} = j \sin \beta \qquad (4.7)$$

$$\cosh \gamma = \frac{e^{\gamma} + e^{-\gamma}}{2} = \frac{e^{j\beta} + e^{-j\beta}}{2} = \cos \beta \qquad (4.8)$$

$$\tanh \gamma = \frac{\sinh \gamma}{\cosh \gamma} = j \tan \beta \qquad (4.9)$$

Thus (4.4) becomes

$$Z_{\mathrm{cl}} = Z_0 j \tan \beta l \qquad (4.10)$$

In case Z_0 is real, representing a resistance, as is usually the case
in practice, we see that the impedance of the short-circuited line
is pure imaginary and is a pure reactance. It is useful to write
(4.10) in terms of the wave length λ of the disturbance on the
line, given by Eq. (1.27) as $\beta = 2\pi/\lambda$. Then we have

$$Z_{\mathrm{cl}} = Z_0 j \tan \frac{2\pi l}{\lambda} \qquad (4.11)$$

We remember that the tangent is zero when its argument is zero;
it increases, at first equaling its argument, then increasing more
rapidly, becoming infinite for the angle $\pi/2$. It then reverses
sign, decreasing from negative infinity to zero as the angle goes
from $\pi/2$ to π, then repeating the cycle, with periodicity of π.
Thus we see that the impedance of the short-circuited line starts
from zero for an infinitely short line (as it must be, on account of
the short circuit), becoming a positive reactance, or inductive
reactance, at first proportional to the length, and then increasing
more rapidly, until for $2\pi l/\lambda = \pi/2$, or the length l equal to one-
fourth wave length, the impedance becomes infinitely great.
Then the impedance changes sign, becoming negative or capacitative as the length increases from a quarter to a half wave length.
At a half wave length the impedance is again zero, as for zero
length, and increasing length carries us through the same cycle,
so that at three quarters of a wave length the impedance is again
infinite, and so on.

The reason for this periodicity is seen when we consider the
pattern of standing waves on the line. We have seen in Sec. 3
that for the short-circuited line, $Z_R = 0$, the amplitude B of the

reflected wave equals the amplitude A of the incident wave. Thus, from (3.3), the current at x is

$$i(x) = Ae^{j\omega t}(e^{-j\beta x} + e^{j\beta x})$$
$$= 2Ae^{j\omega t} \cos \beta x \tag{4.12}$$

The voltage, from (3.5), is

$$V(x) = Z_0 Ae^{j\omega t}(e^{-j\beta x} - e^{j\beta x})$$
$$= -2jZ_0 Ae^{j\omega t} \sin \beta x \tag{4.13}$$

In Fig. 8 we show current amplitude (proportional to $\cos \beta x$) and voltage amplitude (proportional to $- \sin \beta x$) as functions of distance along the line. We see that at the end of the line, the current has a maximum, while the voltage is zero (as is natural from the fact that the line is short-circuited). Thus the imped-

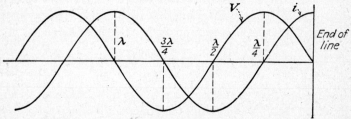

Fig. 8.—Standing waves of voltage and current near end of short-circuited line with no attenuation.

ance, or the ratio of V/i, is zero. On the other hand, a quarter wave length from the end, the voltage has come to a maximum, while the current is zero, so that the impedance is infinite. Increasing the distance changes the sign of the current, and hence of the impedance. We see that, in the standing wave pattern set up in the line, the current is always zero at odd numbers of quarter wave lengths from the end and that the voltage is zero at even numbers of quarter wave lengths from the end. These places where an amplitude of a standing wave is always zero are called nodes; the points midway between are antinodes or loops. We see that nodes are a half wave length apart, explaining the periodicity with this period, and furthermore the nodes of V are at the antinodes of i, and vice versa.

Next let us consider the short-circuited line with attenuation, for which α is not equal to zero. In this case the two traveling waves are not of equal amplitude, so that the exponentials do not combine, as in (4.12) and (4.13), to give a sinusoidal variation of voltage and current along the line. In this case we cannot use the value (4.11) for the impedance, but must instead use the general formula (4.4). Writing $\gamma = \alpha + j\beta$, this becomes

$$Z = Z_0 \tanh (\alpha + j\beta)l \qquad (4.14)$$

We should like to find the real and imaginary parts of Z, or the resistance R and reactance X of the line. To do this, we need the formula for the hyperbolic tangent of a complex number. For convenience, we tabulate a number of relations of hyperbolic functions, which can all be proved in an elementary way from the definitions of these functions in terms of the exponential functions. We have

$$\cosh x = \frac{e^x + e^{-x}}{2}, \qquad \sinh x = \frac{e^x - e^{-x}}{2}, \qquad \tanh x = \frac{\sinh x}{\cosh x}$$
$$(4.15)$$

$$\cosh (x \pm y) = \cosh x \cosh y \pm \sinh x \sinh y \qquad (4.16)$$
$$\sinh (x \pm y) = \sinh x \cosh y \pm \cosh x \sinh y \qquad (4.17)$$
$$\cosh^2 x - \sinh^2 x = 1 \qquad (4.18)$$
$$\cosh jx = \cos x, \qquad \sinh jx = j \sin x \qquad (4.19)$$
$$\cosh (x \pm jy) = \cosh x \cos y \pm j \sinh x \sin y \qquad (4.20)$$
$$\sinh (x \pm jy) = \sinh x \cos y \pm j \cosh x \sin y \qquad (4.21)$$

From (4.20) and (4.21), we have at once

$$\tanh (\alpha + j\beta)l = \frac{\sinh \alpha l \cos \beta l + j \cosh \alpha l \sin \beta l}{\cosh \alpha l \cos \beta l + j \sinh \alpha l \sin \beta l}$$
$$= \frac{\sinh \alpha l \cosh \alpha l + j \sin \beta l \cos \beta l}{\cosh^2 \alpha l \cos^2 \beta l + \sinh^2 \alpha l \sin^2 \beta l} \qquad (4.22)$$

Thus if the characteristic impedance Z_0 of the line is real, which we shall assume, the resistance R and reactance X of the short-circuited line of length l are given by

$$R = Z_0 \frac{\sinh \alpha l \cosh \alpha l}{\cosh^2 \alpha l \cos^2 \beta l + \sinh^2 \alpha l \sin^2 \beta l}$$
$$X = Z_0 \frac{\sin \beta l \cos \beta l}{\cosh^2 \alpha l \cos^2 \beta l + \sinh^2 \alpha l \sin^2 \beta l} \qquad (4.23)$$

A convenient way to plot these relations is to use an ordinary vector diagram, plotting R/Z_0 as abscissa, X/Z_0 as ordinate, and drawing lines of constant αl and lines of constant βl. This gives two families of curves, shown in Fig. 9. From the figure, it appears that the lines of constant αl and constant βl are two families of circles. This is in fact the case. For convenience, let

$$x = \frac{X}{Z_0}, \qquad r = \frac{R}{Z_0} \qquad (4.24)$$

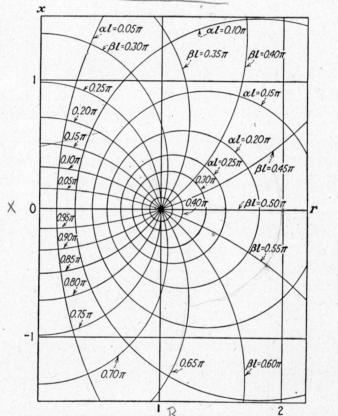

Fig. 9.—Resistance-reactance plot for transmission line.

Then the circles of constant αl have their centers on the r axis, at an abscissa which we shall call r_1, and all surround the point $r = 1$, $x = 0$, as we see from Fig. 9. The circles of constant βl have their centers on the x axis, at an ordinate which we shall call x_1, and all pass through the point $r = 1$, $x = 0$. We shall let the radii of these circles be ρ_α, ρ_β. The circles are shown in

Fig. 10. The equations of the circles, from elementary analytic geometry, are

$$\text{Const. } \alpha l: (r - r_1)^2 + x^2 = \rho_\alpha{}^2 \tag{4.25}$$
$$\text{Const. } \beta l: r^2 + (x - x_1)^2 = \rho_\beta{}^2 \tag{4.26}$$

The values of r_1, ρ_α, x_1, and ρ_β are given by the following expressions:

$$r_1 = \tfrac{1}{2}(\tanh \alpha l + \coth \alpha l) = \coth 2\alpha l \tag{4.27}$$
$$\rho_\alpha = \tfrac{1}{2}(\coth \alpha l - \tanh \alpha l) = \operatorname{csch} 2\alpha l \tag{4.28}$$
$$x_1 = \tfrac{1}{2}(\tan \beta l - \cot \beta l) = -\cot 2\beta l \tag{4.29}$$
$$\rho_\beta = \tfrac{1}{2}(\tan \beta l + \cot \beta l) = \csc 2\beta l \tag{4.30}$$

The proofs of Eqs. (4.25) and (4.26), expressing the lines of constant α and β as circles, are straightforward, though tedious.

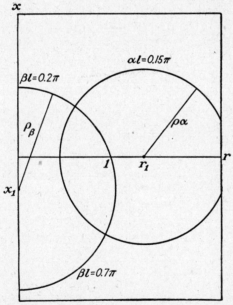

FIG. 10.—Circles of constant αl and constant βl.

We simply substitute x and r from (4.23) and the other quantities from Eqs. (4.27) to (4.30), and the equations prove to be satisfied. We give a proof of (4.25); that for (4.26) is very similar. We have with a little manipulation, reducing to a common denominator,

$$r = \frac{2 \sinh^2 \alpha l \cosh^2 \alpha l}{2 \sinh \alpha l \cosh \alpha l (\cosh^2 \alpha l \cos^2 \beta l + \sinh^2 \alpha l \sin^2 \beta 1)} \quad (4.31)$$

$$r_1 = \frac{2 \sinh^2 \alpha l \cosh^2 \alpha l + \cosh^2 \alpha l \cos^2 \beta l - \sinh^2 \alpha l \sin^2 \beta l}{2 \sinh \alpha l \cosh \alpha l (\cosh^2 \alpha l \cos^2 \beta l + \sinh^2 \alpha l \sin^2 \beta l)}$$

$$(4.32)$$

$$x = \frac{2 \sinh \alpha l \cosh \alpha l \sin \beta l \cos \beta l}{2 \sinh \alpha l \cosh \alpha l (\cosh^2 \alpha l \cos^2 \beta l + \sinh^2 \alpha l \sin^2 \beta l)} \quad (4.33)$$

Thus

$$(r - r_1)^2 + x^2$$

$$= \frac{\left[\begin{array}{c}(- \cosh^2 \alpha l \cos^2 \beta l + \sinh^2 \alpha l \sin^2 \beta l)^2 \\ + (2 \sinh \alpha l \cosh \alpha l \sin \beta l \cos \beta l)^2\end{array}\right]}{[2 \sinh \alpha l \cosh \alpha l (\cosh^2 \alpha l \cos^2 \beta l + \sinh^2 \alpha l \sin^2 \beta l)]^2}$$

$$= \frac{(\cosh^2 \alpha l \cos^2 \beta l + \sinh^2 \alpha l \sin^2 \beta l)^2}{[2 \sinh \alpha l \cosh \alpha l (\cosh^2 \alpha l \cos^2 \beta l + \sinh^2 \alpha l \sin^2 \beta l)]^2}$$

$$= \left(\frac{1}{2 \sinh \alpha l \cosh \alpha l}\right)^2 = \operatorname{csch}^2 2\alpha l = \rho_\alpha^2 \quad (4.34)$$

Thus we verify (4.25), and (4.26) is handled similarly.

Let us now see what our solutions for the resistance and reactance of the short-circuited line mean qualitatively. In many cases the attenuation constant α is small compared to the wave length constant β. In this case, the functions $r_1 = \coth 2\alpha l$ and $\rho_\alpha = \operatorname{csch} 2\alpha l$ from (4.27) and (4.28) stay approximately constant while $x_1 = -\cot 2\beta l$ and $\rho_\beta = \csc 2\beta l$, from (4.29) and (4.30), go through a complete cycle. As we see from Fig. 9 or Fig. 10, a line of constant αl is a circle surrounding the point $r = 1, x = 0$. Thus, so long as we can neglect the variation of αl, the point representing the impedance, in Fig. 9 or 10, traces out a circle of this type, as the length l of the line increases. Let us find how much $2\beta l$ increases as we go once around a circle of constant αl. As $2\beta l$ increases from zero to $\pi/2$, x_1 goes from $-\infty$ to zero, and ρ_β goes from ∞ to 1.. Using the relation (1.27), $\lambda = 2\pi/\beta$, we see that this corresponds to a length of one-eighth wave length. This corresponds to the circle marked $\beta l = 0.25\pi$ in Fig. 9, a circle of unit radius with its center at the origin. An increase of length of another eighth wave length makes x_1 go from zero to $+\infty$, while the radius ρ_β increases again from its minimum value of unity to infinity. Thus the circle representing $2\beta l = \pi$, or $l =$ a quarter wave length, degenerates to the axis of abscissas, corresponding to the notation of $\beta l = 0.5\pi$ on Fig. 9. This carries us halfway around a circle of constant αl; the next quarter wave length carries us back, the values of x_1 repeating exactly, those of ρ_β repeating with opposite sign (which means nothing, since it is only ρ_β^2 which appears in Eq. (4.26) for the circle). In this next quarter wave, we must use the parts of the circles of constant βl which extend to the opposite side of the point $r = 1$, $x = 0$. We see therefore that a half wave length along the line carries us completely around one of the circles surrounding this point $r = 1$, in the plot.

In an actual case, of course, αl is increasing at the same time that βl is, so that the point representing the impedance of the line does not travel around and around a single circle. Instead, we see that the radius

$$\rho_\alpha = \operatorname{csch} 2\alpha l = \frac{2}{e^{2\alpha l} - e^{-2\alpha l}} \qquad (4.35)$$

as given by (4.28) is infinite for $l = 0$ but decreases regularly as l increases, reducing to zero as l becomes infinite. For large values of αl, the first term of the denominator alone is important, and we have the limiting exponential decrease,

$$\rho_\alpha = 2e^{-2\alpha l} \qquad \text{for large } \alpha l \qquad (4.36)$$

Thus instead of staying on one circle, the point representing the impedance in the rx plane travels from one circle to another, of continuously decreasing radius. In other words, it travels on a spiral, gradually winding up onto the point $r = 1$, $x = 0$, or $R = Z_0$, $X = 0$, as we see from (4.24). The longer the line, the more closely the impedance approaches that of an infinite line, and the more completely the effect of the short-circuited end is lost. For a small attenuation, successive turns of the spiral have almost the same radius, so that it decreases gradually; for large attenuation it winds up rapidly. The limiting case of no attenuation would correspond to a spiral that did not wind up at all, so that the impedance would be a pure reactance, increasing to infinity, then changing sign, and repeating every half wave length, as we showed in Eq. (4.10). For a finite attenuation, the impedance of a quarter wave line is not infinite, as for no attenuation, and that of a half wave line is not zero; but nevertheless a quarter wave line has a very high impedance, which as we can see is a resistance, and a half wave line has a very low impedance. We can see this and other features of the

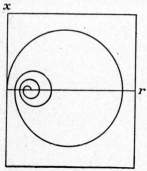

FIG. 11.—Reactance vs. resistance of short-circuited line, as function of length of line.

problem from the spiral as shown in Fig. 11.

The impedance is very large, and the circuit shows antiresonance, for odd numbers of quarter wave lengths, but it is very small, and the circuit shows resonance, for even numbers of quarter wave lengths, or for whole numbers of half wave lengths. This can be best shown by plotting the magnitude of the admittance as a function of β. We recall that the radius vector from the origin to a point of the spiral of Fig. 11 has a

magnitude equal to the impedance, so that the reciprocal of this vector has a length equal to the magnitude of the admittance. To get the mathematical formula for it, we may proceed as in the derivation of (4.22) and (4.23). Letting

Input admittance

$$Y = \frac{1}{Z_\ell} \tag{4.37}$$

where Z is given in (4.14), we have

$$Y = \frac{1}{Z_0} \coth (\alpha + j\beta)l \tag{4.38}$$

where

$$\coth (\alpha + j\beta)l = \frac{\sinh \alpha l \cosh \alpha l - j \sin \beta l \cos \beta l}{\sinh^2 \alpha l \cos^2 \beta l + \cosh^2 \alpha l \sin^2 \beta l} \tag{4.39}$$

The magnitude of Y is then the square root of the sum of the squares of the real and imaginary parts, or is

$$|Y| = \frac{1}{Z_0} \sqrt{\frac{\sinh^2 \alpha l \cosh^2 \alpha l + \sin^2 \beta l \cos^2 \beta l}{(\sinh^2 \alpha l \cos^2 \beta l + \cosh^2 \alpha l \sin^2 \beta l)^2}} \tag{4.40}$$

A plot of $|Y|$ as a function of βl, for a case where α is small compared to β, or where the attenuation is small, is given in Fig. 12. We see that the admittance goes to a sharp maximum whenever βl equals an integer times π, or when the length of the line is a whole number of half wave lengths. Mathematically this comes about in (4.40) because at these points $\sin \beta l = 0$, so that the second term in the denominator is zero, and the term $\sinh^2 \alpha l$ is small anyway on account of the assumed small value of α. Thus the denominator is small and the admittance large for these points.

As is usual in resonance curves, it is interesting to compute the behavior in the neighborhood of the resonant points. Let us continue to assume that α is small compared to β, so that

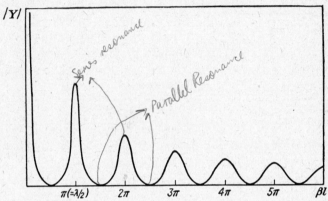

Fig. 12.—Magnitude of admittance of short-circuited line, as function of βl.

for the first few maxima $\sinh^2 \alpha l$ can be replaced by $(\alpha l)^2$, and $\cosh^2 \alpha l$ approximately equals unity. Furthermore, let

$$\beta l = n\pi + \delta \quad \text{(increment on either side of resonance)} \tag{4.41}$$

where δ is a small quantity. Then we shall have approximately $\sin^2 \beta l = \delta^2$, $\cos^2 \beta l = 1$. Using these values, we have

$$\text{(key expansion)} \quad |Y| = \frac{1}{Z_0} \frac{1}{\sqrt{(\alpha l)^2 + \delta^2}} \quad \text{(from 4.40)} \tag{4.42}$$

Since αl varies slowly compared to δ, we may replace it by its approximate value

$$l = \frac{n\pi}{\beta} \text{ near resonance} \qquad \alpha l \sim \frac{\alpha}{\beta} n\pi \tag{4.43}$$

We now see that $|Y|$ has the form of an ordinary resonance curve. This becomes a little more obvious if we compute its square:

$$Y^2 = \frac{1}{Z_0^2} \frac{1}{\delta^2 + \left(\dfrac{\alpha}{\beta} n\pi\right)^2} \quad \text{(Series resonance)} \tag{4.44}$$

at max.

$$Y^2 = \frac{1}{Z_0^2} \left[\left(\frac{1}{\frac{\alpha}{\beta}}\right) n\pi \right]^2 \quad \delta = 0$$

at ½ power pt

$$\frac{1}{2} Y^2 = \frac{1}{2 Z_0^2} \frac{1}{(\alpha/\beta \, n\pi)^2} = \frac{1}{Z_0^2} \frac{1}{\delta_1^2 + [\alpha/\beta \, n\pi]^2}$$

In this formula, δ can play the part either of the length of the line, at constant frequency, or of the frequency, at constant line length, as we see for instance from (2.14). We see from the formula that the admittance has a maximum for $\delta = 0$ but rapidly falls as the frequency departs from this value. Let us find the value of δ for which Y^2 has half its maximum value. This comes when

$$\delta_1 = \frac{\pm \alpha}{\beta} n\pi \qquad (4.45)$$

By this equation, two values of δ are determined, or two values of βl, equally spaced on opposite sides of the resonant value $\beta l = n\pi$, at which Y^2, and consequently the power delivered to the line, has half the value it would have at resonance. The ratio of the difference of these values to the value βl is the same as the ratio of the difference of frequencies to the resonant frequency, since the frequency is proportional to βl. Thus we have

$$\frac{\Delta f}{f} = \frac{2\alpha}{\beta} = \frac{2\delta_1}{\beta l} = \frac{2\frac{\alpha}{\beta}n\pi}{n\pi} \qquad (4.46)$$

As is common in the theory of resonant circuits, this ratio is defined as $1/Q$:

$$\frac{\Delta f}{f} = \frac{2\alpha}{\beta} = \frac{1}{Q} \qquad (4.47)$$

Equation (4.47) can serve as a definition of Q for a transmission line.

The Q as defined in (4.47) ties in with another definition often used with resonant circuits. For a series circuit containing resistance R, inductance L, and capacity C, Q is defined as

$$Q = \frac{\omega L}{R} \qquad (4.48)$$

the ratio of the inductive reactance to the resistance. We can set up an analogous definition for a line. Suppose as in Eq. (2.18) we consider a continuous line, with resistance R, inductance L, and capacity C per unit length. We shall assume the shunt conductance G to be zero, to get a closer analogy to the series circuit. Then from (2.18) we have

$$\frac{2\alpha}{\beta} = \frac{R}{\omega L} = \frac{1}{Q} \qquad (4.49)$$

where Q is given by (4.48), showing that this definition agrees with the previous one (4.47) based on the sharpness of resonance.

It is interesting and easy to get formulas for the impedances (which are pure resistances) of short-circuited lines of any whole number of quarter wave lengths. Let R_n be the resistance of a line n <u>quarter wave lengths</u> long. Then we have $\beta l = n\pi/2$. Substituting in Eq. (4.23), we have

Z_sc for definite length of line

$$R_n = Z_0 \tanh \alpha l \qquad \text{if } n \text{ is even}$$
$$= Z_0 \coth \alpha l \qquad \text{if } n \text{ is odd} \qquad (4.50)$$

The same result can be found at once from (4.27) and (4.28), since we note that

$$r = r_1 - \rho_\alpha \qquad \text{if } n \text{ is even}$$
$$= r_1 + \rho_\alpha \qquad \text{if } n \text{ is odd} \qquad (4.51)$$

OMIT

as is obvious from Figs. 10 and 11. Relations (4.51) are to be combined with the obvious one

$$\alpha l = \frac{\alpha}{\beta} \frac{\pi}{2} n = \frac{\pi}{4} \frac{n}{Q} \qquad (4.52)$$

for a line of n quarter wave lengths. Thus in particular, if α is small enough so that αl can be regarded as a small number for a line of a few quarter wave lengths, we have for the resistance of such a line

Series resonance (4.44)

αl small
tanh αl = αl
coth αl = 1/αl

$$R_n = \frac{\pi}{4} n \frac{Z_0}{Q} \qquad \text{if } n \text{ is even}$$
$$= \frac{4}{\pi} \frac{Q}{n} Z_0 \qquad \text{if } n \text{ is odd} \qquad (4.53)$$

since the hyperbolic tangent becomes equal to αl its argument, and the hyperbolic cotangent to the reciprocal of $\frac{1}{\alpha l}$ its argument, for small arguments. Taking account of the difference in notation (n here means the number of quarter wave lengths, and in (4.44) it means the number of half wave lengths), we see that the value (4.53) for n even agrees with the value given by (4.44) at resonance.

In the discussion from Eq. (4.4) to the present, we have taken up in a good deal of detail the short-circuited line. The discussion of the open-circuited line proceeds in an entirely parallel

way.   Using Eqs. (4.5) and (4.39) we can set up the resistance
and reactance of such a line as a function of βl.   We find

$$R = Z_0 \frac{\sinh \alpha l \cosh \alpha l}{\sinh^2 \alpha l \cos^2 \beta l + \cosh^2 \alpha l \sin^2 \beta l}$$

$$X = Z_0 \frac{- \sin \beta l \cos \beta l}{\sinh^2 \alpha l \cos^2 \beta l + \cosh^2 \alpha l \sin^2 \beta l} \qquad (4.54)$$

The plot of reactance vs. resistance again forms a spiral, similar
to that of Fig. 11, only now starting out when $l = 0$ from an
asymptotic direction at infinity, since in this limit we have

$$R = \frac{Z_0}{l} \frac{\alpha}{\alpha^2 + \beta^2}, \qquad X = -\frac{Z_0}{l} \frac{\beta}{\alpha^2 + \beta^2} \qquad (4.55)$$

The reactance again becomes zero when the length of the line
is a whole number of quarter wave lengths, but now the resonant
points, with small resistance and large admittance, come for odd
numbers of quarter wave lengths, and the antiresonances come
for even numbers of quarter wave lengths.   For the resistances
at these lengths we have

$$R_n = Z_0 \coth \alpha l \qquad \text{if } n \text{ is even}$$
$$= Z_0 \tanh \alpha l \qquad \text{if } n \text{ is odd} \qquad (4.56)$$

Using the same methods employed in deriving (4.53), we see
that for a line of small attenuation the resistances of the first few
resonances and antiresonances are given by

$$R_n = \frac{4}{\pi} \frac{Q}{n} Z_0 \qquad \text{if } n \text{ is even}$$
$$= \frac{\pi}{4} n \frac{Z_0}{Q} \qquad \text{if } n \text{ is odd} \qquad (4.57)$$

A great deal of the discussion that has been given for the
short-circuited and the open-circuited lines can be taken over
to the general case of a line with arbitrary terminal impedance.
In the general equation (4.3) for impedance, let us define a
quantity

$$(\gamma l)_0 = (\alpha l)_0 + j(\beta l)_0 \qquad (4.58)$$

by the equations

$$\cosh (\gamma l)_0 = \frac{Z_0}{\sqrt{Z_0^2 - Z_R^2}}, \qquad \sinh (\gamma l)_0 = \frac{Z_R}{\sqrt{Z_0^2 - Z_R^2}} \qquad (4.59)$$

Then the impedance becomes

$$Z = Z_0 \frac{\sinh \gamma l \cosh (\gamma l)_0 + \cosh \gamma l \sinh (\gamma l)_0}{\cosh \gamma l \cosh (\gamma l)_0 + \sinh \gamma l \sinh (\gamma l)_0}$$

$$= Z_0 \frac{\sinh [\gamma l + (\gamma l)_0]}{\cosh [\gamma l + (\gamma l)_0]}$$

$$= Z_0 \tanh [\gamma l + (\gamma l)_0] \tag{4.60}$$

Thus the impedance of the general line differs from that of the short-circuited line only in having an additive constant added to the quantity γl. The formulas corresponding to (4.23) for resistance and reactance are

$$\frac{R}{Z_0} = \frac{\sinh [\alpha l + (\alpha l)_0] \cosh [\alpha l + (\alpha l)_0]}{\left[\begin{array}{c} \cosh^2 [\alpha l + (\alpha l)_0] \cos^2 [\beta_l + (\beta_l)_0] \\ + \sinh^2 [\alpha l + (\alpha l)_0] \sin^2 [\beta l + (\beta l)_0] \end{array} \right]}$$

$$\frac{X}{Z_0} = \frac{\sin [\beta l + (\beta l)_0] \cos [\beta l + (\beta l)_0]}{\left[\begin{array}{c} \cosh^2 [\alpha l + (\alpha l)_0] \cos^2 [\beta l + (\beta l)_0] \\ + \sinh^2 [\alpha l + (\alpha l)_0] \sin^2 [\beta l + (\beta l)_0] \end{array} \right]} \tag{4.61}$$

It is obvious that the discussion leading to the spiral form of the reactance vs. resistance curve of Fig. 11 holds in the present case as well as in the special case of the short-circuited line, with the only difference that the spiral starts at the point R_R, X_R corresponding to the impedance of the terminal resistance, and then winds around as in Fig. 11. The initial values of r_1, etc., can be found in an obvious way from Eqs. (4.27) to (4.30), by substituting $(\alpha l)_0$ and $(\beta l)_0$ in place of αl and βl. After the spiral starts, its radius ρ_α decreases from its initial value gradually to zero, as in the

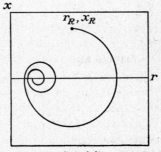

Fig. 13.—Spiral diagram representing line terminated by impedance R_R, X_R.

short-circuited case, and it is still true that an increase of length of half a wave length carries the point once around the spiral. The general form of such a spiral is shown in Fig. 13.

In drawing our spiral diagrams up to the present, we have assumed the characteristic impedance Z_0 of the line to be real. If however it is complex, the situation is altered in a very simple fashion. Our spirals are formed by plotting real and imaginary parts of $Z_0 \tanh [\gamma l + (\gamma l)_0]$, as was shown in Eq. (4.60). Every point in such a diagram is simply the representation of the corresponding impedance, in the complex plane. If now Z_0 is complex rather than real, we can write it as a product of its absolute magnitude, times an exponential representing rotation about the origin by the amount of its phase angle. The whole diagram, then, is to be rotated by this angle, to give the appropriate spiral in this case. In other words, there is still a spiral diagram if Z_0 is complex, but now the spiral winds up on a point that is no longer on the real axis.

Often it is desired to have a diagram representing, not the impedance, but its reciprocal the admittance. We see at once that

$$Y = \frac{1}{Z} = \frac{1}{Z_0} \coth [\gamma l + (\gamma l)_0] \qquad (4.62)$$

We may, however, rewrite this by noting that $\coth x = \tanh (x + \pi j/2)$, which follows simply from Eqs. (4.20) and (4.21). Then we have

$$Y = \frac{1}{Z_0} \tanh \left[\gamma l + (\gamma l)_0 + \frac{\pi j}{2} \right] \qquad (4.63)$$

Since $(\gamma l)_0 + \pi j/2$ is simply another constant, this shows that the curves obtained by plotting real and imaginary parts of the admittance are spirals of the same sort as those found by plotting real and imaginary parts of the impedance. The points that are close to the origin in the impedance spiral are of course far from the origin in the admittance spiral, on account of the reciprocal character of the two spirals. As we should expect, the impedance spiral is particularly useful when lines are connected in series; the admittance spiral when they are in parallel.

As a final point regarding transmission lines of finite length, we may note that a section of line is really a four-terminal network. In Sec. 1 we treated a lumped constant line as being made up of networks connected together; but now we consider them in a different way and consider a finite length of line, of arbitrary length, as a single network. Suppose we have a length of continuous transmission line, of length l, and ask what are the impedance coefficients Z_{aa}, Z_{ab}, Z_{bb}, of this line, as defined in Eq. (1.3). We can find these coefficients easily by using Eq. (4.3) for the impedance of a terminated line.   Thus suppose we have a section of line as in Fig. 14, terminated by an impedance Z_R. We regard the line as a network, as in Fig. 2.   Let us now find the input impedance of the network terminated by Z_R, equate it to the value (4.3), and thus find the impedance coefficients. Equations (1.3) become

$$V_a = Z_{aa}i_a + Z_{ab}i_b$$
$$V_b = -i_b Z_R = Z_{ab}i_a + Z_{bb}i_b \qquad (4.64)$$

In this equation, we have taken account of the fact that the output impedance V_b/i_b of the line must equal the terminal impedance, the negative sign coming on account of the assumption made in deriving Eq. (1.3), to the effect that V_b is positive

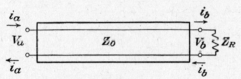

Fig. 14.—Section of transmission line as a network.

if the lower of the terminals b is at higher voltage.   Eliminating i_b between Eqs. (4.64), we now have

$$\frac{V_a}{i_a} = Z_a = Z_{aa} - \frac{Z_{ab}^2}{Z_{bb} + Z_R} \qquad (4.65)$$

This expression must be set equal to (4.3):

$$Z_a = Z(l) = Z_0 \frac{Z_0 \sinh \gamma l + Z_R \cosh \gamma l}{Z_0 \cosh \gamma l + Z_R \sinh \gamma l} \qquad (4.66)$$

To exhibit (4.65) in a form equivalent to (4.66), we reduce both terms of (4.65) to a common denominator and multiply numerator and denominator by $\sinh \gamma l$.   Then (4.65) becomes

$$Z_a = \frac{(Z_{aa}Z_{bb} - Z_{ab}^2) \sinh \gamma l + Z_{aa}Z_R \sinh \gamma l}{(Z_{bb} \sinh \gamma l + Z_R \sinh \gamma l)} \qquad (4.67)$$

(4.67) and (4.66) will now agree if we have

$$Z_{aa}Z_{bb} - Z_{ab}^2 = Z_0^2$$
$$Z_0 \cosh \gamma l = Z_{aa} \sinh \gamma l$$
$$Z_0 \cosh \gamma l = Z_{bb} \sinh \gamma l \qquad (4.68)$$

Solving these equations, making use of Eq. (4.18), we have

$$Z_{aa} = Z_{bb} = Z_0 \coth \gamma l, \qquad Z_{ab} = Z_0 \operatorname{csch} \gamma l \qquad (4.69)$$

Equation (4.69) furnish the necessary impedance coefficients for replacing a section of line of length l, propagation constant γ, and characteristic impedance Z_0, by a four-terminal network, according to Eqs. (1.3). Having these coefficients, we may replace the line by the network in any network calculation.

5. Composite Lines and Impedance Matching.—In practice, composite lines are often encountered, in which the properties change discontinuously from one section of the line to another. Two methods for handling such a line will occur to the reader at once. In the first place, we may use the ideas of reflection met in Sec. 3, in particular in the derivation of Eqs. (3.8) and (3.9). Referring back to the derivation of these formulas for reflection coefficient, we see that there is nothing compelling the terminal impedance Z_R to be a small, finite network. It can perfectly well be another infinite line, or terminated line, so long as its input impedance is Z_R. Thus we see that at a discontinuous boundary between two lines a reflection will be set up, as given by Eq. (3.8) or (3.9). If a wave approaches such a boundary from the left, there will be a reflected wave in the line to the left, a transmitted wave in the line to the right. Similarly a wave approaching a boundary from the right will give rise to a reflected wave on the right, a transmitted wave on the left. By assuming both a reflected and a transmitted wave in each section of line and imposing the boundary condition at each discontinuity that the voltage-current ratio must be the same on each side of the discontinuity, we have enough equations to determine all the amplitudes of the waves and to solve the problem completely.

This method of solving directly for the waves traveling in both directions in each section of line is not so convenient in practice as a method of computing impedances. The thing we generally want to know about a composite line is its input impedance. Suppose the line consists of several sections, of characteristic impedances Z_0, Z_0', Z_0'', etc., terminated by the terminal impedance Z_R; let the lengths of the corresponding sections be l, l', l'', etc. Thus the line has the appearance shown in Fig. 15. Then we may handle the problem in the following way. First we imagine the line broken at the terminals c in the figure and find the impedance of the line Z_0'' terminated by Z_R, the part of the line which we see looking to the right from the terminals c. We do this by the methods of Sec. 4. Next we break it at b, take the impedance just found as a terminal impedance, and find the impedance of the line of characteristic impedance Z_0' terminated by the combined impedance of the circuit to the right of c. This process can be continued indefinitely (one stage more in the special case shown in the figure), to give finally the impedance of the whole line, looking to the right from the input terminals a.

A transmission line is usually used for delivering power from a generator, which we may imagine to be connected across the left-hand end of the line, to a receiver, which may be imagined as an impedance across the right-hand end, a terminal impedance Z_R. We generally wish to design the line so as to transmit the maximum possible power from generator to receiver. We shall

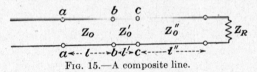

FIG. 15.—A composite line.

ask in this section what conditions the line must satisfy, in order to transmit this maximum power. There are conditions of two sorts. In the first place, it is obvious that if the line has attenuation, there will be power loss along the line. Thus, without any calculation at all, we see that the first condition for maximum power transfer is to have a line without attenuation. Such a line cannot be set up in practice, since resistance is inevitable; but in a well-designed microwave transmission line the attenuation is small, and we can proceed by assuming no attenuation as a first approximation and then by asking what effect the small attenuation necessarily present will have. Even a line without attenuation, however, will not necessarily transmit the maximum possible power from the generator to the receiver. The reason is the same as the well-known one encountered whenever a generator delivers power to a load. For maximum power transfer, the impedance of the generator must be matched to that of the load. There is a similar condition for impedance matching in microwave transmission theory, and as a first step in understanding it we shall write down the proof of the familiar impedance-matching theorem for generators and loads.

Let us suppose that, as in Fig. 16, we have a generator of e.m.f. E, internal impedance Z_I, connected to a load Z_R, and let

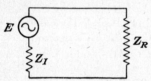

us find the condition on Z_R, for fixed E and Z_I, which will give us maximum power dissipation in the load. As a first step, we must remind ourselves how to find a power loss in terms of voltage and current. Suppose we have a voltage $V_0 e^{j\omega t}$ and a current

FIG. 16.—A generator connected to a load.

$i_0 e^{j\omega t}$, where V_0, and i_0 in general are complex and where the actual voltage and current are the real parts of the quantities written in complex form. That is, if

$$V_0 = V_r + jV_i, \qquad i_0 = i_r + ji_i \qquad (5.1)$$

the real voltage and current are

$$V_r \cos \omega t - V_i \sin \omega t, \qquad i_r \cos \omega t - i_i \sin \omega t \qquad (5.2)$$

The power dissipation in an element carrying the current above, with the voltage above between its terminals, is the product of current and voltage. This instantaneous power is

$$P = (V_r \cos \omega t - V_i \sin \omega t)(i_r \cos \omega t - i_i \sin \omega t)$$
$$= V_r i_r \cos^2 \omega t + V_i i_i \sin^2 \omega t - (V_r i_i + V_i i_r) \sin \omega t \cos \omega t \qquad (5.3)$$

Averaging over a cycle, the average of $\cos^2 \omega t$ and $\sin^2 \omega t$ is $\frac{1}{2}$, and the average of $\sin \omega t \cos \omega t$ is zero. Thus the average power can be written

$$\bar{P} = \frac{1}{2}(V_r i_r + V_i i_i) \qquad (5.4)$$

This expression can be written in a convenient way in terms of the complex voltage and current $V = V_0 e^{j\omega t}$ and $i = i_0 e^{j\omega t}$. Let us write the product of V and the complex conjugate of i. This is

$$V\bar{i} = V_0 \bar{i}_0 = (V_r + jV_i)(i_r - ji_i)$$
$$= V_r i_r + V_i i_i + j(V_i i_r - V_r i_i) \qquad (5.5)$$

Except for the factor $\frac{1}{2}$, the real part of (5.5) is just the same as the expression (5.4). Thus we may write for the average power

$$\bar{P} = \frac{1}{2} \operatorname{Re} V\bar{i} \qquad (5.6)$$

Equation (5.6) gives the standard formula for power dissipation in a network element in which the current i flows, with a voltage V

between terminals.   If we have

$$V = iZ = i(R + jX) \tag{5.7}$$

where Z is the impedance, R the resistance, and X the reactance of the network element, then Eq. (5.6) can be rewritten

$$\bar{P} = \frac{1}{2}|i|^2 R = \frac{1}{2}|V|^2 \frac{R}{R^2 + X^2} \tag{5.8}$$

where $|i|^2$ and $|V|^2$ are the squares of the magnitudes of i and V respectively.

Using these results, let us return to our network of Fig. 16 and find the power dissipated in the load.   We have

$$E = i(Z_I + Z_R) \tag{5.9}$$

where i is the current flowing in the circuit.   The voltage across Z_R is then

$$V = iZ_R \tag{5.10}$$

The average power dissipated in Z_R is

$$P = \frac{1}{2}|i|^2 R_R = \frac{1}{2} \frac{|E|^2 R_R}{|Z_I + Z_R|^2} \tag{5.11}$$

where R_R is the real part and X_R the imaginary part, of the impedance Z_R, with similar expressions for Z_I.   Rewriting, this becomes

$$\bar{P} = \frac{1}{2} \frac{|E|^2 R_R}{(R_I + R_R)^2 + (X_I + X_R)^2} \tag{5.12}$$

We now wish to choose the terminal impedance, R_R and X_R, to make this dissipated power a maximum.   First we choose X_R. By inspection, or by setting the derivative with respect to X_R equal to zero, we see that X_R must be so chosen that the total reactance of the circuit is zero, or the circuit is resonant:

$$X_R = -X_I \tag{5.13}$$

That is, if the generator has an inductive reactance, the load must have a capacitive reactance, and vice versa.   Assuming this condition and differentiating (5.12) with respect to R_R, we have the additional condition

$$\frac{d\bar{P}}{dR_R} = 0 = \frac{1}{2}|E|^2 \frac{R_I - R_R}{(R_I + R_R)^3} \tag{5.14}$$

For this condition to be satisfied, we must have

$$R_R = R_I \qquad (5.15)$$

or the resistances of generator and load must be equal.   In this case, equal powers will be dissipated in the load and in the internal resistance of the generator.   These conditions, that the generator and load must have equal resistances and opposite reactances, are the conditions of impedance match for maximum power transfer to the load.

Now let us ask what similar conditions hold with a transmission line.   Let us assume a generator of e.m.f. E, internal impedance Z_I, feeding power into a line, which is terminated by a load Z_R. The line may be a composite one, as complicated as we please. We now imagine the line broken at an arbitrary point and ask

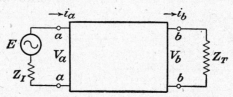

FIG. 17.—Equivalent circuit for generator connected to load through transmission line.

what the condition is for maximum power transfer through the line at this point.   Having found this condition, we can use it to discuss the general problem of optimum conditions for power transfer.   Using the method discussed at the end of Sec. 4, we can replace the part of the line to the left of our arbitrary point by a four-terminal network (though if the line is a composite one the impedance coefficients will not be given by the simple values (4.69)).   The whole terminated line to the right of the arbitrary point can be replaced by a single impedance Z_T. Let us then, as in Fig. 17, assume an equivalent circuit and find the power dissipated in Z_T.   The equations for the four-terminal network are

$$V_a = E - i_a Z_I = Z_{aa} i_a + Z_{ab} i_b$$
$$V_b = -i_b Z_T = Z_{ab} i_a + Z_{bb} i_b \qquad (5.16)$$

Eliminating i_a, we find

$$E = \frac{Z_{ab}^2 - (Z_{aa} + Z_I)(Z_{bb} + Z_T)}{Z_{ab}} i_b \qquad (5.17)$$

By (5.8), the average power dissipation in $Z_T = \frac{1}{2}|i_b|^2 R_T$, where R_T is the resistive part of Z_T. This can be rewritten

$$\bar{P} = \frac{1}{2} \frac{|E|^2 R_T |Z_{ab}|^2}{|Z_{ab}^2 - (Z_{aa} + Z_I)(Z_{bb} + Z_T)|^2} \qquad (5.18)$$

Rather than rewrite this complicated expression in terms of resistances and reactances, we leave it in this form, remembering that the denominator is the square of the absolute magnitude of a complex quantity or is the product of the complex quantity with its complex conjugate. We now wish to apply the condition that $\bar{P}$ is a maximum with respect to variations of the terminal impedance Z_T, keeping the input e.m.f. E and the properties of the input line, described by Z_{aa}, Z_{bb}, Z_{ab}, constant. We can get our information by differentiating (5.18) with respect to R_T. Doing this, we have, after some manipulation,

$$\frac{dP}{dR_T} = 0 = \frac{1}{2} |E|^2 |Z_{ab}|^2$$

$$\frac{\mathrm{Re}\ [\overline{Z_{ab}^2 - (Z_{aa} + Z_I)(Z_{bb} + Z_T)}][Z_{ab}^2 - (Z_{aa} + Z_I)(Z_{bb} - \bar{Z}_T)]}{|Z_{ab}^2 - (Z_{aa} + Z_I)(Z_{bb} + Z_T)|^4}$$

$$(5.19)$$

To make this equal to zero, we set the last factor equal to zero, giving

$$\overline{Z_T} = R_T - jX_T = Z_{bb} - \frac{Z_{ab}^2}{Z_{aa} + Z_I} \qquad (5.20)$$

By a method entirely analogous to that used in deriving Eq. (4.65), we can show that the expression on the right of (5.20) is the impedance looking to the left from the arbitrary point where we are applying our condition, provided we replace the generator by an impedance equal to its internal impedance. Our result, then, is that for maximum power transfer, the impedance looking to the right from our arbitrary point must be the complex conjugate of the impedance looking to the left from the same point; the reactances of the two half networks must be equal and opposite, an inductive reactance balancing a capacitive reactance, and the resistances must be equal. Obviously our earlier theorem of (5.13) and (5.15), relating to a simple generator and load, is a special case of this more general theorem.

The theorem we have just stated gives the general condition for impedance matching. If however the transmission line joining generator and receiver is resistanceless, so that there are no losses in it, we can prove a remarkable further theorem, no matter how complicated the line may be: if the conditions of impedance match are satisfied at one point of such a lossless line, they are automatically satisfied at all points. We can first see why this result should hold physically and can then prove it mathematically. If the line has no losses, that means that the only power dissipation must be in the generator and the receiver; the complete power output of the generator, aside from what is absorbed in its own internal resistance, is delivered to the receiver. The flow of power through any cross section of the line must then be the same and equal to the flow of power into the receiver. If then we match impedances at one point of the line, we ensure that the maximum possible power crosses this point and hence is delivered to the receiver. Further matching at other points must lead to the same condition and hence must automatically be secured by matching at one point.

To prove our theorem mathematically, let us actually show that if the impedance match conditions are satisfied at one point of a resistanceless line, they are satisfied at another. We shall assume the composite line to be made up of a set of sections of uniform line, connected in series. First we shall show our theorem for two points within the same uniform section of line, and later we shall extend it to points in different sections. Let us consider two points a and b in a uniform section. We may replace the whole circuit to the left of a by an impedance Z_l, the whole circuit to the right of b by an impedance Z_R, and the line between a and b by a four-terminal network with the impedance coefficients given in (4.69), where Z_0 is real, γ pure imaginary, as we should have for a line without dissipation. From (4.65), the impedance looking to the right from a is

$$Z_{aa} - \frac{Z_{ab}^2}{Z_{bb} + Z_R} \qquad (5.21)$$

where

$$Z_{aa} = Z_{bb} = -jZ_0 \cot \beta l, \qquad Z_{ab} = -jZ_0 \csc \beta l \qquad (5.22)$$

which follow from (4.69) by putting $\gamma = j\beta$. By the condition of impedance matching which we assume at a, the expression

(5.21) equals the complex conjugate of Z_I. We now wish to prove from this that the conditions of impedance match are satisfied at b; that is, that the impedance looking to the left from b, which we can show is

$$Z_{bb} - \frac{Z_{ab}^2}{Z_{aa} + Z_I} \qquad (5.23)$$

by methods like those used in the derivation of (5.21), is the complex conjugate of Z_R. First we set the expression (5.21) equal to $\bar{Z}_I$. The resulting equation can be written

$$Z_{ab}^2 = (Z_{aa} - \bar{Z}_I)(Z_{bb} + Z_R) \qquad (5.24)$$

The equation which we wish to prove, setting (5.23) equal to $\bar{Z}_R$, is

$$Z_{ab}^2 = (Z_{aa} + Z_I)(Z_{bb} - \bar{Z}_R) \qquad (5.25)$$

Remembering that according to (5.22) the quantities Z_{aa}, Z_{bb}, Z_{ab} are all pure imaginaries, the conjugate of (5.25) is

$$Z_{ab}^2 = (-Z_{aa} + \bar{Z}_I)(-Z_{bb} - Z_R) \qquad (5.26)$$

which is equivalent to (5.24), showing that our theorem is proved.

We have now shown that if the impedance match conditions are satisfied at one point of a uniform resistanceless line, they are satisfied at another arbitrary point of the same line. Thus they are satisfied at the end of that uniform line. This however is the beginning of another section of uniform line; if the conditions are satisfied at the beginning of this section, by our same theorem they are satisfied at any arbitrary point of it, and by extension of this method they are satisfied at any point of the composite line, so long as each section of the line is resistanceless, so that by (5.22) the coefficients of impedance are pure imaginary. If there were losses in any section of the line, the corresponding impedance coefficients would have both real and imaginary parts, so that we could not perform the transformation from (5.25) to (5.24) by taking conjugates, and the theorem would not be true.

Suppose we have a generator, connected by a lossless line to a load. The lossless line and load can be replaced by a single equivalent impedance, so that we can reduce the problem to the elementary one of a generator connected with a simple load. Then, as we showed in (5.13) and (5.15), the condition for maxi-

mum power output from generator to load is that the reactances
of generator and load should be equal and opposite, the resistances equal, and in this case the power dissipations in generator
and load are equal. The same thing must hold in this more
general case, if by load we understand the composite impedance
made up of transmission line and load. Since the line absorbs no
power, all power delivered by the generator goes into the actual
load, and this power is then equal to that used up in the generator. The impedance-matching condition may be applied directly
at the generator, and we see that for maximum power transfer
the internal impedance of the network composed of line and load
must be the conjugate of the internal impedance of the generator.
If this condition is applied and if as we are assuming there are
no losses in the line, then we have seen that the condition of
impedance match is automatically satisfied at every point of the
line.

This does not mean, however, that the load itself must have
an impedance that has any fixed relation to the impedance of
the generator. The lossless transmission line connecting them
has the properties of a transformer. We may replace the line by
a four-terminal network. Then power is fed in from the generator at one voltage and current, or with one impedance, and it
is fed out from the other end to the load with another voltage
and current, or another impedance, but on account of the lossless
nature of the line no power is lost in the line, so that the product
of input voltage and current equals the product of output voltage
and current, the characteristic of a lossless transformer. We
may, then, use a section of transmission line to connect a generator and a load, as a matching transformer, so as to satisfy the
conditions of maximum power transfer. This is a very important use of sections of transmission line, and we shall next
examine it in more detail. We shall show, in a simple manner,
that a section of lossless transmission line can be chosen, such
as to join an arbitrary generator to an arbitrary load, provided
the characteristic impedance of the line (which will necessarily
be real) and the length are properly chosen.

The theorem we have just mentioned can be proved analytically
without trouble, by setting up an equation

$$\bar{Z}_I = Z_{aa} - \frac{Z_{ab}^2}{Z_{bb} + Z_T} \qquad (5.27)$$

similar to (5.20) and by stating that the impedance of the network formed from the line and the terminal impedance Z_T must be the conjugate of the input impedance Z_I. Then we replace Z_{aa}, Z_{bb}, Z_{ab} by the values (5.22) appropriate to a definite length of lossless line. Equation (5.27) then involves the unknowns Z_0, the characteristic impedance of the line, and βl, determining its length in wave lengths. Equation (5.27) really furnishes two equations, one from its real and one from its imaginary part. Thus we have enough equations to determine the two unknowns, and it is a matter of a little algebra to do this. The result, however, can be interpreted much more simply in a resistance-reactance diagram than analytically. For this reason we give only a geometrical discussion. As in Fig. 18, let Z_I, Z_T be represented by two points in the complex plane, and construct the circle passing through these two points and having its center on the real axis. The center of this circle can be found at once as the intersection of the perpendicular bisector of the line joining the points Z_I, Z_T, with the real axis. This circle is then one of the type shown in Fig. 10, and the points on it represent the impedance at various points of a lossless line. The characteristic impedance of this line can be found, as we see for instance from Eqs. (4.56), as the square root of the product of the two resistance values corresponding to the intersections of the circle with the real axis, and the required length of line can be found from the other set of circles in Fig. 10, by noting the values of βl corresponding to the points Z_I

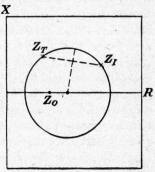

FIG. 18.—Resistance-reactance plot for matching transformer between impedances Z_I and Z_T.

and Z_T. The commonest case is that in which Z_I and Z_T are real. In that case these values are themselves the intercepts, and the required characteristic impedance of the line is

$$Z_0 = \sqrt{Z_I Z_T} \tag{5.28}$$

Furthermore, it is obvious in this case that the length of the line is a quarter wave length (or three quarters, or in general any odd number of quarter wave lengths). Thus we arrive at the very important quarter wave transformer, a quarter wave length of lossless line with characteristic impedance equal to the geometric mean of two resistances, and so designed that it matches these resistances to each other, so that a generator having a real impedance equal to the first resistance will be properly matched by the transformer to a load having a real impedance equal to the second resistance. It is plain, however, that the quarter wave transformer is only a special case, and that to match any two impedances we can equally well set up a transformer of this type, if only the length and characteristic impedance are properly chosen. Another simple case is the half wave transformer. This matches any arbitrary real impedance to itself, since after a half wave length (or any whole number of half wave lengths) the circle returns to its starting place. In other words, if a generator and load have equal resistances and no reactances, so that they are matched without a transmission line between them, we can insert between them any whole number of half wave lengths of lossless transmission line of arbitrary characteristic impedance, and they will still be matched, so that just as much power will flow to the load as before.

We have seen some of the properties of lossless lines in connecting a generator to a load. We have seen that an arbitrary generator can be connected to an arbitrary load by a properly chosen uniform transmission line, of definitely determined characteristic impedance and of length which must be a definite value, or this plus any number of half wave lengths, in such a way as to get the maximum possible power transfer from generator to load. We have seen that we can use composite lines; for, if we for example cut the line just described at any point where the impedance is real (that is, where the impedance circle in the complex diagram cuts the real axis), we may insert at that point an arbitrary number of half wave lengths of line of arbitrary characteristic impedance, without destroying the impedance match. We may now ask, how does this situation change if parts of the lines have attenuation? This is essentially a practical question. Certainly attenuation anywhere in the line will prevent some of the power delivered by the generator from reaching the load, and in any particular case we can calculate how much this power loss will be. Let us however consider the actual sort

of systems likely to be used and see what their situation is
regarding attenuation.

An ordinary transmission system consists of three parts: a
generator, transmission line, and receiver. From the standpoint
of circuit theory, the generator can be replaced by a network or
by a more or less complicated set of transmission lines, of small
length; the transmission line is a long, uniform line; the receiver is
another network or set of short transmission lines. All these
sections of line actually must have some attenuation, even though
it may be small. Generally the transmission part of the line
is much longer than the parts representing generator and receiver,
so that the losses in the line, other things being equal, will be
greater than in the generator and receiver. Let us then ask,
how can we minimize these losses in the transmission line?

So far, we have been quite forgetting reflections; we have paid
no attention to whether there were reflections in a given section
of line or not, and as far as impedance matching between genei-
ator and receiver is concerned, this is entirely immaterial. We
shall now show, however, that to minimize losses it is very
desirable that there be no reflected wave in the main length of
transmission line. This leads us, then, to an additional require-
ment for impedance matching: not only do we try to get the
maximum power from generator to receiver, but we try to do
it in such a way as to have no reflected wave in the line. Before
seeing why this is necessary, we can see very easily the conditions
that it imposes. A practical transmission line generally has an
almost exactly real characteristic impedance, or pure resistance,
and generally this characteristic resistance is determined by some
sort of conditions of convenience, as for example convenient
dimensions. If a single wave transmitted to the right, without
reflected wave, is to be the form of disturbance in this line, then
by the conditions of Sec. 4 we know that it must be terminated
at each end by an impedance equal to its characteristic resistance.
Thus both generator and receiver must be matched to the line,
in the sense of having impedances equal to its characteristic
resistance. Since generator and receiver by themselves would
not ordinarily happen to have impedances of this value, transformer networks must ordinarily be inserted between them and
the line, to transform their impedances to the value necessary
to match the line. These networks, as we have seen in the

preceding paragraphs and in Fig. 18, can be made of suitably
chosen lengths of lossless, or practically lossless, lines of suitable
characteristic impedance.   The matching can also be done by
other devices, some of which we shall describe later.   This type
of impedance matching, in which generator and receiver are
matched to the line by transformers, is as we have just seen not
primarily for the purpose of transmitting maximum power from
generator to receiver; it indirectly accomplishes this purpose by
reducing standing waves and reflections in the transmission line,
thereby reducing losses in the line due to attenuation.   If there
were no attenuation in the lines, this form of impedance matching
would be unnecessary.

Let us now fill in the gap in our argument, by showing that in
an attenuating line, the presence of standing waves, or of reflections, increases the losses.   The reason qualitatively is simple.
If there are reflections, the power transmitted to the right is the
difference of that transmitted by the direct and the reflected
waves.   The greater the reflections, the greater the intensity of
both direct and reflected waves must be, in order that their
difference may represent a constant net power flow.   But both
direct and reflected waves are attenuated, in proportion to their
intensity.   Thus large reflections mean large losses through
attenuation, for a fixed net power flow.   This reasoning is so
obvious that, unless an actual computation of losses is needed,
it seems hardly worth while to write down the analytical formulation of the problem.   In addition to the losses due to resistance
in the line, there is another closely related form of losses, important in practice, which also acts to make reflections undesirable
in transmission lines.   Particularly in coaxial lines, the limit to
the possible transmitted power is generally set by difficulties of
corona or sparking between the two conductors of the line.   This
difficulty is obviously more serious, the greater the voltage on the
line.   For a given flow of power, the voltage is greater, the more
intense the reflected wave, since again it is the difference of the
two waves that determines the net power flow, but the sum, at
the voltage maxima, which is effective in producing corona.
The greatest practical reason for avoiding reflections is to reduce
the magnitude of these voltage maxima.

We can now form a clear picture of the actual procedure used
for impedance matching: the characteristic impedance of the

line is matched to both generator and load by transformer networks or some other device. If we neglect the losses in the transformers, as we usually can on account of their relatively short length in terms of wave lengths, then by this matching we secure the maximum power transfer from generator to line and from line to load, and by avoiding standing waves on the line we obtain the minimum possible loss on the line as a result of heating and of corona losses. Our next task is to examine in more detail the transformer networks used in joining line to generator or load. As a first step, we note that in general it is unavoidable that there should be a reflected wave in a transformer network. For the only object of the transformer is to match a line of one impedance to a load of another, and this can be done only if the transformer has still a different characteristic impedance, which requires that standing waves be set up at the junction of transformer and line. The same objections to standing waves, which we have already raised in connection with the line, hold against standing waves in transformers; they are not serious only because the transformer network is small, the line long, so that losses in the transformer are less important in their total effect than losses in the line. They must be minimized, however, and for this reason reflections should be made as small as possible in transformer design. At the same time there is another difficulty with transformers. They can be easily designed for a given wave length. For another wave length, however, they are no longer correct to perform their function of impedance matching. They are, in other words, resonant or selective. We shall find that the greater the reflections in them, the more selective they are, so that as the reflected wave approaches the incident wave in intensity, and the whole disturbance approaches a standing wave, the transformer approaches a resonant circuit, which will pass only a very narrow band of wave lengths, reflecting all others. To make a nonselective or nonresonant transformer, we then must take the same steps that would lead to small reflections and hence small losses in the transformer. We shall find that this is best done by making the change in characteristic impedance from line to load a gradual change, rather than a sharp one, as we have considered up to date. The more gradual this change, the less the reflections, and the less selective is the transformer. We shall now

proceed to consider the resonant or selective properties of transformers and to see how these are affected by gradual changes in
properties.

Although it is not hard to discuss these problems analytically,
it is qualitative results that we are primarily interested in, and
they can be found easily by graphical methods. Let us first
consider a quarter wave matching transformer, for matching
two pure resistances. For definiteness, let the terminal impedance Z_T be greater than the desired input impedance Z_I. Then
in Fig. 19 we show a resistance-reactance diagram for a quarter

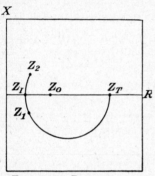

wave line of characteristic impedance
equal to the geometric mean of Z_I
and Z_T, connecting these two impedances. The semicircle includes the
impedances of the various points of
the quarter wave line, and it ends at
Z_I, showing that the line terminated
by Z_T has an impedance Z_I, matching the input. Now let us ask what
would happen if the wave length
changed. Then the line, though of
the same physical size as before, will
no longer be a quarter wave length
long, for the wave length is different.

FIG. 19.—Resistance-reactance plot for quarter-wave
transformer.

In the diagram of Fig. 19, the circle will be the same, but
the line will correspond to more or less than a semicircle.
Thus the impedance of the combination will be like Z_1 or Z_2,
depending on whether the new wave length is longer or shorter
than the original one, and there will be a net reflected wave,
since the impedance no longer matches the input impedance Z_I.
Furthermore, for a given Z_I, it is clear that if Z_T is very different
from Z_I the circle will be very large, so that a small change of
phase angle will correspond to having Z_1 or Z_2 very far from Z_I.
That is, in this case, the reactive component of the impedance
of the line terminated by Z_T is very large, even for a small change
of wave length or frequency. In such a case the resonance
would be sharp and the Q large. It is not hard to set up a
formula for the Q in such a case and to show that it increases
as the ratio Z_T/Z_I increases, while it becomes smaller as Z_T
approaches Z_I. For this case the transformer is almost com-

pletely nonselective. We notice at the same time that the greater the ratio Z_T/Z_I, the greater the discontinuity of characteristic impedance between input and transformer, so that by our reflection equation (3.9) the greater is the reflected wave in the transformer. Thus we verify our previous statement that the case of large discontinuity of impedance has large reflection and is very selective.

It is not hard to devise an impedance-matching device consisting of two successive quarter wave lines of properly chosen impedances, which will give a reflectionless impedance match, just as a single quarter wave line will at a properly chosen frequency, but which will also give an approximate match over

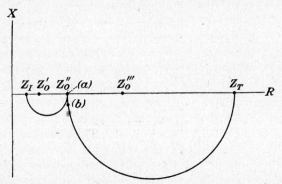

FIG. 20.—Matching transformer of two quarter-wave sections.

a much wider frequency range. The principle of this device is shown in Fig. 20. The problem is to match an input line of characteristic impedance Z_I to an output impedance Z_T. We do this by two quarter wave lines of characteristic impedances Z_0' and Z_0''', so chosen that

$$\frac{Z_0'''}{Z_0'} = \left(\frac{Z_0'}{Z_I}\right)^2 = \left(\frac{Z_T}{Z_0'''}\right)^2. \qquad (5.29)$$

These relations are more easily expressed in terms of the logarithms of the impedances. Then we merely say that on a logarithmic scale, the increment from Z_0' to Z_0''' is twice that from Z_I to Z_0', or from Z_0''' to Z_T. To see how this device works, we draw an additional point at Z_0'' in Fig. 20, such that Z_0'' is the geometric mean of Z_0' and Z_0''', so that Z_I, Z_0', Z_0'', Z_0''', and Z_T are spaced at equal intervals on a logarithmic scale. Then the point a, with impedance Z_0'', represents the impedance of the terminal impedance Z_T and the quarter wave line of impedance Z_0'''. The other line, of characteristic impedance Z_0', is then terminated by the network of impedance Z_0'', so that the impedance of the whole device looking into Z_0' is Z_I, and the network is matched to the input line. But now consider a slightly different wave length, say a slightly longer one. The impedance of the line Z_0''' terminated by Z_T will no longer be the value Z_0'' at the point a but will correspond to a point b, not quite so far around the circle. This will correspond to the terminal impedance for the line of impedance Z_0'.   In traversing the line Z_0', then, the point must start at b, which lies almost exactly on the circle surrounding Z_0', and must go around this circle. Since the wave length is longer, however, the point will not have to go a whole semicircle but will stop at a point which to a first approximation will be the same as Z_I, the impedance which was found for the original wave length. Thus we see that with this network a small change of wave length makes a much smaller change in transmission than it did for the single quarter wave matching line.

We can get a better understanding of this device by considering reflections at discontinuities. This method is useful in considering any impedance-matching device, and we shall think of it first in connection with the ordinary quarter wave transformer. The object of this transformer is to eliminate the reflection that would be present if the impedance Z_I were connected directly to Z_T. The method of eliminating reflections is based on the interference between waves. Two waves half a wave length apart are in opposite phases, and the sum of them, if their amplitudes are numerically equal, is zero. The fundamental principle behind the elimination of reflections is then to have each reflected wave canceled by another wave of equal amplitude and opposite phase. In order that this second wave may have traveled half a wave length farther than the first, it is obvious that it must have gone a quarter wave length farther up the line, and correspondingly a quarter of a wave length back, before it meets the original reflected wave. In other words, two discontinuities in characteristic impedance, of such magnitude as to give equal amplitudes of reflected waves and spaced a quarter of a wave length apart, will give no net reflection and hence will not introduce reflections into the line. Let us now apply this principle to the quarter wave line for matching pure resistances. First we notice, from Eq. (3.9), that the reflection coefficient at a discontinuity depends on the ratio of characteristic impedances. Thus this reflection coefficient between a line of characteristic impedance Z_0 and one of characteristic impedance Z_1 can be written

$$\frac{B}{A} = \frac{Z_0 - Z_1}{Z_0 + Z_1} = \frac{1 - (Z_1/Z_0)}{1 + (Z_1/Z_0)} \qquad (5.30)$$

depending only on the ratio Z_1/Z_0. Then we can see in a crude way that for the reflections at the two boundaries of a quarter wave transformer to be equal, so that the reflected waves should

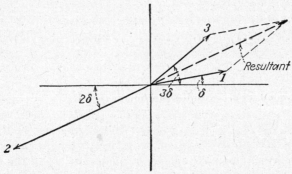

FIG. 21.—Vector diagram illustrating matching with two quarter-wave sections.

cancel, we should have the ratio Z_0/Z_I of the characteristic impedance of the line to the input impedance equal to the ratio Z_T/Z_0 of the terminal impedance to the characteristic impedance. But this leads just to our previous condition that Z_0^2 should equal $Z_I Z_T$, or that the characteristic impedance of the line should be the geometric mean of the impedances of input and output.

Now we can return to our double quarter wave transformer of Fig. 20 and show why it works as well as it does. Let us imagine that we station ourselves at a point in the input line and draw the amplitude and phase of the wave reflected from each discontinuity, as it reaches us. With the wave length for which the device is designed, there will be three reflected waves, coming from the junction between Z_I and Z_0', that between Z_0' and Z_0''',

and that between Z_0''' and Z_T. The first and third will be in
phase; the second will be 180° out of phase and twice as great in
amplitude, so that it will just cancel the other two.   But now
assume that the wave length has changed.   The phases of the
three waves will have been displaced by amounts δ, 2δ, and 3δ,
respectively, where δ is a small quantity.   Thus they will be
represented by the vectors 1, 2, and 3 in Fig. 21.   It is seen
from the figure that the resultant of 1 and 3, shown by the dotted
vector, is very nearly equal and opposite to vector 2, so that the
vector sum of all three is very nearly zero in this case, as well
as for the original wave length.

The device just described was suggested to the writer by Dr.
W. W. Hansen, who points out that similar devices, becoming

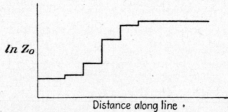

Fig. 22.—Logarithm of characteristic impedance as function of distance along
line, for case where discontinuities are in ratio 1:4:6:4:1.

progressively less selective, can be made by using more and more
sections, with the discontinuities in the logarithms of the impedances following the laws

$$1\ 2\ 1$$
$$1\ 3\ 3\ 1$$
$$1\ 4\ 6\ 4\ 1, \text{ etc.} \tag{5.31}$$

or the successive sets of binomial coefficients.   As more and
more sections are inserted, according to this rule, we see that
the effect is to start the change of impedance gradually, so that
a curve of impedance against distance along the line would be
fairly smooth, joining the initial to the final impedance without
any sudden change of slope.   Such a curve for the case 1 4 6 4 1
is shown in Fig. 22.   The impedance diagram corresponding to
this case is shown in Fig. 23.   This diagram is equivalent to
that of Fig. 20, and the same sort of explanation applies to the
present device that applies to that one.   It is more obvious in
Fig. 23 than in Fig. 20, however, that we are approaching a

gradual, smooth transition from one limiting characteristic impedance to the other. As this happens, since each discontinuity of impedance becomes small, it is plain from the reflection equation (5.30) that the amplitude of the reflected wave in each section of the transformer will become smaller, so that

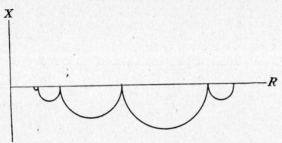

FIG. 23.—Resistance-reactance plot for case of Fig. 22.

we verify our statement that nonselective transformers tend to have small reflections.

An interesting composite line, which can be used to match impedances without reflection, is the exponential line. This is a line in which the impedance varies by a constant fraction for equal increments of length, so that the logarithm of the impedance is proportional to the length. We can make a composite

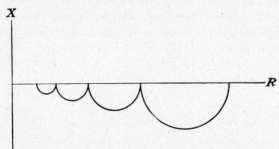

FIG. 24.—Resistance-reactance plot for exponential line.

line of this type out of quarter wave sections, with constant increment of the logarithm of the characteristic impedance from one section to the next. The impedance diagram of such an exponential line is shown in Fig. 24. The same sort of argument used in the discussion of Fig. 20 would show that here too the impedance matching produced by such a line is relatively insensitive to small changes in wave length. This exponential line will be discussed more in the next section, where we take up the continuous exponential line.

The type of impedance-matching problem that we have been discussing in the preceding paragraphs has analogies in many fields. In the first place, in ordinary circuit theory, as we have already seen, a transformer is an impedance-matching device. But there are also analogies in the field of wave propagation, which will be brought out in later chapters. Thus a light wave incident on a discontinuity between two media, as a surface of separation of air and glass, is reflected. If the surfaces are separated by a quarter wave film of material whose index of refraction is the geometric mean of the indexes of the two media, however, the reflection can be eliminated; this is the method used in setting up so-called "invisible glass." If two films are used, with indexes of refraction chosen to agree with our device of Figs. 20 and 21, the reflection can be eliminated over a wider range of wave lengths. In this problem, as in that of impedance matching, it is found that a sufficiently gradual change of index of refraction, extending over a number of quarter wave lengths, results in practically no reflection at any wave length. It is only the sudden discontinuities of properties, in distances short compared to a wave length, that result in reflection. Another analogy to our impedance matching comes when we have waves in pipes, as in acoustics where we have waves of sound, or in microwaves where we have electromagnetic waves in hollow pipes. In such a case, a sudden discontinuity in the size of the pipe, as from a smaller pipe to a larger one or even more from a small pipe to empty space, will result in reflection. This is familiar in acoustics, where a pipe open at one end can sustain standing waves, showing that the sound is reflected as it approaches the discontinuity at the open end of the pipe. Here, as before, to avoid reflection, we must make the change in properties gradual rather than sudden. A single section of pipe a quarter wave length long, inserted between two pipes of differing properties and with properly chosen properties intermediate between the two pipes, will reduce reflection, but this can be done more successfully and for a greater range of wave lengths by a more gradual change of cross section, properly designed. Thus we have a horn, corresponding to a transmission line which changes its properties in many small steps. Its object is again that of matching impedances. An acoustical or electrical horn shooting out into empty space is a device for matching the acoustical or electrical impedance of the pipe feeding the horn, or the generator at its throat, to the impedance of empty space, so that the energy will leave the generator and be radiated, rather than be reflected back to form useless standing waves in the system.

The problems that we have so far taken up in this section relate to a change of impedance from one line to another, and methods of setting up impedance-matching transformers to avoid reflection. Other types of problem arise when short discontinuous elements are inserted into an otherwise continuous line of characteristic impedance Z_0. Several examples will come to mind. First, we can insert an element in series into a line. For instance, in a coaxial transmission line, dielectric beads are necessary to keep the center conductor centered in the line, and they change the impedance of the line. We may be interested in the reflections produced by these beads, and in ways of spacing them so as to minimize reflection. Secondly, we can insert an element in shunt. In a coaxial line, such a shunt is often a section of transmission line, shunted across the line and short-circuited at the outer end by a movable plunger. If the losses in this section of line are neglected, there is formed a variable reactance, adjustable by moving the plunger to any value, positive or negative. Such shunts, as we shall see, can be conveniently used for introducing predetermined reflections into the line, and hence for canceling undesired reflections already present; that is, they can be used for impedance matching. Or in a hollow pipe, a similar purpose is served by introducing an iris diaphragm in the pipe. Such a diaphragm acts like a shunted capacitance or inductance, and hence acts as far as the circuit is concerned like any shunted reactance and can again be used to cancel undesired reflections and match impedances.

First let us consider the effect of a short series element inserted into a continuous line. Ordinarily this element would be a pure reactance, in practical applications. In a resistance-reactance diagram this would then correspond to a certain displacement up or down, the amount of displacement corresponding to the reactive impedance of the series element. Thus for instance consider a line of real characteristic impedance Z_0, terminated

by its characteristic impedance or infinitely long. At a point a
it is broken, and a short element of reactance X is inserted in the
line. Looking to the right into the series element plus line, the
whole thing has a resistance Z_0, a reactance X. If there is again
a line of characteristic impedance Z_0 to the left of a, we see that
a wave approaching the point a from the left will be reflected,
the reflection coefficient B/A being $[Z_0 - (Z_0 + jX)]/[Z_0
+ (Z_0 + jX)] = -jX/(2Z_0 + jX)$, vanishing as X goes to
zero, but being large if X is comparable with Z_0. Such a reflection, as we have mentioned, could be used to cancel a reflection
already present. Thus suppose that in Fig. 25 the circle represents the locus of impedances for a line of characteristic imped-

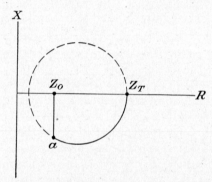

Fig. 25.—Impedance matching by a series reactance.

ance Z_0, but terminated by some different impedance, so that
standing waves are set up on it. We can then break the line
at the point indicated by a in Fig. 25, at which the resistance of
the line is the same as Z_0, and insert a series element whose
reactance equals the negative of the reactance of the line, as
indicated in the figure. The impedance of the whole network
will then be Z_0, so that if it is joined to a line of characteristic
impedance Z_0 on the left, a wave approaching a from the left
will not be reflected, and our inserted series element has canceled
the reflection already present and has matched impedances.
This scheme is perfectly possible in theory; in practice, it is not
easy to set up an arbitrary reactance of physical dimensions
small compared to the wave length. We shall find later that
the corresponding solution by means of a variable shunt reactance
is much simpler.

If the reflection already present in the line is small, however, as for instance that produced by one of the dielectric beads or spacers in a coaxial line, as mentioned before, its reflection can be canceled by another similar reflection from an obstacle a quarter wave length away. Thus in Fig. 26, we assume a line of characteristic impedance Z_0, terminated by its characteristic impedance, so that the impedance at any point of the line is Z_0. At a point a we insert a series reactance X, so that the impedance of this reactance plus the line, looking to the right, is $Z_0 + jX$, as shown by the point a in Fig. 26. Next we assume approximately a quarter wave of line to the left of a. The impedance looking to the right from the point b, at the left of this quarter

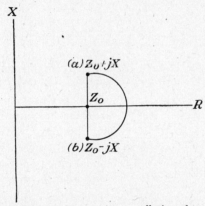

FIG. 26.—Impedance diagram for cancellation of two reflections.

wave length, is indicated by the point b in Fig. 26; we assume the line differs from a quarter wave length just enough so that this impedance is $Z_0 - jX$. Another similar series reactance X inserted at this point b will cancel the reactance already present, giving Z_0 as the impedance of the whole line, so that it will be matched to the line of impedance Z_0, and the two obstacles together will be nonreflective, though one by itself would cause reflection.

In this case, as in the quarter wave transformer previously discussed, there is a resonant or selective effect: although the reflections cancel at the wave length for which the device is designed, they will not cancel at other wave lengths. Here as in the case illustrated in Fig. 21 we can make a less selective device by using more reflecting elements. Thus if we have a scattering element at point a, an element of twice the reactance at point b approximately a quarter wave length away, and a third element like the first at point c approximately another quarter wave length away, we shall have just the situation shown in Fig. 21, with the same desirable properties. We can vary this by replacing the double-strength scattering element at point b by two elements of single strength a half wave length apart, since the two points a half wave length apart are effectively in contact as far as impedance is concerned. Such a device, with four equal scattering elements, spaced approximately one, two, and one quarter wave length apart, will then be nonreflective through a considerable range of wave lengths about the wave length for which it is designed.

Next we can consider the similar case of a reactance in shunt across a line. In this case not the impedances, but the admittances, of the line and of the added reactance must be added. It is then more convenient to use a conductance-susceptance diagram than a resistance-reactance diagram. We saw in Eq. (4.63) that the curve connecting conductance and susceptance of a line is of the same form as that connecting resistance and reactance, only now the spiral winds around the point representing the characteristic admittance Y_0, which is the reciprocal of Z_0.

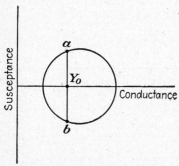

Fig. 27.—Impedance matching by a shunt reactance, admittance diagram.

Thus for instance in Fig. 27 we show the diagram for a line of characteristic admittance Y_0, terminated by some other admittance, so that standing waves are present, as indicated by the circle. We can then break this line at a or b, where the conductance of the line equals the characteristic admittance Y_0, and can shunt the line with a susceptance equal and opposite to the susceptance of the line at that point. The total admittance of the resulting network is then Y_0, so that the line will be matched to a line of characteristic admittance Y_0. Since, as we have mentioned before, this shunting can be done by a length of transmission line of adjustable length, this forms a convenient and practical way of matching impedances.   The one inconvenient feature of it is that it is sometimes impractical to have to break into the line at an arbitrary point.   For this reason matching is often carried out by two such adjustable shunts, at fixed points of the line.   By adjusting both reactances, we have two variables at our disposal for matching, much as if we could adjust the value and position of a single shunt.

We can understand the action of this double-shunt tuner by an admittance diagram.   In Fig. 28, we assume that a line has a certain terminal admittance, in shunt with an arbitrary reactance.   By adjusting this reactance, the terminal admittance can be given any value on the vertical line intersecting the real axis in the conductance G_1, as shown.   Suppose we wish to match this to a line of characteristic admittance Y_0.   Let the distance between the two shunts be l.   From each point a of the vertical line through G_1, a length of line l of characteristic admittance Y_0 will carry us to a point b, as shown.   If the point a is so adjusted that the point b lies vertically above or below Y_0, a reactance can

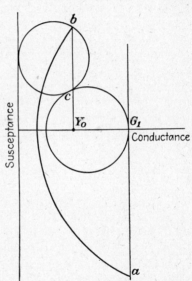

FIG. 28.—Admittance diagram explaining operation of double-shunt tuner.

be inserted in shunt at b which will bring the final reactance of the whole combination to Y_0, matching it to the line.   As will be described in the next paragraph, the points b lie on a circle, as shown.   If this circle extends as far to the right as Y_0, the matching can be accomplished; if it does not, matching is impossible.   It is clear, then, that not all impedances can be matched by this device, but if the distance l between shunts is properly chosen, a considerable range of impedances can be matched.   In practice this device is very useful, particularly in experimental arrangements where the values of the impedances to be matched are not exactly known in advance.   On the other hand, if the values of impedances are well known, the quarter wave transformer mentioned previously can be used. Its disadvantage, or the disadvantage of the double quarter wave transformer described in Fig. 21, is that it is not readily adjustable.

We have mentioned that the locus of the points b in Fig. 28 is a circle. It can be proved that the circle is determined by the following simple geometrical construction, which is clear from the figure. Starting with a terminal admittance of G_1, a pure conductance, we construct the circle surrounding Y_0 representing the admittance of any point on a line of characteristic admittance Y_0 terminated by G_1. We choose the point c, representing the input admittance of a line of length l, terminated by G_1. The circle of points b is then tangent to our first circle at this point c and is also tangent to the vertical axis of our diagram. This fixes the circle completely. Analytically, it can be proved that the equation of this circle of points b has the following value, where G represents the conductance (abscissa), B the susceptance (ordinate) of an arbitrary point of the circle:

$$\left(G - \frac{Y_0^2}{2G_1}\csc^2 \beta l\right)^2 + (B + Y_0 \cot \beta l)^2 = \left(\frac{Y_0^2}{2G_1}\csc^2 \beta l\right)^2 \quad (5.32)$$

Here we remember that G_1 is the conductance of the terminal load that we are trying to match. This is the equation of a circle of radius $(Y_0^2/2G_1)\csc^2 \beta l$, with center at abscissa $(Y_0^2/2G_1)\csc^2 \beta l$, so that it is tangent to the axis of ordinates, and with the ordinate of the center at $-Y_0 \cot \beta l$. The proof that this is the locus of the points b is tedious but not fundamentally difficult, and we shall not reproduce it. To derive it, we first start with an admittance equal to G_1 plus an arbitrary susceptance. By the methods of Sec. 4 we can at once write the admittance of a line of length l, characteristic admittance Y_0, terminated by this terminal admittance. We write down the real and imaginary parts, G and B, of this admittance. Each of these now contains the arbitrary imaginary part of the terminal admittance as a parameter. We eliminate this arbitrary parameter between the two equations, and the result proves to be (5.32).

The circle of points b extends to the right to twice its radius, or to an abscissa equal to $(Y_0^2/G_1)\csc^2 \beta l$. If this value is greater than Y_0, our construction is possible, and matching can be carried out.   This condition for matching can thus be written

$$\frac{Y_0}{G_1} \csc^2 \beta l > 1, \qquad \sin^2 \beta l < \frac{Y_0}{G_1} \qquad (5.33)$$

If G_1 is greater than Y_0, this demands that $\sin^2 \beta l$ be less than unity, which means that the length of the line must be not too close to a quarter wave length (for which $\sin^2 \beta l$ would equal unity).   Ordinarily for practical convenience the distance between shunts is set at some value greater than a quarter wave length and less than a half wave length (since for a half wave length the locus of points b degenerates to the same vertical line through G_1 with which we started, and matching is again impossible).

In this section we have taken up several examples of composite lines which are useful for impedance matching, for joining lines of different impedances without introducing reflection, and for similar purposes.   We shall not go further with this subject at present, but merely remark that the general principles we have already introduced are capable of handling the most complicated problems.

6. The Line with Continuously Varying Parameters.—The composite lines that we have taken up in the preceding sections have been made of sections of uniform lines of various characteristic impedances, with perhaps various discontinuous sections inserted in them.   There is no reason, however, why the characteristic impedance of a line may not be a continuous function of length along the line.   We have mentioned the analogy of a horn to an impedance-matching device; obviously a horn has continuously varying properties, and the lines we take up in this section behave in the same way.   We could treat such a line by the methods of the preceding sections, passing to the limit where the length of each section of line was infinitesimal, but this is a clumsy way of handling the problem.   It is better to introduce differential equations for the line, since this forms the mathematical way of passing to the limit of infinitesimal sections.   Consequently our first step will be to introduce the differential equations of a transmission line, equations that can be applied to the uniform line as well as to the line of varying properties.   We shall verify our previous solutions of the uniform line problem by means of our differential equations and then shall go on to the nonuniform line, giving a general method of approximate

solution for the case where the characteristic impedance varies
slowly in comparison with the wave length, and giving an exact
solution for the exponential line as a particular case.

Let us consider an infinite line with distributed parameters,
as in Sec. 2. As in that section, we shall assume that a section of
line of length dx has a series impedance $Z\,dx$, and a shunt admittance $Y\,dx$. Let us consider an infinitesimal section of length dx,
and let $i(x)$ be the current entering one lead, and leaving the
other, at the point x, and $i(x + dx)$ the current entering one lead
and leaving the other at the other end of the section, at $x + dx$.
(If the line is as in Fig. 7, we might have the point x at the
terminals aa, the point $x + dx$ at the terminals bb, assuming
the sections of the line to be infinitesimal.) Furthermore let
the voltage between the terminals at x (say the terminals aa in
Fig. 7) be $V(x)$, and the voltage between those at $x + dx$ be
$V(x + dx)$, where in each case V is positive if the upper terminal
is at higher voltage. Then we can easily set up two equations for
current and voltage. In the first place, the current flowing
through the shunt element is $i(x) - i(x + dx)$, and this must
equal the voltage V between the two ends of this shunt impedance,
times the shunt admittance $Y\,dx$. That is

$$i(x) - i(x + dx) = VY\,dx$$
$$\frac{i(x + dx) - i(x)}{dx} = -VY \tag{6.1}$$

or, passing to the limit of infinitesimal dx,

$$\frac{di}{dx} = -VY \tag{6.2}$$

To get the other equation, we note that the voltage between the
terminals of the series impedance $Z\,dx$ is $V(x) - V(x + dx)$.
This must equal the current times the impedance. Thus

$$V(x) - V(x + dx) = iZ\,dx$$
$$\frac{V(x + dx) - V(x)}{dx} = -iZ \tag{6.3}$$

or, passing to the limit of infinitesimal dx,

$$\frac{dV}{dx} = -iZ \tag{6.4}$$

Equations (6.2) and (6.4) are the two equations of a transmission line, in one simple form.

We have found two equations in the two unknowns V and i. For many purposes it is more convenient to separate variables, so as to have separate equations for V and for i. To do this, we can first differentiate (6.2) with respect to x:

$$\frac{d^2 i}{dx^2} = -Y\frac{dV}{dx} - V\frac{dY}{dx} = YZi - V\frac{dY}{dx} \qquad (6.5)$$

where we have used Eq. (6.4). From (6.2) we can write V in terms of di/dx, so that (6.5) becomes

$$\frac{d^2 i}{dx^2} - \frac{1}{Y}\frac{dY}{dx}\frac{di}{dx} - YZi = 0 \qquad (6.6)$$

or

$$\frac{d^2 i}{dx^2} - \frac{d\ln Y}{dx}\frac{di}{dx} - YZi = 0 \qquad (6.7)$$

Similarly from (6.4) we can show that

$$\frac{d^2 V}{dx^2} - \frac{d\ln Z}{dx}\frac{dV}{dx} - YZV = 0 \qquad (6.8)$$

The pair of equations (6.7) and (6.8) form the basis for the treatment of nonuniform lines.

First let us verify our equations for the case of a uniform line, where Y and Z are constants. In that case the terms in di/dx and dV/dx do not appear, and the coefficient YZ is a constant, so that we have

$$i = i_0 e^{-\gamma x}, \qquad V = V_0 e^{-\gamma x} \qquad (6.9)$$

where γ is a constant, given by

$$\gamma^2 - YZ = 0, \qquad \gamma = \pm\sqrt{YZ} \qquad (6.10)$$

agreeing with the result (2.7) that we obtained for the same problem by our previous method. Substituting in (6.2) or (6.4), to get the relation between i and V, we then have

$$-\gamma i_0 = -V_0 Y$$

$$\frac{V_0}{i_0} = \frac{V}{i} = Z_0 = \frac{\gamma}{Y} = \pm\sqrt{\frac{Z}{Y}} \qquad (6.11)$$

agreeing with Eq. (2.8).   *X or Y do not vary with distance*

No reflection

In case Y and Z are arbitrary functions of x, Eqs. (6.7) and (6.8) are difficult to solve and, in the general case, cannot be handled by simple analytic methods but must be integrated numerically. There is a useful limiting case, however, in which we can give an approximate solution. This is the case in which the fractional change in Y and in Z in a wave length is small. It is the case that we approached for example in Fig. 22, where we made a transition from a line of one characteristic impedance to a line of another by a number of quarter wave sections, such that the characteristic impedance did not change by a very large fraction from one section to another. The point of that arrangement was that it minimized reflections, and the approximation we are going to present is precisely that which neglects reflections altogether. If there are no reflections, then we may plausibly assume the following character for the solution. It should represent a wave traveling to the right (with an alternative solution representing a wave traveling to the left). The propagation constant γ should vary with position along the line but should be given, at least approximately, by the value (6.10) at each point, where we now have Y and Z depending on x. The ratio of V to i should be given at least approximately by (6.11), again varying from point to point. Finally the power transmitted down the line should decrease as we travel along the line by just the amount to compensate the loss on account of attenuation.

To set up such a solution, let us multiply an amplitude function, varying with x, by an exponential similar to the quantity $e^{-\gamma x}$ appearing in the case of a uniform line. As a matter of fact, the exponential that we must use is $e^{-\int \gamma \, dx}$, in case γ varies with x. We can see this easily from a special case, that in which γ is pure imaginary, equal to $j\beta = 2\pi j/\lambda$. If λ varies from point to point, the quantity dx/λ gives the number of wave lengths in distance dx, so that $\int (1/\lambda) \, dx$ gives the total number of wave lengths in a finite interval, the quantity which should appear in the exponential. Following this suggestion, let us then assume

$$i = i_0(x)e^{-\int \gamma \, dx}, \qquad V = V_0(x)e^{-\int \gamma \, dx} \qquad (6.12)$$

where

$$\gamma = \sqrt{YZ} \quad .$$

and where i_0 and V_0 are functions of x to be determined. We then substitute (6.12) in (6.7) and (6.8), obtaining the equations

NEGLECT   *NEGLECT*   α cannot vary rapidly for decent solution

$$\frac{1}{\gamma^2}\frac{d^2 i_0}{dx^2} + \frac{1}{\gamma}\frac{d i_0}{dx}\left(-2 - \frac{1}{\gamma}\frac{d \ln Y}{dx}\right) + \frac{i_0}{2\gamma}\frac{d \ln (Y/Z)}{dx} = 0$$

$$\frac{1}{\gamma^2}\frac{d^2 V_0}{dx^2} + \frac{1}{\gamma}\frac{d V_0}{dx}\left(-2 - \frac{1}{\gamma}\frac{d \ln Z}{dx}\right) + \frac{V_0}{2\gamma}\cdot\frac{d \ln (Z/Y)}{dx} = 0 \qquad (6.13)$$

Let us now find the order of magnitude of the various terms and see which ones we can neglect in our approximate case where Y and Z vary slowly compared to a wave length. We can see this most easily in the case where $\gamma = 2\pi j/\lambda$. Then for instance $\frac{1}{\gamma}\frac{d \ln Z}{dx}$ equals $\frac{1}{2\pi j}\lambda\frac{d \ln Z}{dx}$, proportional to the change of $\ln Z$ in a wave length, or the fractional change of Z in a wave length, which we are assuming is small compared to unity. Thus to a first approximation we can neglect the terms $\frac{1}{\gamma}\frac{d \ln Y}{dx}$ and $\frac{1}{\gamma}\frac{d \ln Z}{dx}$ compared to unity. On the other hand, presumably we shall find that i_0 and V_0 change by more or less the same fraction in a wave length that Y or Z do, so that the quantities $\frac{1}{\gamma}\frac{d i_0}{dx}$ and $\frac{1}{\gamma}\frac{d V_0}{dx}$ are presumably of the same order of magnitude as $\frac{i_0}{\gamma}\frac{d \ln (Y/Z)}{dx}$ and $\frac{V_0}{\gamma}\frac{d \ln (Z/Y)}{dx}$. The quantities $\frac{1}{\gamma^2}\frac{d^2 i_0}{dx^2}$ and $\frac{1}{\gamma^2}\frac{d^2 V_0}{dx^2}$ are however smaller, for they represent the change in a wave length of the quantity $\frac{1}{\gamma}\frac{d i_0}{dx}$ or $\frac{1}{\gamma}\frac{d V_0}{dx}$, quantities which are themselves small and in addition vary slowly. We shall neglect them.

Leaving out the terms that we consider negligible, Eqs. (6.13) can be rewritten   *LOGARITHMIC LINE*

$$\frac{d \ln i_0}{dx} = \frac{1}{4}\frac{d \ln (Y/Z)}{dx}$$

$$\frac{d \ln V_0}{dx} = \frac{1}{4}\frac{d \ln (Z/Y)}{dx} \qquad (6.14)$$

The solutions are at once

$$i_0 = \text{const.}\left(\frac{Y}{Z}\right)^{1/4}, \qquad V_0 = \text{const.}\left(\frac{Z}{Y}\right)^{1/4} \qquad (6.15)$$

Substitution in Eqs. (6.2) and (6.4) shows that the constants in (6.15) must be equal. Hence our final approximate solution of Eqs. (6.7) and (6.8) is

$$i = A \left(\frac{Y}{Z}\right)^{1/4} e^{-\int \sqrt{YZ}\, dx}$$

$$V = A \left(\frac{Z}{Y}\right)^{1/4} e^{-\int \sqrt{YZ}\, dx} \qquad (6.16)$$

where A is an arbitrary constant. Dividing V by i, we then verify immediately that the ratio V/i equals $\sqrt{Z/Y}$, or the value of characteristic impedance computed for the point in question. Let us next consider the flow of power along the line. This is very easy to do in case there is no attenuation. Then the ratio Z/Y is real, and $\sqrt{YZ}$ is pure imaginary. Then the quantity $V\bar{\imath}$, which appears in the flow of power, is simply equal to $|A|^2$, a constant, showing that the flow of power is the same at any point of the line, as we should expect. On the other hand, if there is attenuation, we should expect that the fractional rate of change of power with distance, $\dfrac{d \ln (V\bar{\imath})}{dx}$, should equal -2α. In this case we have

$$V\bar{\imath} = |A|^2 \left(\frac{Z}{Y}\right)^{1/4} \overline{\left(\frac{Y}{Z}\right)^{1/4}} e^{-2\int \alpha\, dx}$$

$$\ln V\bar{\imath} = \ln |A|^2 + \ln \left(\frac{Z}{Y}\right)^{1/4} \overline{\left(\frac{Y}{Z}\right)^{1/4}} - 2 \int \alpha\, dx \qquad (6.17)$$

If we may neglect the rate of change with x of $\ln (Z/Y)^{1/4}\overline{(Y/Z)^{1/4}}$, compared to -2α, then the power decreases at the proper rate in going along the line. This is the case if α is comparable numerically with β, for then we are simply neglecting the rate of change of $\ln (Z/Y)^{1/4}\overline{(Y/Z)^{1/4}}$ with respect to β or γ, which is essentially what we have done before. If however α is small compared to β, we cannot be sure that the rate of decrease of power down the line is accurately given by our expressions (6.16); but in that case the decrease of power is small anyway and can be neglected to a first approximation.

In our solution (6.16), we have found an approximate solution for the current and voltage in a line with slowly varying properties, the case in which we can neglect reflections. In cases where this solution applies, we have seen that a single wave traveling in one direction forms an approximate solution of the problem and that the ratio of voltage to current in this wave remains constant down the line. In other words, in this case there is an automatic impedance match all the way down the line, independent of the wave length being propagated. The best way to eliminate reflections, and to do it in a nonselective or nonresonant way, as we see from this, is then to change the properties of the line gradually, using a length of a number of wave lengths to make a large change in properties and avoiding any sudden changes or discontinuities. In practice, it is often found that this method is rather better than would be expected at first sight. The properties of a line can be changed considerably even in the distance of one wave length, with very small reflections. In other words, the terms that we have neglected in Eq. (6.13) really seem to be negligible, in many ordinary cases.

The method we have just described is a satisfactory approximation for handling cases of continuously varying impedance, when the variation is not too rapid. Fortunately there is one case which can be treated exactly, and which is useful on its own account and is a valuable check on the correctness of our approximation and an indication as to how far it can be trusted. This is the so-called "exponential line," in which either Z increases exponentially and Y decreases exponentially at the same rate with x, or vice versa. That is, let us assume

$$Z = \text{const. } e^{\delta x}, \qquad Y = \text{const. } e^{-\delta x} \qquad (6.18)$$

where δ is a constant. In this case the quantity YZ appearing in (6.7) and (6.8) is constant, and we have

$$\frac{d \ln Z}{dx} = -\frac{d \ln Y}{dx} = \delta \qquad (6.19)$$

also a constant. Thus Eqs. (6.7) and (6.8) become

$$\frac{d^2 i}{dx^2} + \delta \frac{di}{dx} - YZi = 0$$

$$\frac{d^2 V}{dx^2} - \delta \frac{dV}{dx} - YZV = 0 \qquad (6.20)$$

which are second-order linear differential equations with constant coefficients and therefore have solutions varying exponentially

$$\frac{Y}{Z} = e^{-2\delta x} \qquad \frac{Z}{Y} = e^{2\delta x}$$

with x. To make connection with our approximate solutions (6.16), let us assume

$$i = A \left(\frac{Y}{Z}\right)^{1/4} e^{-\Gamma x} = A e^{-\left(\Gamma + \delta/2\right)x}$$

$$V = A' \left(\frac{Z}{Y}\right)^{1/4} e^{-\Gamma x} = A' e^{-\left(\Gamma - \delta/2\right)x} \quad (6.21)$$

We note from (6.18) that Y/Z varies exponentially with x, so that both i and V from (6.21) vary in this way. We have assumed different constants A and A' multiplying the expressions for i and V in (6.21), so as not to assume that the ratio of V to i is the value given by the approximate theory, and we have inserted an arbitrary constant Γ in the exponential, instead of the value

$$\gamma = \sqrt{YZ} \quad (6.22)$$

which would appear in the approximate theory. Thus our expressions (6.21) are general exponentials, except that we have assumed a relation between the exponentials appearing in i and V, which fortunately proves to be correct.

Substituting the expressions (6.21) in (6.20), we now have

$$\left(\Gamma + \frac{\delta}{2}\right)^2 - \delta\left(\Gamma + \frac{\delta}{2}\right) - \gamma^2 = 0$$

$$\left(\Gamma - \frac{\delta}{2}\right)^2 + \delta\left(\Gamma - \frac{\delta}{2}\right) - \gamma^2 = 0 \quad (6.23)$$

The two Eqs. (6.23) are consistent with each other and lead to the solution

$$\Gamma = \sqrt{\gamma^2 + \left(\frac{\delta}{2}\right)^2} \quad (6.24)$$

Substitution in (6.2) or (6.3) then gives

$$\frac{V}{i} = \frac{A'}{A}\sqrt{\frac{Z}{Y}} = \frac{\Gamma + \delta/2}{\gamma}\sqrt{\frac{Z}{Y}} = \frac{\gamma}{\Gamma - \delta/2}\sqrt{\frac{Z}{Y}} \quad (6.25)$$

the two forms being equivalent on account of (6.24). We thus see that the quantity Γ, appearing in the exponential, differs from the value γ which it would have in the approximate theory by a small quantity of the second order in δ/γ; the ratio V/i differs from the value $\sqrt{Z/Y}$ which it would have in the approximate theory by a ratio differing from unity by a small quantity of the first order in δ/γ. These errors begin to be appreciable when δ becomes numerically of the same order of magnitude as γ; that is, when the proportional change of Y and Z per unit length becomes large, which is just the case where we expected our approximate solution to break down. We can see, in fact, that the behavior in this case of large changes of Y and Z is just what we should expect. For an ordinary line, with small attenuation, or better with no attenuation at all, γ^2 will be a negative real quantity, or at least its real part will be negative and larger than its imaginary part. $(\delta/2)^2$ is positive. If it is small, the leading term of Γ will be pure imaginary, corresponding to small attenuation; in particular, if the line is nonattenuating, Γ will be pure imaginary, and there will be no attenuation at all. If however $(\delta/2)$ becomes larger than the magnitude of γ, the quantity in the radical in (6.24) will change sign, Γ will become real, and the line will have no real propagation at all. This means, if there is no attenuation, and hence no loss, that there is total reflection. In other words, when the fractional change in properties of the line per wave length becomes greater than a critical value, the line will reflect all the energy instead of transmitting it. This is what we should expect, for we have seen throughout that a rapid change of properties of a line produces reflection and that a gradual change does not. If we have a line of fixed properties and pass waves of different frequencies through it, we see that for short waves the change of properties will be gradual and that for long waves it will not. That is, it is the long waves, longer than a critical cutoff value, which will be reflected. An exponential line, in other words, forms a highpass filter, passing only frequencies above a critical value, in case the line is nonattenuating. If it is attenuating, it is not hard to show that the attenuation increases rapidly as we go through a cutoff value, from low attenuation at higher frequencies to very high attenuation for the lower frequencies.

Since Γ is pure imaginary in the transmission region for a nonattenuating line and δ is real, we see that the ratio (6.25) of voltage to current is complex, corresponding to both a resistance and a reactance. If we wish to terminate an exponential line by a nonreflective impedance, we see then that this terminal impedance must have a reactive as well as a resistive component, even though the quantity $\sqrt{Z/Y}$ is a pure resistance. As the wave length becomes longer, or the frequency lower, approaching cut-off, the reactive component of the terminal impedance must be made numerically greater, and the resistive component smaller, until finally at cutoff it must be entirely reactive. Since this terminal impedance varies with frequency, even when $\sqrt{Z/Y}$ is independent of frequency, we see that if a section of exponential line is used as a matching transformer, as is sometimes done, it will be selective, being nonreflective only for the frequency for which it is designed. In this respect it is not so well suited for matching impedances as the type of line discussed in Figs. 22 and 23.

The exponential line, which we have just taken up, furnishes an example of a continuously varying line that can be solved exactly. Many other exact solutions could be set up, since there are many second-order differential equations of the form (6.7), (6.8), with coefficients varying with x, whose exact solutions are known. An example is Bessel's equation; lines can be set up whose solution is in the form of Bessel functions. Problems analogous to those of the present section come up not only in real transmission lines whose properties vary continuously with position, but also in other problems such as horns, which as we have mentioned previously are really transmission lines of varying properties. Thus one can find horns whose solutions are exponentials or Bessel functions, or other simple functions; alternatively we can use a method analogous to our approximate method if an exact solution is not available. Here we note that generally in the throat, or small end, of a horn, the properties vary rapidly in a wave length. Thus our approximate solution must be inaccurate in that region, and we must expect reflections to take place near the throat, with rapid attenuation of the wave. This is actually the case, and it means that exact solutions of simplified problems are the only reliable method of handling the propagation through the throat of a horn.

CHAPTER II

MAXWELL'S EQUATIONS, PLANE WAVES, AND REFLECTION

In our first chapter we have gone about as far as we can, using the ideas of electric circuits alone. To go further, we must think about coaxial lines, wave guides, antennas and radiating systems, and radiation itself. These are problems of the electromagnetic field. It is true that the ideas of impedance and reflection introduced in the preceding chapter in connection with transmission lines can often be advantageously carried over into these problems of the electromagnetic field, but this is by no means always the case; in any case they are valuable rather as analogies than as representing the fundamental theory of the situation. This fundamental theory is always based on Maxwell's equations. When ideas of transmission lines lead to the same results as Maxwell's equations they are right, though superfluous; when they lead to different results they are wrong, an incorrect analogy. This statement is perhaps a little hard on transmission lines, for certainly their theory leads to a good understanding of many problems that deal fundamentally with fields. But, as Dr. W. W. Hansen has said, the first thing to learn about the theory of microwaves is that the idea of impedance cannot be used as a substitute for thought. In this chapter we shall begin to use Maxwell's equations; in later chapters we shall learn how to think by means of them and to apply them to the actual sort of transmission lines used in microwave work.

7. Maxwell's Equations.—This is not a treatise on electromagnetic theory, and we shall not start at the beginning with our discussion of Maxwell's equations. We assume that the reader has a bowing acquaintance with them, such as he would get from one of the standard books on electromagnetic theory. We shall also assume that he is familiar with the elements of vector analysis, as he will be if he has read these works on electromagnetic theory. Nevertheless, in case his acquaintance with these matters is merely a casual one and does not reach the point of intimacy, we shall start with a statement of the vectors concerned in Maxwell's equations and the equations themselves and their meaning, before going on to their use.

Maxwell's equations deal with four vector fields, vectors defined as functions of position and time. These form two pairs: E, the electric field intensity, and B, the magnetic induction, forming one pair, and D, the electric displacement, and H, the magnetic field intensity, forming the other. (The more familiar grouping of E and H in one pair and B and D in another is less fundamental than the grouping that we have indicated.) The first pair, E and B, are the vectors determining the forces acting on electric charges and current elements in space. By definition, the force acting on a charge q at rest is qE, in the direction of the vector E, so that E measures the force acting on unit charge. Similarly the force acting on an element of current I is a vector at right angles to the plane of the vector I and of B, equal in magnitude to the product of B and of the component of I at right angles to B. Thus B measures the force on unit current element at right angles to B. The force on a current element is symbolized in terms of vector analysis by the equation that the force equals $I \times B$, the vector product of I and B, where by definition the vector product of two vectors equals a vector normal to the plane of the two vectors, equal to the magnitude of one of the vectors times the component of the second vector at right angles to the first. In terms of components, it is proved in vector analysis that the x component of the vector product is

$$(I \times B)_x = I_y B_z - I_z B_y \qquad (7.1)$$

with corresponding formulas for the other two components, if I_x, I_y, I_z are the x, y, z components of current, and similarly for B. We have stated the forces acting on charges or currents at rest. A charge in motion, however, is equivalent to a current. Thus a charge q moving with velocity v is equivalent to a current $I = qv$. The force acting on a charge q moving with velocity v is then

$$F = q[E + (v \times B)] \qquad (7.2)$$

This equation is particularly important in applications to electronics, where we wish the forces acting on individual electrons.

The second pair of vectors, D and H, are determined from charges and currents in the field, as lines of force originating from the charges and currents. Lines of D emanate from electric charges, and, if we use rationalized units, as we shall, we find that the total number of lines of D originating on a charge, or the total flux of D outward from the charge, is numerically equal to the charge itself. By the flux of a vector such as D, we mean the following: the flux of a vector D across an element da of area equals the component D_n of the vector normal to the area, times the area. This definition is set up in analogy to the flux of a vector representing the velocity of a fluid: the flux of fluid across an area, or the volume crossing the area per second, equals the component of velocity normal to the area, times the area. The total flux of D outward across a closed surface is denoted by $\iint D_n \, da$, where the double integral indicates that we are to sum the elements of flux $D_n \, da$ through each element of the surface, over the whole surface. Our statement is then

$$\iint D_n \, da = q \tag{7.3}$$

where q represents the total charge within the surface.

Although lines of D start out from charges, the situation is quite different with H: lines of H form closed paths surrounding currents. We can state the law governing these lines in terms of line integrals. A line integral is defined as follows. We first take a curve and consider a short element ds of this curve. We then take the component H_s of H in the direction of the curve and multiply by ds. The sum of these quantities for all the elements of the curve, or $\int H_s \, ds$, is called the line integral of H along the curve. It is set up by analogy with the total work done on a body by a force F, as the body moves along a given path. The work done in the element ds is $F_s \, ds$, the product of component of force along the direction of motion, times the distance moved, and the total work done is $\int F_s \, ds$, the line integral of force along the curve. Let us now take a closed curve enclosing a current I. The law governing H is now the following: the line integral of H around any closed curve enclosing the current I is numerically equal to I (if we use rationalized units). That is,

$$\int H_s \, ds = I \tag{7.4}$$

Maxwell showed that this equation could be correct only in static problems, in which the currents do not change with time. For suppose we have a current changing with time and flowing into a condenser. Then in the wire leading to the condenser there may be a current I, while in the condenser there is no current. It is then impossible to say whether a closed curve surrounds the wire, in which there is a current I, or the condenser, in which there is no current. To avoid this difficulty Maxwell introduced the displacement current. This is a quantity that plays the part of a current in a condenser, or in any place in which the displacement D is changing with time. To get at the correct value for the displacement current, let us consider a closed volume. If there are bodies within this volume having a certain capacity, there can be a net flow of real current into this volume. Maxwell's displacement current must be so defined that there is an equal and compensating flow of displacement current out of the volume, so that the total current, real plus displacement, will not be able to pile up, even on condensers, but as much will flow into a volume as out again, so that essentially the total current will obey Kirchhoff's law that the total current entering any point of a circuit equals the current leaving it. The total current entering our closed volume equals the time rate of increase of charge within the volume. This in turn, by (7.3), equals $(\partial/\partial t)\int\int D_n\, da$. The total displacement current leaving the volume must then equal this amount, and the natural assumption is that the amount of displacement current crossing any element da of the area is $(\partial/\partial t)D_n\, da$. This was the assumption which Maxwell made. Then in the general case, in which currents are changing with time, we must modify (7.4) by adding the total displacement current flowing through the closed curve around which we are integrating H. This is the flux of displacement current across a surface bounded by the closed curve. Writing the flux in terms of a double integral, as before, we can write the modified form of (7.4) as

$$\int H_s\, ds = I + \frac{\partial}{\partial t}\int\int D_n\, da \qquad (7.5)$$

There are now two experimental laws of electromagnetism which we must state. One is that lines of magnetic induction B are always closed, never starting or stopping. That is, the total flux of B out of any closed surface is always zero, or

$$\iint B_n \, da = 0 \tag{7.6}$$

where the integration is carried out over any closed surface. The other law is Faraday's induction law. This states the electromotive force developed in a circuit as a result of electromagnetic induction, or of changing magnetic fields. The electromotive force in a circuit by definition is the work done on unit charge carrying it once around the circuit. If we have a closed curve representing the circuit, then the force on unit charge is E, and the work done on this charge carrying it around the circuit is $\int E_s \, ds$, integrated around the curve. Faraday's law states that such an electromotive force is produced by change in the flux of magnetic induction B through the circuit and is numerically equal to the rate of change of flux, with a negative sign, if the line integral is carried out in a positive direction (going counterclockwise around the curve) and the positive direction of B is upward. That is, the induction law may be stated

$$\int E_s \, ds = -\frac{\partial}{\partial t} \int \int B_n \, da \tag{7.7}$$

In addition to these laws already stated, which are quite general, there are relations between the various vectors, depending on the nature of the material media in which they are found. In ordinary materials, D is proportional to E and in the same direction, and in nonferromagnetic materials B is proportional to H and in the same direction. The relations are written

$$D = \epsilon E, \qquad H = \frac{B}{\mu} \tag{7.8}$$

where ϵ is called the electric inductive capacity, μ the magnetic inductive capacity. In the system of units which we shall use, ϵ and μ have definite dimensions and numerical values, though in some units they are pure numbers. In our units, empty space has quite definite values of ϵ and μ, which we shall denote by ϵ_0 and μ_0. Then the ratio of the electric inductive capacity of a medium to that of empty space is called the specific inductive capacity, or dielectric constant, of the medium. We shall denote it by

$$\kappa_e = \frac{\epsilon}{\epsilon_0} \tag{7.9}$$

Similarly the ratio of the magnetic inductive capacity of a medium to that of empty space is called the magnetic permeability. We shall write it

$$\kappa_m = \frac{\mu}{\mu_0} \tag{7.10}$$

For most ordinary materials, ϵ is really a constant, though for crystalline media the relation is more complicated, the three vector components of D being linear functions of the three components of E, so that instead of one constant ϵ there are really nine coefficients of the three linear equations. We shall not have to consider that case, however, in our discussion. For nonferromagnetic materials, μ is constant and very closely equal to μ_0, so that the permeability is almost exactly equal to unity. For ferromagnetic materials, μ is not even a constant; it is well known that the relation between B and H is a complicated one, showing phenomena of hysteresis, saturation, etc. We shall not consider these complications, since iron is ordinarily not used in microwave work.

In addition to the four vectors E, B, D, and H, we need quantities expressing the charge density and current density. The charge density is denoted by ρ and measures the amount of charge in unit volume, a function of position. The quantity q, which we have used previously, is the total charge in a volume, or the integral of ρ over the volume:

$$q = \iiint \rho \, dv \tag{7.11}$$

Similarly the current density is denoted by J, a vector, measuring the amount of current per unit area. Our quantity I, the current flowing through an area, is the integral of J over the area:

$$I = \iint J_n \, da \tag{7.12}$$

These two quantities satisfy the equation of continuity, an equation stating that the current flowing out of a volume equals the rate of decrease of charge within the region. This equation may be written

$$\iint J_n \, da = -\frac{\partial}{\partial t} \iiint \rho \, dv \tag{7.13}$$

where the left side represents the flux of current out of a volume, the right side the rate of decrease of charge within the volume.

In a conductor obeying Ohm's law, there is a relation between the current density J and the electric field E. Ohm's law in this form is

$$J = \sigma E \tag{7.14}$$

where σ is the electrical conductivity. In materials not obeying Ohm's law, the relation between field and current is more complicated. For instance, in a discharge tube, the intensity E determines the force on the electrons or ions in the discharge, they move according to Newton's laws of motion under the action of this force, and from their resultant average velocity we can find the current density J.

We have now derived a number of relations between the electromagnetic quantities. Let us repeat these, in the form in which they lead to Maxwell's equations. From Eqs. (7.7), (7.6), (7.5), and (7.3), respectively, we have

$$\text{(I)} \qquad \int E_s \, ds + \frac{\partial}{\partial t} \int \int B_n \, da = 0$$

$$\text{(II)} \qquad \int \int B_n \, da = 0$$

$$\text{(III)} \qquad \int H_s \, ds - \frac{\partial}{\partial t} \int \int D_n \, da = I$$

$$\text{(IV)} \qquad \int \int D_n \, da = q \tag{7.15}$$

These equations are the integral forms of Maxwell's equations. We note that the surface integrals $\int\int B_n \, da$ and $\int\int D_n \, da$ appearing in Eqs. (I) and (III) are over surfaces spanning the curves around which the line integrals $\int E_s \, ds$ and $\int H_s \, ds$, respectively, are to be computed, while the surface integrals $\int\int B_n \, da$ and $\int\int D_n \, da$ in (II) and (IV) are over closed surfaces enclosing volumes. It is now possible by vector methods to transform the four integral equations (I) to (IV) into differential equations. This is done by the use of two vector theorems, Gauss's theorem and Stokes' theorem. These theorems are stated in terms of two vector differential quantities, the divergence and the curl. By definition the divergence of a vector is a scalar, given by

$$\text{div } A = \frac{\partial A_x}{\partial x} + \frac{\partial A_y}{\partial y} + \frac{\partial A_z}{\partial z} \tag{7.16}$$

The curl of a vector is a vector, whose x component is

$$\text{curl}_x A = \frac{\partial A_z}{\partial y} - \frac{\partial A_y}{\partial z} \tag{7.17}$$

with corresponding formulas for the other components, formed by advancing the letters. In terms of them Gauss's theorem is stated as follows:

$$\iiint \text{div } A \; dv = \iint A_n \; da \tag{7.18}$$

That is, the volume integral of the divergence of any vector, over a finite volume, equals the surface integral of the normal component of the vector, or the total flux of the vector, over the surface enclosing the volume, n representing the outer normal to the surface. Similarly Stokes' theorem is

$$\iint \text{curl}_n A \; da = \int A_s \; ds \tag{7.19}$$

or the surface integral of the normal component of the curl of a vector, over a surface spanning a closed curve, equals the line integral of the tangential component of the vector around the closed curve.

We may now use Gauss's theorem and Stokes' theorem to rewrite Eqs. (7.15). Using (7.11) and (7.12), the equations become

$$\text{(I)} \qquad \iint \text{curl}_n E \; da + \frac{\partial}{\partial t} \iint B_n \; da = 0$$

$$\text{(II)} \qquad \iiint \text{div } B \; dv = 0$$

$$\text{(III)} \qquad \iint \text{curl}_n H \; da - \frac{\partial}{\partial t} \iint D_n \; da = \iint J_n \; da$$

$$\text{(IV)} \qquad \iiint \text{div } D \; dv = \iiint \rho \; dv \tag{7.20}$$

Since Eqs. (I) and (III) hold for any arbitrary surface and (II) and (IV) for any arbitrary volume, the integrands themselves must obey corresponding relations, and we have

$$\text{(I)} \qquad \text{curl } E + \frac{\partial B}{\partial t} = 0$$

$$\text{(II)} \qquad \text{div } B = 0$$

$$\text{(III)} \qquad \text{curl } H - \frac{\partial D}{\partial t} = J$$

$$\text{(IV)} \qquad \text{div } D = \rho \tag{7.21}$$

In Eqs. (7.21) we have the differential form of Maxwell's equations. Remembering the definitions of (7.16) and (7.17), these give relations between derivatives of the various field vectors. When combined with Eqs. (7.8), (7.14) in a medium having a definite dielectric constant, permeability, and conductivity, the equations form a complete system. These supplementary relations, often called the constitutive equations of the medium, are then

$$D = \epsilon E, \qquad B = \mu H, \qquad J = \sigma E \qquad (7.22)$$

For more complicated material media, other relations must be substituted for (7.22), but these simple equations are satisfactory for most of the materials encountered in microwave work, with the one restriction that ϵ, μ, and σ must in general be considered functions of frequency.

Maxwell's equations hold at any point where the fields are not changing discontinuously. At a surface of discontinuity, however, there are certain boundary conditions, which are derived by limiting processes, assuming that the discontinuity is the limiting case of a more and more rapid continuous change, and finding the limiting form of Maxwell's equations. These conditions are the following:

(I) E_t is continuous
(II) B_n is continuous
(III)   Discontinuity in H_t = surface current density
(IV)   Discontinuity in D_n = surface charge density   (7.23)

at a surface of discontinuity, where the subscript t refers to the tangential component, and the subscript n to the normal component, of a vector, and where the relations numbered (I) to (IV) follow from the correspondingly numbered Maxwell's equations. The surface current density and surface charge density mean the current crossing unit length line in the surface, and charge per unit area in the surface, in cases where charge and current are assumed to be localized in the surface layer.

The discussion of Maxwell's equations which we have given is not, as we have said earlier, intended to be a complete derivation, but it should serve to recall the equations to those who have met them before, and to introduce them in usable form to those who are meeting them for the first time. It should be understood that our introduction of them in the integral form, from Faraday's law of induction and other similar relations, is not in any sense a derivation, but merely an indication of their relation to well-known elementary laws. The proper point of view to take is that Maxwell's equations are the postulates of electromagnetic theory, not to be proved or derived from anything else, but to be assumed as the foundation of the theory. They can be proved only by deriving results from them that are in agreement with experiment.

The units that we shall use in Maxwell's equations are rationalized m.k.s. (that is, meter-kilogram-second) or Georgi units. In these units, the electrical quantities are expressed in practical units, distances in meters, masses in kilograms, times in seconds, and the whole forms a consistent set of units. Let us consider the units to be used for each quantity appearing in Maxwell's equations. The electric field intensity E is measured in volts per meter, where of course 1 volt per meter equals $\frac{1}{100}$ volts per centimeter. The magnetic induction $\iint B_n \, da$ is measured in webers, so that B is in webers per square meter, where 1 weber per square meter equals 10^4 gauss. From (I) we can see that there is a relation between volts and webers: volts per square meter = webers per square meter-second, or volts = webers per second. The charge density ρ is in coulombs per cubic meter, and the current density J in amperes per square meter. From Eq. (IV) we then see that the units of D are coulombs per square meter, and from (III) the units of H are amperes per meter. These units are not ordinarily given different names. We see that in these units, the quantities ϵ and μ, the electric and magnetic inductive capacities, have dimensions, unlike the situation with some other systems of units. The units of ϵ are those of D/E, or (coulombs per square meter)/(volts per meter) or coulombs/(volt-meter). We note that the farad, the unit of capacity, is equal to the number of coulombs per volt; thus ϵ has the dimensions of farads per meter. Similarly the units of μ are those of B/H or (webers per square meter)/(amperes per meter) or webers/(ampere-meter). But the henry, the unit of inductance, has the dimensions of volts/(amperes per second) or (volt-seconds)/ampere or webers per ampere, so that μ has the dimensions of henry per meter. The values of the quantities ϵ_0 and μ_0, for empty space, are

$$\mu_0 = 4\pi \times 10^{-7} \text{ henry per meter} \qquad (7.24)$$

$$\epsilon_0 = \frac{1}{\mu_0 c^2} = \frac{1}{4\pi \times 10^{-7} \times (3 \times 10^8)^2}$$
$$= 8.85 \times 10^{-12} \text{ farad per meter} \qquad (7.25)$$

where

$$c = \frac{1}{\sqrt{\epsilon_0 \mu_0}} = 3.00 \times 10^8 \text{ m. per second} \qquad (7.26)$$

is the velocity of light, as we shall show later. Of the two quantities ϵ_0, μ_0, the second, μ_0, given by (7.24), is pure definition; when it is determined, the value of ϵ_0 is also determined. The two quantities ϵ_0 and μ_0 are really the only numerical quantities that one must remember to keep this system of units straight, which is certainly simpler than all the powers of 10 and of c that must be remembered in changing from either the absolute electromagnetic system or the Gaussian system to practical units. A derived numerical quantity that is often encountered is

$$\sqrt{\frac{\mu_0}{\epsilon_0}} = 376.6 \text{ ohms} \qquad (7.27)$$

To check the units in (7.27), we note that μ_0/ϵ_0 is of the dimensions of (webers/ampere-meter)/(coulombs/volt-meter) or (weber $\times$ volt)/(ampere $\times$ coulomb). Using the relation that 1 weber = 1 volt $\times$ 1 second, and 1 coulomb = 1 ampere $\times$ 1 second, our quantity becomes (volt^2)/(ampere^2) = ohm^2. The quantity (7.27) appears later in connection with the characteristic impedance of empty space, regarded as a transmission line.

Certain other units appear in connection with our equations. In the force equation (7.2), if the electrical quantities are in the units we have used, the force F is given in newtons, where by definition 1 newton equals 10^5 dynes. That is, a newton is the force required to give a unit kilogram mass an acceleration of 1 meter per second per second. With the force given in (7.2), we can solve the equations of motion by methods of mechanics, getting distances in meters as a function of time. If we compute energy in our units, it comes out in joules, where 1 joule is 10^7 ergs, or the work done by a force of 1 newton acting through a distance of 1 meter. When we compute a rate of working, or a power, it comes out in joules per second, or watts. In materials obeying Ohm's law (7.22), the conductivity of the material, σ, must be expressed in the same units as J/E. That is, its units are 1/(ohm-meter) = mhos per meter, where 1 mho is defined as the reciprocal of 1 ohm. It is to be noted that 1 mho per meter is $\frac{1}{100}$ of 1 mho per centimeter, the usual unit of conductivity.

8. Poynting's Vector, the Wave Equation, the Potentials.—In the present section we shall collect a number of familiar electromagnetic theorems, which follow from Maxwell's equations and which we shall need in later work. These theorems will all be proved for the case where the constants ϵ and μ are really constants, independent of the field strengths, and furthermore independent of position and of time. That is, we deal only with homogeneous media. For that reason one must be on his guard in applying these theorems to cases in which ϵ and μ change from point to point, for some of the theorems do not hold in that case. The ordinary cases met in practice, fortunately, involve a number of regions in each of which the properties are homogeneous. Thus one can apply the theorems of the present section in each homogeneous region and use the continuity conditions (7.23) to join solutions together in different regions.

First we prove Poynting's theorem, relating to energy flow and energy density in the electromagnetic field. We begin by computing the quantity div $(E \times H)$. By a well-known vector identity this is

$$\text{div } (E \times H) = H \cdot \text{curl } E - E \cdot \text{curl } H \qquad (8.1)$$

Using Maxwell's equations (7.21), this becomes

$$\text{div } (E \times H) + E \cdot \frac{\partial D}{\partial t} + H \cdot \frac{\partial B}{\partial t} = -E \cdot J \qquad (8.2)$$

If we assume $D = \epsilon E$, $B = \mu H$, we have

$$\text{div } (E \times H) + \frac{\partial}{\partial t} \frac{1}{2} (\epsilon E^2 + \mu H^2) = -E \cdot J \qquad (8.3)$$

This equation reminds us of an ordinary equation of continuity,[1] which states that the divergence of the flux of any quantity, plus the rate at which the density of the quantity increases with time, equals the rate at which the quantity is produced. In other

[1] See for instance Slater and Frank, "Introduction to Theoretical Physics," p. 186, McGraw-Hill Book Company, Inc., New York.

words, applying the equation to a small volume, it states that the rate at which the quantity increases within the volume equals the rate at which it is produced within the volume, minus the rate at which it flows out over the surface. We can give such an interpretation to Eq. (8.3). The quantity $-E \cdot J$ represents the rate at which energy is produced (that is, $E \cdot J$ represents the rate at which energy is lost) per unit volume on account of ordinary Joulean or resistance heating. Thus the quantity for which (8.3) forms the equation of continuity is the energy. We can then interpret the vector

$$S = E \times H \tag{8.4}$$

which is known as Poynting's vector, as the flux of energy, the amount of energy crossing unit area perpendicular to the vector, per unit time, and the scalar

$$\tfrac{1}{2}(\epsilon E^2 + \mu H^2) \tag{8.5}$$

as the energy density, the amount of energy per unit volume. In our units, S comes out in joules per square meter per second or watts per square meter, and the energy density is in joules per cubic meter. The interpretation of S as an energy flux, and (8.5) as an energy density, is well known not to be unique, but it is the most convenient interpretation and will not involve us in error.

Next we shall derive the wave equations for propagation of electromagnetic waves in homogeneous media. We shall assume a conducting medium satisfying Ohm's law, for generality, and shall therefore set $J = \sigma E$, as in (7.22). If we wish to deal with a nonconducting medium, we need only set $\sigma = 0$. We may now take Maxwell's equation (I) and take its curl. Using the vector identity curl curl $F = $ grad div $F - \nabla^2 F$, where F is any vector, this is

$$\text{grad div } E - \nabla^2 E + \frac{\partial}{\partial t} \text{ curl } B = 0 \tag{8.6}$$

In the first term, we write $E = D/\epsilon$ and assume ϵ to be a constant, so that we can disregard it in differentiating. We replace div D by ρ, according to Maxwell's equation (IV), and set $\rho = 0$ since we are in the interior of a conducting medium. In the third term, we write $B = \mu H$, assume μ to be a constant, and rewrite curl H from Maxwell's equation (III). Thus we have

$$\text{curl } H = \epsilon \frac{\partial E}{\partial t} + \sigma E$$
$$\text{div } D = \rho = 0 \quad (\text{no electrostatic chgs})$$

$$-\nabla^2 E + \mu \frac{\partial}{\partial t}\left(\epsilon \frac{\partial E}{\partial t} + \sigma E\right) = 0$$

$$\nabla^2 E - \sigma\mu \frac{\partial E}{\partial t} - \epsilon\mu \frac{\partial^2 E}{\partial t^2} = 0 \qquad (8.7)$$

Similarly, starting by taking the curl of Eq. (III), we find

$$\nabla^2 H - \sigma\mu \frac{\partial H}{\partial t} - \epsilon\mu \frac{\partial^2 H}{\partial t^2} = 0 \qquad (8.8)$$

Thus both E and H, as well as each component of each of these vectors, must satisfy the same equation. For the case of a non-conducting medium, these equations reduce to (for free space)

$c = \dfrac{1}{\sqrt{\mu\epsilon}}$ when $\sigma = 0$

$$\nabla^2 E - \epsilon\mu \frac{\partial^2 E}{\partial t^2} = 0, \qquad \nabla^2 H - \epsilon\mu \frac{\partial^2 H}{\partial t^2} = 0 \qquad (8.9)$$

the familiar wave equation. If we deal with a disturbance varying as $e^{j\omega t}$, Eqs. (8.7) and (8.8) take the form

$$\begin{Vmatrix} \nabla^2 E + (\epsilon\mu\omega^2 - j\sigma\mu\omega)E = 0, \\ \nabla^2 H + (\epsilon\mu\omega^2 - j\sigma\mu\omega)H = 0 \end{Vmatrix} \qquad (8.10)$$

Finally we shall set up the electromagnetic potentials and derive the equations that they satisfy. We assume a scalar potential ϕ and a vector potential A, in terms of which E and B are given by

dynamic case - for static $A = 0$

$$E = - \operatorname{grad} \phi - \frac{\partial A}{\partial t}, \qquad B = \operatorname{curl} A \qquad (8.11)$$

Then, using the facts that the curl of any gradient and the divergence of any curl are zero, we find that Maxwell's equations (I) and (II) are automatically satisfied. Next we substitute (8.11) in Maxwell's equations (III) and (IV), treating ϵ and μ as constants, and again assuming $J = \sigma E$ and $\rho = 0$. From (III) we have

$$\frac{1}{\mu} \operatorname{grad}\left(\operatorname{div} A + \sigma\mu\phi + \epsilon\mu \frac{\partial\phi}{\partial t}\right)$$

$$-\frac{1}{\mu}\left(\nabla^2 A - \sigma\mu \frac{\partial A}{\partial t} - \epsilon\mu \frac{\partial^2 A}{\partial t^2}\right) = 0 \quad (8.12)$$

From (IV) we have *by adding*

$$-\epsilon \frac{\partial}{\partial t}\left(\operatorname{div} A + \sigma\mu\phi + \epsilon\mu\frac{\partial\phi}{\partial t}\right)$$

$$-\epsilon\left(\nabla^2\phi - \sigma\mu\frac{\partial\phi}{\partial t} - \epsilon\mu\frac{\partial^2\phi}{\partial t^2}\right) = 0 \quad (8.13)$$

We find that we can now assume, *though God knows why & He won't tell*

$$\operatorname{div} A + \sigma\mu\phi + \epsilon\mu\frac{\partial\phi}{\partial t} = \overset{0}{\text{cons.}} \quad (8.14)$$

without involving ourselves in any contradictions or difficulties. Then Eqs. (8.12) and (8.13) become

$$\nabla^2 A - \sigma\mu\frac{\partial A}{\partial t} - \epsilon\mu\frac{\partial^2 A}{\partial t^2} = 0$$

$$\nabla^2\phi - \sigma\mu\frac{\partial\phi}{\partial t} - \epsilon\mu\frac{\partial^2\phi}{\partial t^2} = 0 \quad (8.15)$$

so that the potentials satisfy the same wave equation that we have already seen in (8.7) and (8.8) to be satisfied by E and H. The equations that we have found are those which hold in a conducting region obeying Ohm's law, where there is no concentration of charge. They hold for a nonconducting region, such as empty space, if it likewise contains no charge.

9. Undamped Plane Waves.—The wave equations (8.9), or the more general form (8.10), have a great variety of solutions; in fact, a large part of our work will consist of a study of different forms of solutions of these equations. Using the principle of starting with simplest things first, we begin with the most elementary type of plane wave. We shall assume that E and H are functions of z and t alone and shall assume that E has a component only along the x axis; it will turn out that in that case H has a component only along y. Furthermore, we may assume that both E and H vary with t according to the familiar exponential $e^{j\omega t}$, and with z according to the exponential $e^{-\gamma_0 z}$, in complete analogy with the continuous transmission line, as discussed in Secs. 1 and 2. Thus we assume

$$E_x = E_0 e^{j\omega t - \gamma_0 z}$$
$$H_y = H_0 e^{j\omega t - \gamma_0 z} \quad (9.1)$$

where E_0 and H_0 are constants to be determined and where all other components of E and H are assumed to be zero.

E_x and H_y, as given in (9.1), must in the first place satisfy the wave equation. To start with simplest cases first, we shall assume a nonconducting medium, so that the wave equation is (8.9). Substituting, we then have

$$\gamma_0^2 - \epsilon\mu(j\omega)^2 = 0, \qquad \gamma_0 = \pm j\omega \sqrt{\epsilon\mu} \qquad (9.2)$$

Thus there are two possible waves, varying as $e^{j\omega(t \pm \sqrt{\epsilon\mu}z)}$. These obviously represent waves traveling along the positive or negative z axis, the $+$ sign in Eq. (9.2) for γ_0 corresponding to the positive z axis, the $-$ sign to the negative z axis. Comparing with Eq. (1.19), we see that the velocity of propagation is given by

$$v = \frac{1}{\sqrt{\epsilon\mu}} \qquad (9.3)$$

In the case of empty space, this becomes

$$v = c = \frac{1}{\sqrt{\epsilon_0\mu_0}} = 3 \times 10^8 \text{ m. per second} \qquad (9.4)$$

as we see from Eq. (7.26). In optical theory it is convenient to define an index of refraction n, as the ratio of c to the velocity of light in the medium in question:

$$n = \frac{c}{v} = \sqrt{\frac{\epsilon\mu}{\epsilon_0\mu_0}} = \sqrt{\kappa_e\kappa_m} \qquad (9.5)$$

where κ_e is the dielectric constant, κ_m the magnetic permeability, as defined in (7.9) and (7.10). That is,

$Z_0 = \sqrt{Z_s Z_p}$

$$n^2 = \kappa_e\kappa_m \qquad (9.6)$$

Since most materials of interest for microwave propagation have permeabilities nearly equal to unity, this means practically that the square of the index of refraction equals the dielectric constant. Since ordinarily both κ_e and κ_m are greater than unity, the index of refraction is commonly greater than unity, and the velocity of propagation of the wave in a material medium is commonly less than that in free space. This does not necessarily have to be the case, however. (This may seem at first sight to contradict the result of the theory of relativity, that no signal can be propagated

faster than the velocity c.   It does not, however, for the velocity
we are speaking of is the phase velocity, which does not in general
agree with the group velocity, the velocity with which a signal
travels in the medium.)

The wave equations by themselves are not the only conditions
which E and H must satisfy; they must satisfy Maxwell's equations.   We derived the wave equations from Maxwell's equations,
so that it is obvious that it is necessary for E and H to satisfy the
wave equation, but that is not a sufficient condition to make them
satisfy Maxwell's equations.   Using Eq. (7.21), we have

$$\text{(I)} \qquad \frac{\partial E_x}{\partial z} + \mu \frac{\partial H_y}{\partial t} = 0, \qquad -\gamma_0 E_0 + \mu j\omega H_0 = 0$$

$$\text{(III)} \qquad -\frac{\partial H_y}{\partial z} - \epsilon \frac{\partial E_x}{\partial t} = 0, \qquad \gamma_0 H_0 - \epsilon j\omega E_0 = 0 \qquad (9.7)$$

The two equations above result from Maxwell's equations (I) and
(III); Eqs. (II) and (IV) are identically satisfied by our assumptions (9.1).   Equations (I) and (III), (9.7), both give values for
the ratio of E_0 to H_0:

$$\frac{E_0}{H_0} = \frac{\mu j\omega}{\gamma_0} = \frac{\gamma_0}{\epsilon j\omega} \qquad (9.8)$$

The two values of the ratio E_0/H_0 agree on account of the relation
(9.2).   Substituting this relation, we have

$$\frac{E_0}{H_0} = \pm \sqrt{\frac{\mu}{\epsilon}} \qquad (9.9)$$

The positive sign corresponds to the wave traveling along the
positive z axis, the negative sign to the negative z axis.

Referring to Eq. (7.27), we see that the ratio of E_0 to H_0, just
computed, has the dimensions of a resistance; in empty space it
has the specific value of 376.6 ohms.   This is the simplest of a
considerable number of reasons which lead us to regard this ratio
as an analogy, in wave propagation, to impedance in the theory
of transmission lines.   For discussion of this analogy, see for
instance Stratton;[1] the analogy was developed particularly by
Schelkunoff.[2]   The analogy is based on a resemblance between

[1] "Electromagnetic Theory," p. 282, McGraw-Hill Book Company, Inc.
[2] *Bell System Tech. J.*, **17,** 17 (1938).

E_x and the voltage in a transmission line, and between H_y and the current. We shall later see physical reasons why this resemblance is a close one. For the moment, however, we shall simply point out the mathematical reasons for the resemblance. These come from the similarity between Maxwell's equations, in the form (9.7) which they take in this problem, and the differential equations of a transmission line, (6.2) and (6.4). For a disturbance whose time variation is given by $e^{j\omega t}$, Maxwell's equations (9.7) become

$$\frac{\partial E_x}{\partial z} = -\mu j \omega H_y, \qquad \frac{\partial H_y}{\partial z} = -\epsilon j \omega E_x \qquad (9.10)$$

while the transmission line equations are

$$\frac{dV}{dx} = -Zi = -(R + j\omega L)i$$

$$\frac{di}{dx} = -YV = -(G + j\omega C)V \qquad (9.11)$$

where we have used the definitions (2.10) and (2.11) of series impedance and shunt admittance. For a line without attenuation, so that R and G are zero, we see that there is a mathematical parallelism between (9.10) and (9.11), if we identify E_x with the voltage V, H_y with the current i, μ with the inductance L, and ϵ with the capacity C. The units are not the same; following the discussion of Sec. 7, we see that while E_x is measured in volts per meter, V is in volts; H_y is measured in amperes per meter, i in amperes. Thus to make the quantities appearing in (9.10) have the same dimensions as those in (9.11), we must somehow multiply each one by a length, and we shall see later how this can be done, so as to get an exact parallelism between our wave problem and a transmission line. The quantities μ and ϵ, however, are exactly analogous to L and C; μ is measured in henrys per meter, and so is L, since it is the inductance per unit length; and ϵ and C are both measured in farads per meter. With this mathematical parallelism between Maxwell's equations and the equations of a transmission line, it is obvious that they must lead to the same solutions. We have seen, for example in (2.3) and (9.1), that this is the case. Our value (9.2) for γ_0 follows immediately from that of (2.13) by replacing L by μ and C by ϵ. And our formula (9.9) for the characteristic impedance follows from (2.20) by making the same replacement.

$$Z_0 = \sqrt{Y_c} \qquad \beta = \omega \sqrt{LC}$$
$$\gamma = \alpha + j\beta \quad \text{where } \alpha = 0$$
$$\gamma_0 = \pm j\omega \sqrt{\mu\epsilon}$$

Not only in propagation in a single medium, but in the boundary conditions between two media and the conditions for reflection, our quantity (9.9) plays the part of an impedance. Let us suppose that there are a number of planes normal to the z axis, dividing space into different media of different dielectric constants and magnetic permeabilities; we shall still for the moment retain our restriction that the media be nonconducting. Within each medium we can express the fields as a sum of two waves, traveling along the positive and negative z directions, so that if we make the definition

$$\frac{E_0}{H_0} = Z_0 = \sqrt{\frac{\mu}{\epsilon}} = \sqrt{\frac{\mu}{\epsilon}}$$ (9.12)

following (9.9), we have

$$H_y = A e^{j\omega t - \gamma_0 z} + B e^{j\omega t + \gamma_0 z} \quad current$$
$$E_x = Z_0 A e^{j\omega t - \gamma_0 z} - Z_0 B e^{j\omega t + \gamma_0 z} \quad voltage$$ (9.13)

exactly analogous to (3.5), where here as in Sec. 2 we write γ_0 as the positive root of (9.2). At a surface of separation of two media, following (7.23), (I), the tangential component of E, or E_x, is continuous, and from (III) the tangential component of H, or H_y, is continuous, since we are dealing with nonconductors and there can be no surface current. Since there are no normal components of E or H in this case, the conditions (II) and (IV) of (7.23) are automatically satisfied. In other words, since both E_x and H_y have the same values in the two media, their ratio must also be continuous from one medium to the other. That is, the condition determining the behavior of E_x and H_y at a boundary is just the same as that we had in Secs. 3 and 4 for the behavior of V and i at a discontinuity in a transmission line, and all our discussion of reflection coefficients, of input impedance of composite lines, of impedance matching, and such things, in Chap. I, can be carried through without change to our present problem of plane wave propagation. This is a very far-reaching and valuable analogy between our previous theory of transmission lines and our present problem of plane waves.

We have seen the mathematical explanation for the interpretation of the ratio of E_x to H_y in a plane wave as an analogue to the impedance of a transmission line. Now let us examine the physical interpretation of the same thing. To do this, we shall set up a simple type of transmission line, in which on the one hand the electric and magnetic fields are just the plane wave we have been considering, but in which on the other hand we can find the current, voltage, inductance, and capacity, and so treat it as an ordinary transmission line. Let us imagine that the two

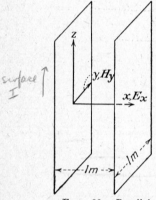

conductors of the transmission line are two parallel strips of a perfect conductor, each of unit width (that is, one meter) and spaced unit distance apart. Let them extend indefinitely along the z axis, and let the normal to the strips be the x axis. Between them we shall show that the field is just the plane wave we have described, provided that, in order to eliminate edge effects, we imagine that the strips are really only part of conducting planes extending to infinity and acting as guards, so that the field will not depend on y. The arrangement is shown in Fig. 29. In this figure we show the electric field along the x axis and the magnetic field along the y axis. We now have to ask about the effect of the

Fig. 29.—Parallel-strip transmission line.

field along the y axis. We now have to ask about the effect of the perfectly conducting strips forming the transmission line.

In (7.23) we have seen that at a boundary the tangential component of E and the normal component of B must be continuous, while the discontinuity in the tangential component of H equals the surface current and the discontinuity in the normal component of D equals the surface charge. In the arrangement of Fig. 29, the tangential component of E and the normal component of B are zero just outside the conducting plate, and by continuity they are zero inside as well. Inside a perfect conductor, in fact, all components of both the electric and the magnetic field must vanish. We shall show this in detail later, when we consider waves in conductors and go to the limit of the perfect conductor. For the present, we can argue merely that on account of the infinite conductivity, any electric field different from zero would be accompanied by infinite current, and, if the electric field is zero everywhere within the volume, then by Maxwell's equations the magnetic field must be zero also. In Fig. 29, then, since the magnetic field H is tangential to the surface just outside the conductor and is zero inside, the discontinuity at the surface is equal to the surface current flowing on the surface of the conductor. This surface current is the limit of a volume current, which on account of skin effect, which we take up later, is confined to a thinner and thinner depth below the surface as the conductivity becomes greater and greater. H_y, then, measures the surface current, in amperes per meter; or, with a strip of conductor 1 m. wide, it measures directly the current flowing in the strip. The sign is such that, if E_x points along the positive x axis, H_y along the positive y axis, as shown in Fig. 29, the surface current is upward in the left-hand conductor, downward in the right-hand conductor. At the same time, there is a discontinuity in the normal component of D at the surface of the conductor, equal to D itself, or to ϵE_x. Thus there must be a surface charge of ϵE_x coulombs per square meter, positive on the left-hand conductor, negative on the right-hand one, in the case shown. It is the motion of this surface charge along the positive z direction, the direction of propagation of the wave, which gives rise to the surface current. To see this, let us note that the current carried by a charge equals the charge times its velocity. In this case the charge per square meter of area is ϵE_x, and its velocity, by Eq. (9.3), is $1/\sqrt{\epsilon\mu}$. Thus the current is $\epsilon E_x/\sqrt{\epsilon\mu} = \sqrt{\epsilon/\mu}\,E_x = H_y$, using (9.9). But this is just the value that we found previously, by direct use of the tangential component of H.

In the preceding paragraph, we have shown that in the parallel strip transmission line shown in Fig. 29, the current flowing in the line is equal to H_y. Furthermore the voltage between the two conductors is plainly E_x, since this measures the number of volts per meter, and the field extends over a distance of one meter. Thus we have made the fundamental identification of H_y with current, E_x with voltage, which we desired to justify our definition of the ratio E_x/H_y as an impedance, in (9.9) and (9.12). We still wish to compute the inductance per unit length, L, and the capacitance per unit length, C, however, and show that these are respectively equal to μ and ϵ. Unit length of the line corresponds to a square meter of conducting plate, or a cubic meter of the space between the plates. The number of lines of B threading this region is μH_y, so that the time rate of change of this number of lines is $\mu(\partial H_y/\partial t)$. The current flowing in the conductor is H_y, so that its time rate of change is $\partial H_y/\partial t$. Thus the rate of change of magnetic flux, for unit rate of change of

$$\text{Induced } EMF = -\mu\,\frac{\partial N_y}{\partial t} = -\frac{\partial B}{\partial t}$$
$$= -L\,\frac{di}{dt}$$

(margin annotations: $D_n = q$ *;* $J = qv$ *)*

current, is just μ, which is the inductance per unit length. Similarly, regarding a square meter of each plate as forming a condenser, the charge on each plate is $\pm D_x = \pm \epsilon E_x$, and the voltage between plates is E_x. Thus the charge per unit voltage is ϵ, which is just the capacity of the condenser. From this example, then, we get a very vivid picture of the meaning of the numerical values of the magnetic and electric inductive capacities of a medium, or of empty space, as given in (7.24) and (7.25). The magnetic inductive capacity μ_0 of empty space, $4\pi \times 10^{-7}$ henry per meter, is the inductance of one meter length of a circuit like that of Fig. 29, consisting of two conducting strips a meter in width and separated by a meter; the electric inductive capacity ϵ_0 of empty space, 8.85×10^{-12} farad per meter, is the capacity of a condenser whose plates are each one square meter in area, spaced a meter apart. In each case, it is assumed that the parallel strips are parts of infinite parallel plane conductors, so as to avoid edge effects.

10. Reflection of Plane Waves at Oblique Incidence.—In Sec. 9, we have investigated plane waves, we have shown that a quantity analogous to the impedance of a transmission line can be set up for them, and we have shown that at a boundary between two media the conditions governing reflection are stated in terms of this impedance just as they would be for a discontinuity in properties of a transmission line, so that practically all of the analysis of Chap. I can be applied to waves propagated through a medium with a set of parallel planes separating materials of different properties. We assumed throughout that the waves were traveling along the normal to the surfaces of separation, however; that is, we assumed that the waves struck these surfaces at normal incidence. In this section we shall take the more general case of oblique incidence, studying the laws of reflection and refraction, and we shall see that the concept of impedance can be used here too.

Let us assume as before that any surfaces of discontinuity between different media are perpendicular to the z axis, so that the z axis is the direction of the normal, for any reflection or refraction. We shall not lose in generality if we also assume that the direction of propagation lies in the yz plane. Let us then establish a set of coordinates as in Fig. 30, with the x' axis coinciding with the x axis, and the z' axis in the direction of propagation, making an angle θ with the z axis, where θ is ordinarily called the angle of incidence. We have seen in Sec. 9 that in a plane wave the vectors E and H are at right angles to each other and to the direction of propagation, and that the ratio of E to H is the impedance of the medium. To be specific, we shall refer to this ratio of E to H in a plane wave as the intrinsic impedance of the medium and shall denote it by Z_0; this will distinguish it from other quantities that also play the part of impedance. Now if E and H are perpendicular to the direction of propagation in the present case, they must lie in the $x'y'$ plane. There is a preferred direction in this plane, the x' axis. Consequently there are two simple cases: that in which the electric vector E lies along x', so that H must lie along y'; and that in which the magnetic vector H lies along x' and E is along $-y'$. In optics, these two cases are ordinarily described by saying that the electric vector is normal to the plane of incidence in the first

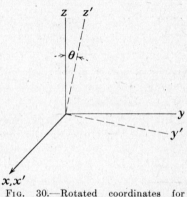

FIG. 30.—Rotated coordinates for oblique incidence.

case, parallel in the second. In the theory of wave guides and transmission lines, which is essentially built up on the basis of this simple problem, the first case is sometimes called the transverse electric case, since the electric field is entirely transverse to the z direction, and the second is called the transverse magnetic case. Sometimes another notation is used, however, in which the first case is called an H wave (since H has a component along the z direction, or a longitudinal component as far as the direction normal to the reflecting surfaces is concerned), and the second case is called an E wave (since E has a longitudinal component).

Let us first consider the case where E is in the x direction (the transverse electric case) and write down the components of E and H in the original, xyz, coordinates, and consider Maxwell's equations in those coordinates. We still consider the case of a nonconducting medium, as in the preceding section, so as to avoid attenuation. It is easy to write down the components of

E and H. In the first place, each component will be multiplied by the same exponential function, which as we can see from the value of γ_0 found in (9.2) can be written $e^{j\omega(t - \sqrt{\epsilon\mu}z')} = e^{j\omega[t - \sqrt{\epsilon\mu}(y \sin \theta + z \cos \theta)]}$. Furthermore, using the value of the intrinsic impedance $Z_0 = \sqrt{\mu/\epsilon}$ of the medium as given in (9.12), we see that the magnitude of E will be $\sqrt{\mu/\epsilon}$ times as great as the magnitude of H. Finally E will be along the x axis, H along the y' axis, so that it will have components along both y and z axes. Then it is easy to see that E and H may be written

$$E_x = \sqrt{\frac{\mu}{\epsilon}}\, A e^{j\omega[t - \sqrt{\epsilon\mu}(y \sin \theta + z \cos \theta)]}$$

see p 93 for reason

$$E_y = E_z = 0$$
$$H_x = 0$$
$$H_y = A \cos \theta e^{j\omega[t - \sqrt{\epsilon\mu}(y \sin \theta + z \cos \theta)]}$$
$$H_z = -A \sin \theta e^{j\omega[t - \sqrt{\epsilon\mu}(y \sin \theta + z \cos \theta)]} \tag{10.1}$$

It is simple to verify by direct substitution that these values of E and H satisfy Maxwell's equations.

We shall now show that even in this case of oblique incidence, H_y, the transverse component of magnetic field, still plays the part of a current, and E_x still plays the part of a voltage, and their ratio E_x/H_y is analogous to an impedance. As a first step in this, let us write down those components of Maxwell's equations which are of essential importance in this particular case. From Eq. (I) (as given in (7.21)) we have

$$\frac{\partial E_x}{\partial z} = -\mu j\omega H_y \tag{10.2}$$

$$-\frac{\partial E_x}{\partial y} = -\mu j\omega H_z \tag{10.3}$$

From Eq. (III) we have

$$\frac{\partial H_z}{\partial y} - \frac{\partial H_y}{\partial z} = \epsilon j\omega E_x \tag{10.4}$$

Equation (10.2) is already of the form of the first equation of (9.10) and hence is analogous to the first of the transmission line equations of (9.11). Equation (10.4) can be made to resemble the second transmission line equation by the following steps:

$$\frac{\partial H_y}{\partial z} = -\epsilon j\omega E_x + \frac{\partial H_z}{\partial y}$$

$$= -\epsilon j\omega E_x + \frac{1}{\mu j\omega} \frac{\partial^2 E_x}{\partial y^2}$$

$$= -\left(\epsilon j\omega - \frac{1}{\mu j\omega} \frac{1}{E_x} \frac{\partial^2 E_x}{\partial y^2}\right) E_x \qquad (10.5)$$

in which we have used (10.3).   Now we use (10.1) to show that

$$\frac{1}{E_x} \frac{\partial^2 E_x}{\partial y^2} = -\omega^2 \epsilon \mu \sin^2 \theta \qquad (10.6)$$

Substituting (10.6) in (10.5), we have

$$\frac{\partial H_y}{\partial z} = -\epsilon j\omega(1 - \sin^2 \theta)E_x = -\epsilon j\omega \cos^2 \theta E_x \qquad (10.7)$$

We have now, in Eqs. (10.2) and (10.7), two equations similar to (9.10) or (9.11), and we see that they are equivalent to transmission line equations, if we make the identification

$$\begin{aligned} L &= \mu \\ C &= \epsilon \cos^2 \theta \end{aligned} \qquad (10.8)$$

Following (2.13), we have

$$\gamma = j\omega \cos \theta \sqrt{\epsilon\mu} \qquad (10.9)$$

which is correct, since we note that the part of the exponential in (10.1) can be written

$$e^{-\gamma z} = e^{-j\omega \cos \theta \sqrt{\epsilon\mu}\, z} \qquad (10.10)$$

The impedance of the line is

$$Z(\theta) = \sqrt{\frac{\mu}{\epsilon}} \sec \theta \qquad (10.11)$$

using (2.20), and this is also correct, since it is the ratio of E_x to H_y, as we see from (10.1).   The impedance $Z(\theta)$, which depends on the angle of incidence, is to be distinguished from the intrinsic impedance Z_0 of (9.12); the intrinsic impedance is the particular value that $Z(\theta)$ takes on for $\theta = 0$, or for normal incidence.

From the results of the preceding paragraph, we see that mathematically we can regard a plane wave traveling obliquely to a fixed z direction as equivalent to a disturbance traveling in a transmission line along that direction.   The correspondence is not quite so definite physically as for normal incidence, however.   The value of the capacity C, given in (10.8), in connection with the shunt admittance of the line, is not really entirely a capacity at all. As we can see from the derivation in (10.5), the shunt admittance is made up of a capacitative admittance $\epsilon j\omega$, in parallel with an inductive admittance $-\epsilon j\omega \sin^2 \theta$, resulting from the voltage induced across the line on account of magnetic lines of force in the z, or longitudinal, direction. This term is perfectly easy to understand, but it is a term of a sort that would not occur in the simplest type of transmission line. Nevertheless the analogy with a transmission line is mathematically as good in the present case as before, and it is just as useful. In particular, as we shall see in the next paragraph, we can discuss reflection coefficients in the present case by means of the impedance, just as with a transmission line.

Let us assume a surface of separation at the plane $z = 0$, the medium for negative values of z having constant μ, ϵ, and that for positive values having μ', ϵ'. We shall first consider the problem of reflection and refraction at this surface by ordinary methods of imposing boundary conditions at the surface, and then we shall show that the same results can be obtained by using the method of the impedance. We assume an incident wave in the medium at negative z, just like the wave of (10.1). In that medium we also assume a reflected wave, which can be got from (10.1) by changing the sign of z and of E_x and H_z. We shall let the amplitude of that wave be B, corresponding to A for the incident wave. Finally in the second medium, at positive z, we assume a single refracted wave, like (10.1), only with primed values of A, μ, ϵ, and θ. Thus in the first medium we have

$$E_x = \sqrt{\frac{\mu}{\epsilon}}\, e^{j\omega(t - \sqrt{\epsilon\mu}\,y\,\sin\,\theta)}\left(A e^{-j\omega\sqrt{\epsilon\mu}z\,\cos\,\theta} - B e^{j\omega\sqrt{\epsilon\mu}z\,\cos\,\theta}\right)$$

$$H_y = \cos\,\theta e^{j\omega(t - \sqrt{\epsilon\mu}\,y\,\sin\,\theta)}\left(A e^{-j\omega\sqrt{\epsilon\mu}z\,\cos\,\theta} + B e^{j\omega\sqrt{\epsilon\mu}z\,\cos\,\theta}\right)$$

$$H_z = \sin\,\theta e^{j\omega(t - \sqrt{\epsilon\mu}\,y\,\sin\,\theta)}\left(-A e^{-j\omega\sqrt{\epsilon\mu}z\,\cos\,\theta}\right.$$
$$\left. + B e^{j\omega\sqrt{\epsilon\mu}z\,\cos\,\theta}\right) \quad (10.12)$$

In the second medium we have

$$E_x = \sqrt{\frac{\mu'}{\epsilon'}}\, e^{j\omega(t - \sqrt{\epsilon'\mu'}\,y\,\sin\,\theta')}A' e^{-j\omega\sqrt{\epsilon'\mu'}z\,\cos\,\theta'}$$

$$H_y = \cos\,\theta' e^{j\omega(t - \sqrt{\epsilon'\mu'}\,y\,\sin\,\theta')}A' e^{-j\omega\sqrt{\epsilon'\mu'}z\,\cos\,\theta'}$$

$$H_z = -\sin\,\theta' e^{j\omega(t - \sqrt{\epsilon'\mu'}\,y\,\sin\,\theta')}A' e^{-j\omega\sqrt{\epsilon'\mu'}z\,\cos\,\theta'} \quad (10.13)$$

We now must satisfy the boundary conditions of (7.23) at the surface $z = 0$. These lead, since the surface $z = 0$ can carry no current, to the conditions that E_x, H_y, and μH_z are continuous at the boundary. That is, setting $z = 0$, we must first have

$E_{x_1} = E_{x_2}$
from 7.23

$$\sqrt{\epsilon\mu}\, \sin\theta = \sqrt{\epsilon'\mu'}\, \sin\theta' \tag{10.14}$$

so that the exponentials will cancel, and then

$E_{x_1} = E_{x_2}$

$$\sqrt{\frac{\mu}{\epsilon}}\,(A - B) = \sqrt{\frac{\mu'}{\epsilon'}}\,A' \tag{10.15}$$

$H_{y_1} = H_{y_2}$

$$\cos\theta(A + B) = \cos\theta'\,A' \tag{10.16}$$

$\mu H_{z_1} = \mu' H_{z_2}$

$$\mu\sin\theta(A - B) = \mu'\sin\theta'\,A' \tag{10.17}$$

The relation of Eq. (10.14) is the ordinary Snell's law of refraction, which may be written

$$\frac{\sin\theta}{\sin\theta'} = \frac{\sqrt{\epsilon'\mu'}}{\sqrt{\epsilon\mu}} = \frac{n'}{n} \tag{10.18}$$

where n and n' are the indexes of refraction of the two media, as defined in (9.5). We note that (10.17) is not an independent condition, for each side is obtained by multiplying the corresponding sides of (10.14) and (10.15) together. In other words, if Snell's law is satisfied and the tangential components of E and H are continuous, then the normal component of B is automatically continuous. We can then handle (10.15) and (10.16) by dividing the first by the second, obtaining

$$\sqrt{\frac{\mu}{\epsilon}}\,\sec\theta\,\frac{(A - B)}{(A + B)} = \sqrt{\frac{\mu'}{\epsilon'}}\,\sec\theta' \tag{10.19}$$

But we notice that, using the definition in (10.11), this can be written

$$Z(\theta)\,\frac{(A - B)}{(A + B)} = Z'(\theta') \tag{10.20}$$

which is exactly equivalent to (3.7), the corresponding equation for a transmission line, using the method of impedances. Proceeding as in the derivation of (3.9), we have

$$\frac{B}{A} = \frac{Z(\theta) - Z'(\theta')}{Z(\theta) + Z'(\theta')} \tag{10.21}$$

Thus our method of satisfying boundary conditions has led to the same result that we should have found directly by use of the impedance. It is easy to see why this should be the case. As we see from Sec. 3, Eq. (10.20) states that the impedance of the actual disturbance, consisting of incident, reflected, and refracted wave, is the same on both sides of the boundary. This is equivalent to the conditions (10.15) and (10.16) for the continuity of the tangential components of E and H. But if the tangential component of E is continuous at the surface, its derivative with respect to y must obviously be continuous, so that by Maxwell's equation (10.3) the component μH_z must be continuous, and (10.17) must be automatically satisfied, as we have seen that it is.

The reflection coefficient of Eq. (10.21) can be easily put in a more familiar form, by writing out the value of $Z(\theta)$ and $Z'(\theta')$ and by using Eq. (10.18). We find at once

$$\frac{B}{A} = \frac{\mu \tan \theta - \mu' \tan \theta'}{\mu \tan \theta + \mu' \tan \theta'} \tag{10.22}$$

Equation (10.22) gives the reflection coefficient for a wave with E in the plane of incidence. In the case $\mu \approxeq \mu'$, which ordinarily occurs in practice, it reduces to

$$\frac{B}{A} = \frac{\tan \theta - \tan \theta'}{\tan \theta + \tan \theta'} = \frac{\sin \theta \cos \theta' - \cos \theta \sin \theta'}{\sin \theta \cos \theta' + \cos \theta \sin \theta'}$$
$$= \frac{\sin (\theta - \theta')}{\sin (\theta + \theta')} \tag{10.23}$$

which is one of the familiar Fresnel's equations for reflection.

Having taken up the case of a transverse electric field in considerable detail, we can give the essential steps in the entirely similar treatment of the transverse magnetic case. Corresponding to (10.12), the field in the first medium is

$$H_x = e^{j\omega(t - \sqrt{\epsilon\mu}y \sin \theta)} \left(A e^{-j\omega\sqrt{\epsilon\mu}z \cos \theta} + B e^{j\omega\sqrt{\epsilon\mu}z \cos \theta} \right)$$
$$H_y = H_z = E_x = 0$$
$$E_y = \sqrt{\frac{\mu}{\epsilon}} \cos \theta e^{j\omega(t - \sqrt{\epsilon\mu}y \sin \theta)} \left(-A e^{-j\omega\sqrt{\epsilon\mu}z \cos \theta} + B e^{j\omega\sqrt{\epsilon\mu}z \cos \theta} \right)$$
$$E_z = \sqrt{\frac{\mu}{\epsilon}} \sin \theta e^{j\omega(t - \sqrt{\epsilon\mu}y \sin \theta)} \left(A e^{-j\omega\sqrt{\epsilon\mu}z \cos \theta} + B e^{j\omega\sqrt{\epsilon\mu}z \cos \theta} \right)$$

$$\tag{10.24}$$

and the field in the second medium, like (10.13), can be obtained from (10.24) by setting $B = 0$ and replacing all appropriate unprimed quantities by the corresponding primed ones. On account of the rotation of coordinates in comparison with the earlier case, the current corresponds to H_x, the voltage to $-E_y$. From Maxwell's equations we have

$$\frac{\partial H_x}{\partial z} = -\epsilon j\omega(-E_y) \qquad (10.25)$$

$$\frac{\partial(-E_y)}{\partial z} = -\mu j\omega H_x - \frac{\partial E_z}{\partial y} = -\left(\mu j\omega - \frac{1}{\epsilon j\omega} \frac{1}{H_x} \frac{\partial^2 H_x}{\partial y^2}\right) H_x$$
$$= -(\mu j\omega - \mu j\omega \sin^2 \theta) H_x = -\mu j\omega \cos^2 \theta H_x \qquad (10.26)$$

From Eqs. (10.25) and (10.26) we see that the quantity corresponding to the inductance L is $\mu \cos^2 \theta$, and the capacity C is replaced by ϵ. Then, following the pattern of (10.8) to (10.11), we have

$$\gamma = j\omega \cos \theta \sqrt{\epsilon\mu} \qquad (10.27)$$

as before; and

$$Z(\theta) = \sqrt{\frac{\mu}{\epsilon}} \cos \theta \qquad (10.28)$$

The reflection coefficient (10.21), written in terms of the impedance (10.28), becomes

$$\frac{B}{A} = \frac{\mu \sin \theta \cos \theta - \mu' \sin \theta' \cos \theta'}{\mu \sin \theta \cos \theta + \mu' \sin \theta' \cos \theta'} \qquad (10.29)$$

In the case $\mu = \mu'$, we can use the trigonometric relations

$$\sin (\theta \pm \theta') \cos (\theta \mp \theta') = (\sin \theta \cos \theta' \pm \cos \theta \sin \theta')$$
$$(\cos \theta \cos \theta' \pm \sin \theta \sin \theta')$$
$$= \sin \theta \cos \theta (\cos^2 \theta' + \sin^2 \theta')$$
$$\pm \sin \theta' \cos \theta' (\sin^2 \theta + \cos^2 \theta)$$
$$= \sin \theta \cos \theta \pm \sin \theta' \cos \theta' \qquad (10.30)$$

from which we have

$$\frac{B}{A} = \frac{\sin (\theta - \theta') \cos (\theta + \theta')}{\sin (\theta + \theta') \cos (\theta - \theta')} = \frac{\tan (\theta - \theta')}{\tan (\theta + \theta')} \qquad (10.31)$$

Equation (10.31) is the other one of Fresnel's equations, analogous to (10.23) and applying in this case to the transverse magnetic wave. There is one interesting feature met in this case, which is not present with the transverse electric wave: if $\theta + \theta' = 90°$, a perfectly possible situation, the denominator of (10.31) is infinite, so that the reflection coefficient is zero. Going back to (10.21), this means that for this particular angle there is automatically an impedance match between the two media. This angle is called the polarizing angle; if unpolarized radiation, consisting of a mixture of both transverse electric and transverse magnetic radiation, falls on the reflector at this angle, only the transverse electric radiation will be reflected, and the reflected radiation will be polarized. To find the polarizing angle, we note that if $\theta + \theta' = 90°$, we have $\cos \theta = \sin \theta'$. But from (10.18), $\sin \theta' = (n/n') \sin \theta$. Thus the polarizing angle is given by

Brewster's Law

$$\tan \theta = \frac{n'}{n} \qquad (10.32)$$

11. Poynting's Vector and Plane Waves.—We have shown in Eq. (8.3) that the Poynting vector $E \times H$ represents the energy flow, and the quantity $\frac{1}{2}(\epsilon E^2 + \mu H^2)$ represents the energy density. Let us first consider an undamped wave at normal incidence, as in Sec. 9, and show the analogy of these quantities to the corresponding quantities for a transmission line. In that case the magnitude of H is equivalent to the current i in the transmission line, and the magnitude of E is the voltage V. Thus the Poynting vector becomes equivalent to Vi, which is equal to $i^2 Z_0$, where Z_0 is the characteristic impedance. If Z_0 is real, which is the case we are considering at the moment, this is the expression for the energy flux in the transmission line. Similarly the expression $\frac{1}{2}\epsilon E^2$ for the electric energy becomes $\frac{1}{2}CV^2$, and $\frac{1}{2}\mu H^2$ for the magnetic energy becomes $\frac{1}{2}LI^2$, both the correct values for unit length of a transmission line which has capacity C and inductance L per unit length.

Before considering the case of oblique incidence, let us ask what is the correct formulation of Poynting's theorem, when we are writing E and H in complex form. At a given point of space, E is given by the real part of $E_0 e^{j\omega t}$ and H by the real part of $H_0 e^{j\omega t}$, where E_0 and H_0 are complex vector functions of position. Let the real part of E_0 be E_r, and the imaginary part E_i, with similar notation for H_0. Then E is given by

$$\text{Re}\,(E_0 e^{j\omega t}) = \text{Re}\,(E_r + jE_i)(\cos \omega t + j \sin \omega t)$$
$$= E_r \cos \omega t - E_i \sin \omega t \qquad (11.1)$$

$E_0 = E_r + j E_i$

$H_0 = H_r + j H_i$

Similarly H is given by

$$\text{Re } (H_0 e^{j\omega t}) = H_r \cos \omega t - H_i \sin \omega t \qquad (11.2)$$

Poynting's vector is then

$$E \times H = (E_r \times H_r) \cos^2 \omega t + (E_i \times H_i) \sin^2 \omega t$$
$$- [(E_r \times H_i) + (E_i \times H_r)] \sin \omega t \cos \omega t \quad (11.3)$$

We notice that there are two types of terms: the first two, whose time average is different from zero, since $\cos^2 \omega t$ and $\sin^2 \omega t$ average to $\frac{1}{2}$; and the last term, whose time average is zero, since $\sin \omega t \cos \omega t$ averages to zero. Thus the time average Poynting vector is

$$\text{Average } (E \times H) = \tfrac{1}{2}(E_r \times H_r + E_i \times H_i) \qquad (11.4)$$

This can be rewritten in a convenient way, by using the notation of complex conjugates, where the complex conjugate of a complex number is the number obtained from the original one by changing the sign of j wherever it appears, and is indicated by a bar over the number. In terms of this notation, let us consider the quantity $(E \times \bar{H})$. This is

$$(E \times \bar{H}) = (E_0 e^{j\omega t}) \times (\bar{H}_0 e^{-j\omega t})$$
$$= E_0 \times \bar{H}_0 = (E_r + jE_i) \times (H_r - jH_i)$$
$$= (E_r \times H_r + E_i \times H_i)$$
$$+ j(E_i \times H_r - E_r \times H_i) \quad (11.5)$$

We see that, except for the factor of $\frac{1}{2}$, the real part of (11.5) is just the same as the quantity appearing in (11.4). That is, we have

$$\text{Average } (E \times H) = \tfrac{1}{2} \text{ Re } (E \times \bar{H}) \qquad (11.6)$$

where the E and H appearing on the right side of the equation are the complex quantities whose real parts give the real E and H appearing on the left of the equation. This derivation is obviously exactly parallel to that of the corresponding theorem (5.6) for transmission lines.

In case we are dealing with plane waves of the type discussed in this section, we have been interested in E_x and H_y, for example, and are particularly concerned in that case with the z component of Poynting's vector. This would then be

$$\text{Average } (E \times H)_z = \tfrac{1}{2} \text{ Re } (E_x \bar{H}_y) \qquad (11.7)$$

We have been using the concept of impedance, where we have had

$$E_x = ZH_y \qquad (11.8)$$

where Z has been real in the cases we have considered, but in general might be complex, given by a relation

$$Z = R + jX \qquad (11.9)$$

Then we have

$$\text{Average } (E \times H)_z = \tfrac{1}{2} \text{ Re } ZH_y \bar{H}_y \qquad (11.10)$$

But $H_y \bar{H}_y$ is the square of the absolute magnitude of H_y and is a real quantity, so that (11.10) becomes

$$\text{Average } (E \times H)_z = \tfrac{1}{2}R|H_y|^2 \qquad (11.11)$$

where R is the real part of the impedance, as given by (11.9) and where $|H_y|$ is the absolute magnitude of H_y. We see from (11.11) that it is only the real part of the impedance, the resistance, that contributes to flow of power; the reactance leads to a term that averages to zero. It is to be noted that the values of E_x, H_y, etc., here and throughout, are peak amplitudes, as follows from the fact that we take the real part of our complex exponential to give the real field. If we had used root mean square values instead, the $\tfrac{1}{2}$ would have been absent in (11.11) and similar formulas.

Now that we have considered the form of Poynting's vector, we shall proceed to the case of oblique incidence and shall show in that case that the flow of energy toward the reflecting plane, carried by the incident wave, minus the energy carried away by the reflected wave, equals the energy transmitted through and carried by the refracted wave. We wish the z component of Poynting's vector. In the case of the transverse electric vector, given in (10.12) and (10.13), we first take the incident wave, given by the first term in each equation of (10.12). For this wave, we have

from (11. 7) $\qquad \text{Average } (E_x \bar{H}_y) = \dfrac{1}{2}\sqrt{\dfrac{\mu}{\epsilon}}\, A^2 \cos \theta \qquad (11.12)$

Similarly for the reflected wave we have

$$\text{Average } (E_x \bar{H}_y) = -\dfrac{1}{2}\sqrt{\dfrac{\mu}{\epsilon}}\, B^2 \cos \theta \qquad (11.13)$$

For the refracted wave, using (10.13), we have

$$\text{Average } (E_x \overline{H_y}) = \frac{1}{2} \sqrt{\frac{\mu'}{\epsilon'}} A'^2 \cos \theta' \qquad (11.14)$$

We should now expect that the sum of (11.12) and (11.13) should equal (11.14). That is, we should expect

$$\sqrt{\frac{\mu}{\epsilon}} (A^2 - B^2) \cos \theta = \sqrt{\frac{\mu'}{\epsilon'}} A'^2 \cos \theta' \qquad (11.15)$$

To prove this, we need only multiply (10.15) and (10.16); the result follows immediately. The proof for the case of the transverse magnetic wave is carried through in an identical way, using (10.24).

12. Damped Plane Waves, Normal Incidence.

We shall now give up the restriction that the conductivity of our medium is zero and shall consider conducting materials, in which the waves will be damped or attenuated. First we consider the case of normal incidence, in which E is along the x axis, H along y, and the propagation is along z, as in the case of undamped waves in Sec. 9. We make the same assumption as in (9.1) for the values of the field components, but must use the wave equation (8.10) instead of (8.9). Then we find at once

$$\gamma_0^2 = -(\epsilon \mu \omega^2 - j \sigma \mu \omega) \qquad \text{from } 8.10 \sigma 9.1$$

$$\gamma_0 = j \omega \sqrt{\epsilon \mu - \frac{j \sigma \mu}{\omega}} = \pm j \omega \sqrt{\epsilon \mu} \sqrt{1 - j \frac{\sigma}{\epsilon \omega}} \qquad (12.1)$$

Instead of being pure imaginary, as in the case of an undamped wave, we see that γ_0 is complex, so that it has a real part, resulting in attenuation. It is important to see the order of magnitude of this attenuation, for the sorts of materials and wave lengths we are interested in, and for that reason we give some numerical values.

Let us first consider the ratio $\sigma/\epsilon \omega$ of the second term inside the radical to the first. Let us take copper as an example. The resistivity of copper at 20°C. is given in the tables as 1.74×10^{-6} ohm-cm. Thus its conductivity is $(1/1.74) \times 10^6 = 0.58 \times 10^6$ $= 5.8 \times 10^5$ mhos per centimeter, or 5.8×10^7 mhos per meter. (This value, as well as values for other materials, is given in Appendix III of Stratton, "Electromagnetic Theory.") The value of ϵ for a conductor is very hard to estimate, but we shall probably not be seriously in error if we take the value for empty space, which as we have seen in (7.25) is 8.85×10^{-12} farad per meter. For ω we may write $2\pi c/\lambda_0$, where c is the velocity of light in empty space, or 3.0×10^8 meters per second, and where λ_0 is the equivalent wave length in empty space, in meters. Then we have

$$\frac{\sigma}{\epsilon\omega} = \frac{5.8 \times 10^7 \lambda_0}{8.85 \times 10^{-12} \times 2\pi \times 3 \times 10^8}$$
$$= 3.5 \times 10^9 \lambda_0 \qquad (12.2)$$

For a wave length of 1 m. the ratio is thus 3.5×10^9, showing that at such a wave length the first term in (12.1) is entirely negligible. This first term, if we look back at Maxwell's equations, is the one coming from the displacement current; the second comes from the conduction current, so that we see that the displacement current in a conductor like copper is entirely negligible compared to the conduction current even at ultrahigh frequencies. To get to wave lengths small enough so that the ratio (12.2) is comparable to unity, so that the displacement current becomes appreciable, we must go to the range of very short ultraviolet wave lengths. This checks the experimental fact that in the ultraviolet region metals become much more transparent to light, the attenuation term becoming less important. It is obvious from this why the dielectric constant of a metal is hard to estimate: it enters in the first term of (12.1), which is entirely masked by the conduction effect, until we get to wave lengths so short that, though we can measure ϵ for those wave lengths perfectly well, we are not justified in thinking that that value would agree with the static or radio frequency value.

Copper of course is a good conductor, and it is interesting to consider our ratio of (12.2) for poor conductors. For sea water, the conductivity is about 4 mhos per meter, and the dielectric constant of the order of 80. Then proceeding as in (12.2) the ratio $\sigma/\epsilon\omega$ is about $3\lambda_0$. For 1 m., then, the ratio is about 3, so that the two terms of (12.1) are of the same order of magnitude. Ordinary insulators are much poorer conductors, so that the conductivity term is a very small correction only for them. On the other hand, though the other metals are poorer conductors than copper, they are still all so good that the same situation holds for them as for copper, namely that the displacement current is entirely negligible.

The physical meaning of the ratio $\sigma/\epsilon\omega$ can be made clearer by computing the relaxation time for a distribution of charge within a conductor. We start with the equation of continuity for the current and charge, or $\mathrm{div}\, J + \partial\rho/\partial t = 0$, write $J = \sigma E$ from Ohm's law, and $D = \epsilon E$. Finally we use Maxwell's equation (IV), of (7.21), $\mathrm{div}\, D = \rho$. Then we have the equation

$\mathrm{div}\, J = \mathrm{div}\, \sigma E$

$= \mathrm{div}\, \dfrac{\sigma D}{\epsilon} = \dfrac{\sigma\rho}{\epsilon}$

$$\frac{\sigma\rho}{\epsilon} + \frac{\partial\rho}{\partial t} = 0 \tag{12.3}$$

The solution of this differential equation is

$$\rho = \rho_0 e^{-\frac{\sigma}{\epsilon}t} = \rho_0 e^{-\frac{t}{\tau}} \qquad \tau = \frac{\epsilon}{\sigma} \tag{12.4}$$

where ρ_0 is a function of x, y, z representing the value of the charge density at $t = 0$, and where

$$\tau = \frac{\epsilon}{\sigma} \tag{12.5}$$

is the time in which the original charge density falls to $1/e$ of its value at $t = 0$ and is called the relaxation time. In terms of it and of the period

$$T = \frac{2\pi}{\omega} \tag{12.6}$$

of the oscillation, we see that our ratio $\sigma/\epsilon\omega$ can be rewritten

$$\frac{\sigma}{\epsilon\omega} = \frac{1}{2\pi}\frac{T}{\tau} \tag{12.7}$$

Since we have shown in (12.2) that this ratio is very large for microwave frequencies and high conductivity, we see that this means that the relaxation time is very small compared to the period of the oscillation in such a case, so that any distribution of charge which is set up in a metal will fall off to zero in a time which is insignificantly small compared to a period of the vibration.

We shall now limit ourselves to the case of metals, for which we can neglect the first term of (12.1). We then have

$$\gamma_0 = \pm j\omega\sqrt{-j\sigma\frac{\mu}{\omega}} \tag{12.8}$$

But $\sqrt{-j} = (1 - j)/\sqrt{2}$, so that this becomes

$$\gamma_0 = \alpha_0 + j\beta_0 = \sqrt{\frac{\sigma\mu\omega}{2}}\,(1 + j) \qquad (12.9)$$

and

attenuation const = phase constant

$$\alpha_0 = \beta_0 = \sqrt{\frac{\sigma\mu\omega}{2}} \qquad (12.10)$$

In terms of these quantities, the exponential appearing in the expression (9.1) for field intensities can be written

wave in metal $\quad E = E_0\,e^{-\alpha_0 z}e^{j(\omega t - \beta_0 z)} \quad H_y = H_0\,e^{-\alpha_0 z}e^{j(\omega t - \beta_0 z)}$ (12.11)

from which we see that the field is damped to $1/e$ of its value in a distance of $1/\alpha_0$ and that the velocity of propagation, given by (1.28) as ω/β_0, is

velocity of conduction in metal $\quad \dfrac{\omega}{\beta_0} = v = \sqrt{\dfrac{2\omega}{\sigma\mu}}$ *this does not hold for the limit $\rho = 0$, $\omega = \infty$* (12.12)

If we define δ as the distance $1/\alpha_0$ and use the relation $\omega = 2\pi c/\lambda_0$, where c is the velocity of light in empty space, λ_0 the equivalent wave length in empty space, we have

attenuated to 1/e of original value at

$$\delta = \frac{1}{\alpha_0} = \sqrt{\frac{\lambda_0}{\pi\sigma\mu c}} \qquad (12.13)$$

For copper, using the same numerical values as in (12.2), this gives us

$$\delta = 3.8 \times 10^{-6}\,\sqrt{\lambda_0} \qquad (12.14)$$

so that for $\lambda_0 = 1$ m., we have $\delta = 3.8 \times 10^{-6}$ m. $= 3.8 \times 10^{-4}$ cm. Thus for microwaves in good conductors the disturbance penetrates only a very small distance into the conductor before being damped off practically to zero. From (12.13) we see that poorer conductors will have greater values of δ; for sea water at 1 m. wave length, the distance δ is about 1 cm. Even here, however, it is small compared to the wave length in free space. The velocity (12.12) is best compared to the velocity of light in free space, which is $c = 1/\sqrt{\epsilon_0\mu_0}$. Using this, we have without trouble

$$\frac{v}{c} = \sqrt{\frac{2\epsilon\omega}{\sigma}}\,\sqrt{\frac{\epsilon_0\mu_0}{\epsilon\mu}} = \sqrt{\frac{4\pi\tau}{T}}\,\sqrt{\frac{\epsilon_0\mu_0}{\epsilon\mu}} \qquad (12.15)$$

From our previous discussion we see that this is a very small quantity. Thus for instance if we put in the value for copper at 1 m. wave length, v/c is 0.24×10^{-4}, so that v is 0.72×10^4 m. per second, a value in the range of ordinary acoustic velocities. The effective wave length in the conductor has the same ratio to the value in free space that the velocity in the conductor does to that in free space; thus in this case the wave length in the conductor is only 2.4×10^{-3} cm., which as we can at once see is $2\pi\delta$. The velocity of propagation, as given by (12.12) or (12.15), depends on the wave length or frequency of the disturbance, unlike the case of propagation in free space.

The intrinsic impedance Z_0 of the conducting medium can be found at once from Eq. (9.8), as modified for the presence of conductivity. It is given by

$$Z_0 = \frac{\mu j\omega}{\gamma_0} \tag{12.16}$$

where γ_0 is given in (12.1) and where its value for good conductors is given in (12.9). Substituting that value, we have

Z_0' in conducting medium

$$Z_0' = \sqrt{\frac{\mu\omega}{2\sigma}}\,(1 \mp j) = \sqrt{\frac{\mu_0}{\epsilon_0}}\sqrt{\frac{\epsilon_0}{\epsilon}\frac{\mu}{\mu_0}}\sqrt{\frac{\epsilon\omega}{2\sigma}}\,(1 \mp j) \tag{12.17}$$

From the second form of (12.17), we see that the ratio of Z_0 to the impedance of empty space, which is $\sqrt{\mu_0/\epsilon_0} = 377$ ohms, as we have seen, depends on the very small ratio $\epsilon\omega/\sigma$. Thus the electric field in a conductor is a much smaller value in comparison to the magnetic field than would be the case in free space, and in the limiting case of perfect conductivity, $\sigma = \infty$, the electric field vanishes, though the magnetic field does not. In addition to the small magnitude of the intrinsic impedance, we see that it is a complex quantity, so that the magnetic field is out of phase with the electric field. In fact, since $(1 - j)/\sqrt{2} = e^{-\pi j/4}$, we see that there is a phase difference of 45° between them. Using (9.1), we can write

$$E_x = H_0\sqrt{\frac{\mu\omega}{\sigma}}\,e^{-z/\delta}e^{j(\omega t - z/\delta - \pi/4)}$$
$$H_y = H_0 e^{-z/\delta}e^{j(\omega t - z/\delta)} \tag{12.18}$$

in conducting medium / in voltage phase differs in voltage & current

Often we have a wave in empty space, striking a conducting surface at normal incidence and being reflected. Let the ampli-

The phase shift is in time & E_x & H_y are still ⊥

tude of the magnetic vector in the incident wave be A, and in the reflected wave B.   Then, as in (3.9), we shall have

$$\frac{B}{A} = \frac{Z_0 - Z_0'}{Z_0 + Z_0'} \qquad (12.19)$$

assume $\varepsilon = \varepsilon_0$
$\mu = \mu_0$

where Z_0 is the impedance of free space, or $\sqrt{\mu_0/\epsilon_0}$, and Z_0' is the impedance of the conductor, given in (12.17). Since we have seen that Z_0' is very small compared to Z_0, this means that the ratio B/A is very nearly unity, so that almost all of the incident radiation is reflected.   We can easily find the coefficient R giving the fraction of incident energy which is reflected, for this is the ratio of the square of the magnitude of B to the square of the magnitude of A.   For simplicity we shall assume that the ϵ and μ of the conductor equal those of empty space; then we have

$$\frac{B}{A} = \frac{1 - \sqrt{\epsilon\omega/2\sigma}\,(1-j)}{1 + \sqrt{\epsilon\omega/2\sigma}\,(1-j)} = 1 - \frac{2\sqrt{\epsilon\omega/2\sigma}\,(1-j)}{1 + \sqrt{\epsilon\omega/2\sigma}\,(1-j)} \qquad (12.20)$$

In the denominator we can neglect the second term, since it is so small compared to unity.   We then have

$R \propto$ intensities $\propto$ amplitude$^2 = |B/A|^2$

$$R = \left|\frac{B}{A}\right|^2 = 1 - 4\sqrt{\frac{\epsilon\omega}{2\sigma}} = 1 - \sqrt{\frac{8\epsilon\omega}{\sigma}} \qquad (12.21)$$

where we have neglected terms of higher order.   The quantity $1 - R$, measuring the fraction of the incident energy absorbed by the reflector, is extremely small for good conductors at microwave frequencies, and as we see from (12.21) it decreases still more as the frequency decreases, or as the conductivity increases.   For a wave length of 1 m. and the conductivity of copper, we have $1 - R = 0.5 \times 10^{-4}$, a practically negligible amount.   The frequency must increase to values in the infrared before $1 - R$ becomes appreciable, for copper.

We can get at R in another way by finding the power flowing into the metal, directly from Poynting's vector.   To satisfy the boundary conditions at the surface, the resultant E from the incident and reflected waves must be very small, so that the electric fields of these two waves must almost exactly cancel.   As a result the magnetic fields must be in the same phase and must add.   Thus the H_0 for the wave inside the metal, just at the surface, as in (12.18), must be almost exactly equal to $2A$.   The

Poynting vector in the metal will be the real part of the impedance, times the mean square value of H_0, as we saw in (11.11),
and the Poynting vector of the incident wave is the impedance of
free space, times the mean square value of the H of the incident
wave. Thus $1 - R$, which represents the ratio of the power
flowing into the metal to the power in the incident wave, must be

$$1 - R = \frac{\sqrt{\mu\omega/2\sigma}\,(2A)^2}{\sqrt{\mu/\epsilon}\,A^2} = \sqrt{8\epsilon\omega/\sigma} \qquad (12.22)$$

Show

in agreement with (12.21). We shall find in the next chapter
that this type of calculation will be very useful in calculating the
attenuation in wave guides. There we shall have a field inside
the conducting walls of the guide which is almost identical with
what we have here. It will penetrate to the same depth, and the
fact that the current flows only in this narrow surface layer is
what is called the skin effect. There, as here, the electric field
at the surface of the conductor will be almost, but not quite, zero,
with the result that there will be a small Poynting vector directed
toward the surface and resulting in energy flow into the metal.
It is this energy flow which goes into heating up the conductor
and which is responsible for the power loss and attenuation in
the conductor.

13. Damped Plane Waves, Oblique Incidence.—The general
case of attenuated plane waves, striking a reflecting surface at an
arbitrary angle of incidence, is complicated enough so that it is
best to use more general methods than we have employed so far,
to make it understandable. In this section we shall set up these
general methods and shall describe qualitatively how to treat
such problems, though without going into great detail. The
reason for the complication, from the mathematical side, is that
all the vectors concerned in Maxwell's equations become complex
vectors. In such a case it is not necessary for the real and complex parts of a vector to have the same direction in space, any
more than it is necessary for them to have the same magnitude.
Thus the direction of propagation can have both a real and an
imaginary component, meaning that the surfaces of constant
phase, or the wave fronts, are perpendicular to one direction,
and that the surfaces of constant amplitude are perpendicular to
another direction. This is clearly necessary in problems of
reflection from absorbing media: the wave normal in general is at

an oblique angle to the normal to the surface, and yet the surfaces of constant amplitude are parallel to the surface, the intensity being damped off as we travel into the absorbing medium from the surface. Similarly the electric and magnetic fields can have both real and imaginary parts, pointing in different directions in space. This means that they show elliptical polarization, rather than plane polarization. We shall investigate the relations between these various quantities by setting up the fields and the direction of polarization, as complex vectors, and then investigating the meaning of Maxwell's equations in terms of these vectors.

Let us suppose *K is a direction vector*

$$E = E_0 e^{j\omega t} e^{-jk \cdot r}, \qquad H = H_0 e^{j\omega t} e^{-jk \cdot r}, \qquad (13.1)$$

where E_0, H_0, and k are complex vectors, given by

$$E_0 = E_r + jE_i$$
$$H_0 = H_r + jH_i \qquad \text{*like β*}$$
$$k = k_r + jk_i \qquad \text{*= jK*} \qquad (13.2)$$

and where r is the radius vector, of components x, y, z. The quantity k is analogous to the corresponding quantity introduced in (1.18) and (1.26), where it was shown that jk was equivalent to γ, only now we have set k up as a vector. Then, assuming an absorbing medium, Maxwell's equations (I) to (IV) become

K⊸H₀ are ⊥

$$-j(k \times E_0) = -\mu j\omega H_0, \qquad (k \times E_0) = \mu\omega H_0 \quad (I) \qquad (13.3)$$
$$k \cdot H_0 = 0 \quad (II) \qquad (13.4)$$
$$-j(k \times H_0) = (\epsilon j\omega + \sigma)E_0,$$
$$(k \times H_0) = -(\epsilon\omega - j\sigma)E_0 \quad III \quad (13.5)$$

K⊸E₀ are ⊥

$$k \cdot E_0 = 0 \quad (IV) \qquad (13.6)$$

where in the last equation we have set the charge density inside a conductor equal to zero, as we have found it will be in the preceding section, after the expiration of the relaxation time. From (13.4) and (13.6) we see that both H_0 and E_0 are at right angles to k. From (13.3), we see that E_0 and H_0 are at right angles to each other, since the vector product of E_0 with another vector must be at right angles to E_0. These relations do not have their simple meanings, however, on account of the complex nature of the vectors. We shall see later just what the relative directions are in this case.

We can easily find the value of the constant k, by taking the vector product of k and the expression (13.3). Thus we have

$$k \times (k \times E_0) = k(k \cdot E_0) - E_0(k \cdot k) = -E_0 k^2$$
$$= \mu\omega(k \times H_0) = \mu\omega(-\epsilon\omega + j\sigma)E_0 \quad (13.7)$$

where we have used a vector identity to find $k \times (k \times E_0)$ and have substituted from (13.5). Canceling E_0, this gives

$$k \cdot k = k^2 = \mu\omega(\epsilon\omega - j\sigma) \quad (13.8)$$

Using (13.2) for k, this becomes

$$k_r^2 - k_i^2 + 2jk_r \cdot k_i = \epsilon\mu\omega^2 - j\sigma\mu\omega$$
$$k_r^2 - k_i^2 = \epsilon\mu\omega^2, \quad 2k_r \cdot k_i = -\sigma\mu\omega \quad (13.9)$$

Equation (13.9) shows that we can set up propagation for any arbitrary value of k_i, the quantity determining the attenuation. From the first of the two equations we can then find the magnitude of k_r; from the second we can find the angle between the two vectors. It is interesting to note that a damped wave, with k_i different from zero, is possible even in a nonabsorbing medium, with $\sigma = 0$. In this case, k_r and k_i must be at right angles. This is a case that we meet in connection with total internal reflection. It is also interesting to note, from the first equation, that the greater the damping is, or the greater k_i, the greater also must be k_r. Remembering that k_r is inversely proportional to the wave length, this means that a highly damped wave must have a very short wave length. This has already been pointed out in the special case of normal incidence in the preceding section. The results of that section are plainly in agreement with the more general case considered here. Equation (13.8) agrees with (12.1), and the preceding case is the one in which k_r and k_i are parallel to each other.

The general case is that in which E_0 and H_0 are both complex vectors. However, on account of the linear nature of Maxwell's equations, it follows that if for example E_0 is complex, we can set up solutions consisting only of the real, or only of the imaginary, part of E_0, combined with appropriate magnetic fields. Thus there are simple solutions in which E_0 is real, or pure imaginary. Similarly there are solutions in which H_0 is real, or pure imaginary. The general solution can be built up out of linear combinations of

[handwritten note] If σ is large, then k_r & k_i are $\parallel$, or nearly so, then $k = \omega\sqrt{\epsilon\mu} - \frac{j\sigma\mu}{\omega}$ & compare to 12.1 ($\gamma_0 = jk$)

these. Let us first take the case in which E_0 is real. Then Eq. (13.6) has a simple result: we have both

$$k_r \cdot E_0 = 0$$

and

$$k_i \cdot E_0 = 0 \tag{13.10}$$

That is, the vector E_0 is at right angles to both k_r and k_i or is in the direction normal to the plane determined by k_r and k_i. This direction is unique, except in the special case of the preceding section, where k_r and k_i are parallel to each other and thus do not determine a plane. Using (13.3), we then have

$$k_r \times E_0 = \mu\omega H_r, \qquad k_i \times E_0 = \mu\omega H_i \tag{13.11}$$

showing, since k_r and k_i are perpendicular to E_0, that H_r and H_i are proportional to k_r and k_i but at right angles to them. The situation, in the plane containing k_r and k_i, is then as shown in Fig. 31. E_0 in this figure is at right angles to the paper. The

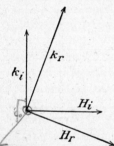

FIG. 31.—Direction of magnetic and propagation vectors in damped plane wave with real electric vector.

situation is not essentially altered if E_0 is pure imaginary instead of real. This type of wave might well be considered a transverse electric wave, since E has no component along either k_r or k_i, while H does have such a component. We can equally well set up a transverse magnetic wave, by assuming H_0 to be real. In that case, E_r and E_i will be at right angles to k_r and k_i, as H_r and H_i are in Fig. 31. We note that in Poynting's vector, whose average value is determined by Re $(E \times \bar{H})$, as we have seen in Sec. 11, it is only the component H in Fig. 31 that will contribute to the energy flow. Thus the flow of energy is along k_r, the normal to the surfaces of constant phase, and it is entirely justifiable to consider this direction as the direction of propagation of the wave.

Let us now ask how to satisfy boundary conditions at a surface of separation between two media. In the first place, the tangential component of k must be continuous at the surface, in order that the exponentials in (13.1) may join continuously in the two media. This means that both the tangential components of k_i and of k_r must be continuous at the surface. This leads to one

very simple result: if one of the two media is not absorbing and if
the wave in that medium is not damped, k_i in it is zero.   To get
continuity of the tangential component of k_i, then, we see that k_i
in the absorbing medium must be normal to the surface, so as to
have no tangential component.   In addition to this, the tangential component of k_r must be continuous, and this leads to the
law of refraction in this case.   It is not Snell's law in the ordinary
form, however, for as we see from (13.9), it is not true in this case
that $k_r = \omega \sqrt{\epsilon\mu}$, which is the condition on which Snell's law
depends.   It is not hard to get the actual law from (13.9), but we
shall not derive it; it is rather complicated.   In addition to continuity of the tangential component of k, we must have continuity of the tangential components of E and H and of the normal
components of D and B.   Let us define an impedance of the
wave, as the ratio of the tangential components of E and H.
Then it is clear that if we compute the impedance for a disturbance consisting of an incident and reflected wave in the first
medium and a refracted wave in the second medium, the continuity of this quantity is necessary in order that the tangential
components of E and H should be continuous.   From Eq. (13.3)
we then see that if the tangential components of k and of E are
continuous, the normal component of $\mu H = B$ will be continuous.
Finally from (13.5) we see that if the tangential components of k
and H are continuous, the normal component of $\dot{D} + \sigma E$, the
sum of the displacement current and the conduction current, will
be zero.   This is really the correct condition in this case, not the
continuity of the normal component of D; it is the condition, in
the case of conducting media, which is the limit of the divergence
equation div $D = \rho$, in the limit of sudden changes at a surface.
In other words, we see that the situation is the same that we have
encountered before: to satisfy boundary conditions at a surface,
we must impose the correct law of refraction and the continuity of
impedance on both sides of the surface, computed for the disturbance actually present.   Then all conditions demanded by
Maxwell's equations will be met.

Two cases of reflection involving the principles of this section
are familiar.   The first is the case of total internal reflection.
This is met where both of the media in question are nonconducting, but where the second medium has a smaller index of refraction than the first, and the angle of incidence is greater than the

In air, $K_i = 0$, no attenuation $K_r = \omega \sqrt{\epsilon\mu}$

critical angle.   In the first medium, there is no damping, and k_i is zero.   The magnitude of k_r in this medium, from (13.9), is then $\omega \sqrt{\epsilon\mu}$.   If the angle of incidence is θ, the tangential component of k_r is $\omega \sqrt{\epsilon\mu} \sin \theta$.   If we could satisfy the boundary conditions with a real vector k in the second medium, we should have

$$\omega \sqrt{\epsilon\mu} \sin \theta = \omega \sqrt{\epsilon'\mu'} \sin \theta' \qquad (13.12)$$

where primed quantities refer to the second medium.   This would give

$$\frac{\sin \theta'}{\sin \theta} = \frac{n}{n'} \qquad (13.13)$$

where n is the index of refraction, as in (10.18).   If n' is less than n, the ratio is greater than unity, so that for angles greater than a certain critical angle, $\sin \theta'$ as defined by (13.13) would be greater than unity, and θ' would be imaginary.   It is in this case that we must use the damped solution in the second medium. We must then have k_i' normal to the surface, so that k_r' is tangential to the surface, meaning that in the second medium there is no flow of energy normal to the surface, but only parallel to the surface.   Since this carries no energy across the surface, the reflected wave must carry as much energy away from the surface as the incident wave carries to it, and the reflection coefficient is unity.   For this reason the case is referred to as total reflection. The rate of attenuation of the wave in the second medium is given by (13.9):

$$k_i'^2 = k_r'^2 - \omega^2\epsilon'\mu' = \omega^2(\epsilon\mu \sin^2 \theta - \epsilon'\mu') \qquad (13.14)$$

where we have used the condition that the tangential component of k_r is continuous.   Just at the critical angle, where $\epsilon\mu \sin^2 \theta = \epsilon'\mu'$, there is no attenuation, but as the angle of incidence increases from the critical angle the attenuation becomes more rapid, so that the disturbance does not penetrate far into the rare medium.

The other important case of our equations comes in reflection from a metallic surface.   Again we ordinarily assume the incident medium to the nonabsorbing, so that we have an undamped incident wave.   The vector k_i' in the second medium must then be normal to the surface, but since σ is not zero in the second medium, (13.9) tells us that in this case k_r' is not parallel to the surface but instead has a normal component.   In fact, in any ordinary case, if the second medium is a metal, k'_r is almost exactly normal to the surface itself. To see that, we note that in such a case, as we saw in Sec. 12, $\epsilon' \mu' \omega^2$ is very small compared to $\sigma' \mu' \omega$. Thus in (13.9) we see that k'^2_r is almost exactly equal to k'^2_i. We shall see in a moment that the angle between k'_r and k'_i is very small; thus from the second equation of (13.9) we see that k'_r and k'_i in magnitude are approximately equal to $\sqrt{\sigma' \mu' \omega/2}$. On the other hand, the tangential component of k'_r, by the condition of continuity, must equal the tangential component of k_r, which is $\omega \sqrt{\epsilon \mu} \sin \theta$. Thus the ratio of the tangential component of k'_r to the magnitude of k'_r is

$$\frac{k'_{rt}}{|k'_r|} = \sqrt{\frac{\mu}{\mu'}} \sqrt{\frac{2\epsilon\omega}{\sigma'}} \sin \theta \qquad (13.15)$$

From the arguments of Sec. 12, we see that this ratio is very small, so that we are justified in saying that k'_r is almost normal to the surface. In other words, no matter what the angle of incidence may be, the wave in a good conductor will be very nearly the same that it is at normal incidence, so that the discussion of Sec. 12 applies with only small corrections to the general case of arbitrary angle of incidence. The equations of the present section can be used to investigate the reflected wave and show that in general it is elliptically polarized. However, since we shall not use the results at present, we shall not carry them through.

The cases taken up in the present section are not intrinsically of great importance in microwave work. Nevertheless the principles underlying damped waves at oblique incidence are important and will come up again in a number of connections. Thus in the next chapter we shall consider attenuation in wave guides and in the general nature of skin effect. This is merely a special case of the equations of the present section. Again, we shall encounter waves that are attenuated as we pass down wave guides, even though they are traveling in empty space. These are solutions essentially like those met in the problem of total reflection, where the wave in the rare medium is attenuated, even though there is no absorption in the medium.

CHAPTER III
RECTANGULAR WAVE GUIDES

An infinitely long hollow pipe, of rectangular cross section and conducting walls, transmits many types of electromagnetic waves with small attenuation and is a practical transmission line. On the one hand, it has many of the properties of the transmission lines of Chap. I; on the other, it forms a simple and natural extension of the study of plane waves taken up in Chap. II. In this chapter we consider such rectangular wave guides. Later we shall go on to wave guides of more complicated cross section than rectangles and to composite wave guides, whose properties change from point to point along the length of the guide, introducing reflections like those found in a composite transmission line. The theory of rectangular wave guides is given in a number of papers.[1]

14. Wave Propagation between Parallel Perfectly Conducting Planes.—As a first step, we shall consider wave propagation in the space between two infinite parallel perfectly conducting planes. A special case of this was considered in the arguments illustrated by Fig. 29, in Sec. 9. We shall base our argument on Sec. 10, which treated the reflection of plane waves at oblique incidence. We shall show that if two plane waves are superposed in a suitable way, they automatically set up a disturbance that satisfies correct boundary conditions at the surfaces of the planes and hence forms the solution of our problem.

Figure 32 shows a diagram of the set of coordinates that we shall use. We imagine two conducting planes perpendicular to the y axis, as indicated by the sections of planes in Fig. 32. The type of disturbance that we shall consider is propagated along the z axis. Let us now make up the disturbance out of two plane waves, traveling along the z' and z'' directions, as shown in Fig. 32. These directions are both in the yz plane, making angles of θ with the z axis. It is reasonable that we should superpose these two

[1] Barrow, *Proc. I.R.E.*, **24**, 1298 (1936); Carson, Mead, and Schelkunoff, *Bell System Tech. J.*, **15**, 310 (1936); Chu and Barrow, *Proc. I.R.E.*, **26**, 1520 (1938).

waves to set up the disturbance between the planes. If we started with the wave traveling along z' alone, it would be reflected from the right-hand plane, and the reflected wave would travel along z''. Similarly the wave along z'' would be reflected by the left-hand plane, the reflected wave traveling along z'. Thus the superposition of these two waves should form a complete solution for the space between the reflectors.

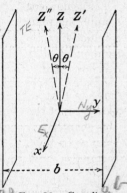

FIG. 32.—Coordinate system for propagation between parallel planes.

As in Sec. 10, there will be two types of particularly simple solutions: the transverse electric wave (abbreviated *TE*), in which the electric field is along the x axis, and the magnetic field has y and z components; and the transverse magnetic wave (*TM*), in which the magnetic field is along x, and the electric field has y and z components. Let us start with the *TE* wave. We now have in (10.1) the values of the components of E and H for a *TE* wave propagated along the direction z'. To get the wave propagated along z'', we need only change the sign of θ wherever it appears. Let us then superpose waves of equal amplitude and, for convenience, opposite phase along z' and z''. The result is

$$E_x = -\sqrt{\frac{\mu}{\epsilon}}\, 2Aj \sin\left(\omega\sqrt{\epsilon\mu}\,\sin\theta y\right)e^{j\omega(t-\sqrt{\epsilon\mu}\,\cos\theta z)}$$

$$E_y = E_z = H_x = 0$$

$$H_y = -2Aj \cos\theta \sin\left(\omega\sqrt{\epsilon\mu}\,\sin\theta y\right)e^{j\omega(t-\sqrt{\epsilon\mu}\,\cos\theta z)}$$

$$H_z = -2A \sin\theta \cos\left(\omega\sqrt{\epsilon\mu}\,\sin\theta y\right)e^{j\omega(t-\sqrt{\epsilon\mu}\,\cos\theta z)} \quad (14.1)$$

By addition of expansion of $e^{jk_y y}$ $z' + z''$ waves 180° out of phase (see p. 102)

Formulas (14.1) may be simplified by using as abbreviations

$$\gamma = j\omega\sqrt{\epsilon\mu}\,\cos\theta = j\beta \quad (14.2)$$

$$k_y = \omega\sqrt{\epsilon\mu}\,\sin\theta \quad (14.3)$$

$$Z(\theta) = \frac{E_x}{H_y} = \sqrt{\frac{\mu}{\epsilon}}\,\sec\theta \quad (14.4)$$

Then they become

$$E_x = Z(\theta)H_0 \sin k_y y\, e^{j\omega t - \gamma z}$$

$$H_y = H_0 \sin k_y y\, e^{j\omega t - \gamma z}$$

$$H_z = H_0 \frac{k_y}{\gamma} \cos k_y y\, e^{j\omega t - \gamma z} \quad (14.5)$$

$H_0 = -2Aj \cos\theta$

where H_0 is another constant. We can easily verify by direct calculation that (14.5) are solutions of Maxwell's equations. We see that they represent a wave propagated along the z axis, with propagation constant γ along this axis and varying sinusoidally with y.

Let us now consider the boundary conditions on the two parallel conducting planes. We remember that on a surface of infinite conductivity the tangential component of E and the normal component of H must be zero. From the results of Sec. 13, we can now justify these boundary conditions completely. In the first place, in (12.17) we found the impedance at the surface of a conductor, and from the formula we see that it becomes zero as the conductivity becomes infinite. Thus the tangential component of E is zero inside the surface; hence by continuity it must be zero outside the surface as well. Then from (13.15) we see that in a perfect conductor the wave normal inside the conductor must be along the normal to the surface, no matter what may be the direction of the normal outside. Then from the construction of Fig. 31 we see that the magnetic field in the conductor must be perpendicular to the normal and must have no normal component, so that by continuity there is no normal component of H outside the surface. Considering Fig. 32, then, we see that at the conducting planes E_x and H_y must be zero. That is, at these planes $\sin k_y y$ must equal zero. Let us suppose that the planes are located at $y = 0$ and $y = b$. The condition at $y = 0$ is automatically satisfied; for the condition at $y = b$ we must have

$$k_y b = n\pi, \qquad k_y = \frac{n\pi}{b} \tag{14.6}$$

where n is an integer greater than zero. The wave associated with an integer n is called the $TE_{0,n}$ wave; the first subscript, equal to zero in this case, refers to another term varying sinusoidally with x, which we shall find in the general case.

Let us consider the $TE_{0,n}$ wave more in detail. First we may find the angle θ in terms of the wave length of the disturbance in empty space, and b. Thus let

$$\lambda_0 = \frac{2\pi}{\omega \sqrt{\epsilon\mu}} \tag{14.7}$$

$C = \frac{1}{\sqrt{\mu\epsilon}}$

$\frac{c}{b}$

$\omega = 2\pi f$

There is no $TE_{0,0}$ wave

be the wave length in empty space.   Then from (14.3) and (14.6) we have at once

(handwritten: $K_y = \omega \sqrt{\varepsilon \mu} \sin \theta$
$= \frac{n\pi}{b}$ *)*

$$\sin \theta = \frac{n\lambda_0}{2b}, \qquad \cos \theta \doteq \sqrt{1 - \left(\frac{n\lambda_0}{2b}\right)^2} \qquad (14.8)$$

Since the sine cannot be greater than unity, we see that such a wave is only possible if

$$n\lambda_0 < 2b \qquad (14.9)$$

In other words, n half wave lengths must be smaller than the distance between the parallel conductors, in order to have real propagation.   If the wave length is greater than this, then from (14.8) the cosine is pure imaginary, so that from (14.2) the propagation constant γ is real, and the wave is damped exponentially as we go along z, instead of varying sinusoidally.   The attenuation constant can be found at once from (14.2) and (14.8).   The set of parallel conductors, then, forms a high-pass filter, only frequencies above a critical frequency being propagated through it.   Instead of having one critical frequency for cutoff, however, like an ordinary filter, we have an infinite number, one given by each value of n.   If the frequency is so low that the wave is attenuated, the resulting field (14.5) is the type that would be set up by superposing two damped waves of the type discussed in Sec. 13, with their vectors k_i pointing along the z axis, and their real vectors k_r pointing along the y axis, so that the resulting disturbance is damped along z but varies sinusoidally along y.

Using Eq. (14.8), we can rewrite our wave in terms of λ_0 and b rather than in terms of θ.   Thus we have

(handwritten: $n\lambda_0 = 2b$, then $\gamma = 0$ *)*

$$\gamma = \frac{2\pi j}{\lambda_0} \sqrt{1 - \left(\frac{n\lambda_0}{2b}\right)^2} \qquad (14.10)$$

The impedance Z is given by

(handwritten: $n\lambda_0 = 2b$ then $Z = \infty$ *)*

(handwritten: $\sqrt{\frac{\mu}{\varepsilon}} \sec \theta =$ *)* $Z = \sqrt{\frac{\mu}{\epsilon}} \frac{1}{\sqrt{1 - (n\lambda_0/2b)^2}} \qquad (14.11)$

The phase velocity of propagation along the z axis, which by (1.28) equals ω/β, is given by

(handwritten: $n\lambda_0 = 2b$, then $V = \infty$ *)*

(handwritten: $\frac{\omega}{\beta} =$ *)* $v = \frac{1}{\sqrt{\epsilon\mu}} \frac{1}{\sqrt{1 - (n\lambda_0/2b)^2}} \qquad (14.12)$

(handwritten: The group vel is signal on wave = 0 when $n\lambda_0 = 2b$
" phase " " vel of wave front
We are trying to measure velocity along wave front $(t=0)$
$\therefore v = \infty$ *)*

For any given n or any given mode, we see that as the frequency becomes infinite, or λ_0 becomes zero, the impedance and velocity approach those characteristic of empty space. At the same time the angle θ, given by (14.8), approaches zero, so that we have the simple case of a plane wave propagated along the z axis. As the frequency decreases toward the cutoff frequency, however, both impedance and velocity of propagation increase, becoming infinite at cutoff. At the same time the angle θ increases, becoming 90° at cutoff, so that there is no real propagation along the z axis at all, a fact which is shown also by the fact that γ becomes zero at this point. It is interesting to note that for any arbitrary wave length λ_0, we shall in general find some modes that have real propagation along z and others that are attenuated. Thus those for which n is less than $2b/\lambda_0$ will be propagated, those with higher n will be attenuated. As the frequency decreases and λ_0 increases, fewer and fewer will be propagated. For example, if a half wave length is less than b but greater than $b/2$, only the mode $n = 1$ will be propagated; all higher values of n will represent attenuated modes. This is a common condition for the operation of a type of wave guide based on this example.

The $TE_{0,n}$ wave which we have just been considering can be propagated in a rectangular wave guide, constructed from the two parallel conducting planes of Fig. 32 by adding two additional planes perpendicular to the x axis, at arbitrary points. From (14.5) it is obvious that E has no tangential components, and H no normal components, over these planes, so that the boundary conditions are automatically satisfied. The lines of E terminate in surface charges on these planes perpendicular to x, just as they did in the case illustrated in Fig. 29, and the tangential magnetic field H_y results in currents flowing along the z axis in these conductors. We approach exactly the case of Fig. 29, if b becomes so great that the planes perpendicular to y may be considered to recede to infinity. In this case θ becomes zero, and the propagation constant and impedance reduce to the values for empty space. In the formulas (14.5) for the fields, it is more convenient in this case to use a factor $\cos k_y y$ in E_x and H_y and $- \sin k_y y$ in H_z, having as a result that the mid-point between the two planes is at the origin instead of one of the planes. Then if the planes recede to infinity, by making b infinite, k_y goes to zero, so that E_x becomes $ZH_0 e^{j\omega t - \gamma z}$, H_y becomes $H_0 e^{j\omega t - \gamma z}$, and H_x becomes zero, just as in the case of empty space.

Distribution of E is half sine wave

Next we consider the transverse magnetic waves. Starting with Eq. (10.24) and combining as in the derivation of (14.5), only now combining the two waves in the same phase rather than in opposite phases, we have

$$E_x = 0$$
$$E_y = -ZH_0 \cos k_y y e^{i\omega t - \gamma z}$$
$$E_z = Z \frac{k_y}{\gamma} H_0 \sin k_y y e^{i\omega t - \gamma z}$$
$$H_x = H_0 \cos k_y y e^{i\omega t - \gamma z}$$
$$H_y = H_z = 0 \qquad\qquad (14.13)$$

[handwritten: Two plane waves along z' & z'' Show this]

with

$$Z = Z(\theta) = -\frac{E_y}{H_x} = \sqrt{\frac{\mu}{\epsilon}} \cos \theta \qquad (14.14)$$

and with γ and k_y as defined in (14.2) and (14.3). We note that the value of $Z(\theta)$ found in (14.14) agrees with that found in (10.28) for the transverse magnetic wave in empty space, just as the value (14.4) agrees with (10.11). We see, then, that as far as propagation vectors are concerned the transverse magnetic wave is just like the transverse electric case, but that the impedance, or ratio of E to H, is different.

Next let us impose boundary conditions. On a conducting surface perpendicular to the y axis, the normal component of magnetic field is automatically zero, and the tangential component of electric field is E_z. Since this depends on y through the term $\sin k_y y$, we see that the boundary condition is just the same as (14.6), already met in the transverse electric case, with one exception: the integer n can be zero, as well as other values, for the TM wave; with the TE wave the value zero was excluded. The reason is that the field components of (14.5) all automatically become zero if n is zero, but this is not the case with the components of (14.13). In the TM case, in fact, if $n = 0$, we see from (14.8), which applies here also, that $\theta = 0$, the propagation is like that of a wave along the z axis in free space, and the fields reduce to $E_y = -ZH_0 e^{i\omega t - \gamma z}$, $H_x = H_0 e^{i\omega t - \gamma z}$, with all other components zero, just as in (9.1), except that the axes are rotated. Thus the $TM_{0,0}$ wave is essentially just like a wave in free space and is equivalent to that used in Fig. 29. Since $\theta = 0$ for it, the velocity of propagation is equal to that in free space, there is no attenuation or cutoff at any frequency, and the impedance is

[handwritten right margin: E_x & E_z are E_t $H_y = H_n$]

[handwritten bottom: $\sin k_y = 0$ at $y = 0 = b$ $k_y = \frac{n\pi}{b}$]

equal to that for free space. This wave is often called the principal wave. The other transverse magnetic waves, $TM_{0,n}$ for n different from zero, are not unlike the $TE_{0,n}$ waves. The formulas (14.8) for θ are the same, and consequently as far as propagation is concerned they are exactly equivalent. The only mathematical difference comes in the impedance. There is one other important difference, however. We have seen that for the TE waves, it is possible to put up an extra set of conducting surfaces perpendicular to the x axis and make the system into a rectangular wave guide, in which case the boundary conditions on the new surfaces are automatically satisfied. This is not the case, however, with the TM waves. We see from (14.13) that at a surface perpendicular to x, E_y and E_z are transverse components of E, and H_x is a normal component of H, and all three are in general different from zero. Thus these waves $TM_{0,n}$ can exist in the present case of two parallel conductors but cannot exist in a rectangular wave guide. In particular, the principal wave, $TM_{0,0}$ does not exist in a wave guide. We shall see in a later chapter that principal waves exist only in systems, like that of two parallel planes, in which there are two separated conductors, but cannot exist in systems like a rectangular pipe, with only one conductor. Thus a coaxial line has a principal mode, but a hollow pipe does not. The reason is essentially that in the principal mode the electric vector goes across from one conductor to the other, being terminated by opposite charges on the two conductors. If the two conductors are connected, so as to make a hollow pipe, this inevitably results in a short-circuiting of this mode, since the lines of force otherwise would run tangentially to the side walls.

15. Undamped Waves in Rectangular Pipes.—In the preceding section we have taken up the problem of wave propagation between parallel conducting planes and have seen that by superposing two elementary plane waves, representing the waves incident on and reflected by each surface, we can satisfy the boundary conditions and get a solution of our problem. Corresponding to the two types of polarization of a plane wave, there are two types of solution, the transverse electric and transverse magnetic, corresponding to the polarizations where the electric and magnetic vectors respectively are in the planes perpendicular to the z axis. Similarly with a rectangular pipe, with boundaries perpendicular to both the x and the y axis, we can build up the general disturbance out of a sum of elementary plane waves. Here in general we need four waves, however: an incident wave, and the reflections of this wave in both sets of planes. That is, writing the exponential part of the wave, we need all combinations of $+$ and $-$ signs in the expression $e^{j(\omega t \pm k_x x \pm k_y y - k_z z)}$, where k_x, k_y, k_z are three constants. Again we can have either transverse electric or transverse magnetic waves; but now, since the wave normals are no longer in the yz plane, the transverse field is no longer along the x axis but has both x and y components. Similarly the other field, which is not transverse, now has not only y and z components but an x component as well. The whole situation thus becomes rather involved and, although we can continue if we please to set up a solution by superposing plane waves, it becomes simpler to proceed directly, assuming fields that vary exponentially along z, sinusoidally along x and y, and choosing the constants so as to satisfy Maxwell's equations. Let us first consider the transverse electric wave and see what Maxwell's equations give, on the assumption that only E_z is zero.

For a case where $E_z = 0$, Maxwell's equations become

$$-\frac{\partial E_y}{\partial z} + \mu j \omega H_x = 0$$

$$\frac{\partial E_x}{\partial z} + \mu j \omega H_y = 0$$

(I) $$\frac{\partial E_y}{\partial x} - \frac{\partial E_x}{\partial y} + \mu j \omega H_z = 0$$

(II) $$\frac{\partial H_x}{\partial x} + \frac{\partial H_y}{\partial y} + \frac{\partial H_z}{\partial z} = 0$$

$$\frac{\partial H_z}{\partial y} - \frac{\partial H_y}{\partial z} - (\epsilon j \omega + \sigma) E_x = 0$$

$$\frac{\partial H_x}{\partial z} - \frac{\partial H_z}{\partial x} - (\epsilon j \omega + \sigma) E_y = 0$$

(III) $$\frac{\partial H_y}{\partial x} - \frac{\partial H_x}{\partial y} = 0$$

(IV) $$\frac{\partial E_x}{\partial x} + \frac{\partial E_y}{\partial y} = 0 \qquad (15.1)$$

In the case of the wave guide, we assume that the variation of each field component with z is given by the expression $e^{-\gamma z}$.

Inserting this assumption, the equations become

$$\gamma E_y + \mu j\omega H_x = 0 \quad (1)$$
$$-\gamma E_x + \mu j\omega H_y = 0 \quad (2)$$
$$\frac{\partial E_y}{\partial x} - \frac{\partial E_x}{\partial y} + \mu j\omega H_z = 0 \quad (3)$$

(3) = (4) from (9)

$$\frac{\partial H_x}{\partial x} + \frac{\partial H_y}{\partial y} - \gamma H_z = 0 \quad (4)$$

$$\frac{\partial H_z}{\partial y} + \gamma H_y - (\epsilon j\omega + \sigma)E_x = 0 \quad (5)$$

$$-\gamma H_x - \frac{\partial H_z}{\partial x} - (\epsilon j\omega + \sigma)E_y = 0 \quad (6)$$

Satisfied by (10)

$$\frac{\partial H_y}{\partial x} - \frac{\partial H_x}{\partial y} = 0 \quad (7)$$

$$\frac{\partial E_x}{\partial x} + \frac{\partial E_y}{\partial y} = 0 \quad (8) \qquad (15.2)$$

Of these equations, the first two serve to express E_x and E_y in terms of H_x and H_y:

From (1) & (2)

$$\frac{E_x}{H_y} = \frac{E_y}{(-H_x)} = Z = \frac{\mu j\omega}{\gamma} \quad (9) \qquad (15.3)$$

In the third equation, we can express E_x and E_y in terms of H_x and H_y, and then find that it becomes identical with the fourth equation. Using (15.3), the fifth and sixth equations then serve to express H_x and H_y in terms of derivatives of H_z:

Placing (9) in (5) & (6)

$$H_x = \frac{-\gamma}{\gamma^2 - \mu j\omega(\epsilon j\omega + \sigma)} \frac{\partial H_z}{\partial x}$$
$$H_y = \frac{-\gamma}{\gamma^2 - \mu j\omega(\epsilon j\omega + \sigma)} \frac{\partial H_z}{\partial y} \qquad (15.4)$$
$$(10)$$

Using (15.3) and (15.4), we find that the seventh and eighth equations are automatically satisfied. This then leaves only the third, or fourth, equation, and it becomes an equation for H_z. Substituting from (15.4), this equation is

Placing (10) in (4)

$$\frac{\partial^2 H_z}{\partial x^2} + \frac{\partial^2 H_z}{\partial y^2} + (\gamma^2 - \mu j\omega(\epsilon j\omega + \sigma))H_z = 0 \qquad (15.5)$$

or

$$\frac{\partial^2 H_z}{\partial x^2} + \frac{\partial^2 H_z}{\partial y^2} + k^2 H_z = 0 \qquad (15.6)$$

where

$$k^2 = \gamma^2 - \mu j\omega(\epsilon j\omega + \sigma) \qquad (15.7)$$

In the preceding paragraph we have set up a procedure for handling the TE waves, which is applicable to any form of wave guide. We first find a solution of (15.6) for H_z. This equation is simply the familiar wave equation in two dimensions, in the form where the time is eliminated. Then from the H_z so determined we may find H_x and H_y by (15.4), and E_x and E_y by (15.3). In addition to satisfying the wave equation, we must satisfy our boundary conditions at the surface of the conductors. For the moment let us consider the general problem of a wave guide of arbitrary cross section in the xy plane, but whose boundaries are parallel to the z axis. Then the component of H in the xy plane perpendicular to the surface, and the component of E in the xy plane parallel to the surface, must both vanish, at the surface of a perfect conductor. The first condition, using (15.4), means that the rate of change of H_z along the normal to the surface must be zero. The second condition is equivalent to the first; for Eq. (15.3) tells us that the components of E and of H in the xy plane are perpendicular to each other, since it can be written $E_x/E_y = -H_y/H_x$. Thus if the normal component of H is zero, the tangential component of E will automatically be zero also.

Now that we have set up the general formulation of our problem, let us specialize for the case of a rectangular wave guide, bounded by perfectly conducting planes at $x = 0$, $x = a$, $y = 0$, $y = b$. We can plainly set up a solution of (15.6) which varies sinusoidally with both x and y. In order that the derivative of H_z with respect to the normal to the surface may be zero, we must use a cosine function and must have the boundaries come at points where the cosine has a maximum or minimum. To satisfy these conditions, we must have

$$H_z = H_0 \cos \frac{m\pi x}{a} \cos \frac{n\pi y}{b} e^{j\omega t - \gamma z} \qquad (15.8)$$

where m, n, are integers, which as far as we can see at the moment can be zero as well as different from zero. The wave equation (15.6) then gives

$$\left[-\left(\frac{m\pi}{a}\right)^2 - \left(\frac{n\pi}{b}\right)^2 + k^2 \right] H_z = 0 \qquad (15.9)$$

If we write

$$k_x = \frac{m\pi}{a}, \qquad k_y = \frac{n\pi}{b} \tag{15.10}$$

Equation (15.9) can be rewritten

$$k_x^2 + k_y^2 = k^2 \tag{15.11}$$

Using (15.3), (15.4), we then have

$$E_x = \frac{\mu j \omega k_y}{k^2} H_0 \cos k_x x \sin k_y y e^{j\omega t - \gamma z}$$

$$E_y = - \frac{\mu j \omega k_x}{k^2} H_0 \sin k_x x \cos k_y y e^{j\omega t - \gamma z}$$

$$E_z = 0$$

$$H_x = \frac{\gamma k_x}{k^2} H_0 \sin k_x x \cos k_y y e^{j\omega t - \gamma z}$$

$$H_y = \frac{\gamma k_y}{k^2} H_0 \cos k_x x \sin k_y y e^{j\omega t - \gamma z}$$

$$H_z = H_0 \cos k_x x \cos k_y y e^{j\omega t - \gamma z} \tag{15.12}$$

In these expressions, k_x and k_y are given by (15.10), k^2 is determined in terms of them by (15.11) and γ by (15.7). It will be seen that there are a doubly infinite set of solutions, one for each pair of integers m, n. A particular one is denoted as a $TE_{m,n}$ wave. Let us consider the special cases where one or both of the indexes are equal to zero. If for instance $m = 0$, we have exactly the solution given in (14.5), except that the H_0 which appears in (15.12) is equal to the quantity $H_0 k_y / \gamma$ in (14.5). Since the solution in that case is independent of x, it is immaterial whether the wave guide is terminated at $x = 0$, $x = a$, as in the present case, or whether it extends to infinity along the x axis, as in Sec. 14. If $n = 0$, so that we have the $TE_{m,0}$ wave, the situation is of course just like the $TE_{0,n}$, only with the axes interchanged. Finally, we see particularly easily from (14.5) that there is no solution when both m and n are zero; in that case all field components automatically reduce to zero.

The transverse magnetic case is handled in a manner practically identical with that already used for the transverse electric case. In this case all field components except H_z are different from zero. We find E_x and E_y from E_z, by equations that are exactly like (15.4), except with E substituted for H, and E_z

satisfies a wave equation that is exactly like (15.6). The ratio of E_x to H_y and of E_y to $-E_x$ is a quantity that we can again call an impedance, but it is different from its value for the TE case, as given in (15.3); instead, we find

$$\frac{E_x}{H_y} = \frac{E_y}{(-H_x)} = Z = \frac{\gamma}{\epsilon j \omega + \sigma} \qquad (15.13)$$

The boundary conditions at the boundaries of the wave guide are different from the TE case. E_z is now a tangential component of the electric field; consequently it must be zero at the boundaries of the wave guide. From the equations analogous to (15.4), we then see that E_x and E_y, regarded as the components of a two-dimensional vector in the xy plane, are proportional to the gradient of E_z, regarded as a scalar function of x and y. But the gradient is a vector at right angles to the surfaces on which the function whose gradient is taken is constant. Thus the vector of components E_x, E_y is at right angles to the surfaces on which E_z is constant. Since E_z is zero over the surface of the wave guide, this means that the vector E_x, E_y is normal to the surface, so that the condition that the tangential component of E should be zero is satisfied. Finally from (15.13) we see that the vector H is perpendicular to E, so that since E is normal to the surface of the wave guide, H must be tangential, and the condition that the normal component of H should be zero is also satisfied.

Using these relations, we find that the expressions for the field components in the TM case, analogous to (15.12) for the TE case, are

$$E_x = -\frac{\gamma k_x}{k^2} E_0 \cos k_x x \sin k_y y e^{j\omega t - \gamma z}$$

$$E_y = -\frac{\gamma k_y}{k^2} E_0 \sin k_x x \cos k_y y e^{j\omega t - \gamma z}$$

$$E_z = E_0 \sin k_x x \sin k_y y e^{j\omega t - \gamma z}$$

$$H_x = \frac{(\epsilon j \omega + \sigma) k_y}{k^2} E_0 \sin k_x x \cos k_y y e^{j\omega t - \gamma z}$$

$$H_y = -\frac{(\epsilon j \omega + \sigma) k_x}{k^2} E_0 \cos k_x x \sin k_y y e^{j\omega t - \gamma z}$$

$$H_z = 0 \qquad (15.14)$$

Here, as for the TE case, k_x, k_y, and k^2 are defined by (15.10) and (15.7). Contrary to the TE case, however, we see by inspection of (15.14) that neither m nor n can be zero; if either one is zero, all components of field vanish. This verifies our conclusion of Sec. 14, that waves of the form $TM_{0,n}$ can exist in the case of two infinite parallel conductors but cannot exist in a rectangular wave guide.

As in the case of propagation between two parallel conductors, discussed in Sec. 14, each type of wave in the rectangular pipe can be propagated only above a critical or cutoff frequency. Let us find this frequency. First we write (15.7) for γ^2, substituting from (15.10) and (15.11) for k^2 and assuming a perfect dielectric within the pipe, so that $\sigma = 0$. Then we have

$$\gamma^2 = -\omega^2 \epsilon \mu + \left(\frac{m\pi}{a}\right)^2 + \left(\frac{n\pi}{b}\right)^2 \tag{15.15}$$

For low frequencies, the first term in (15.15) is smaller than the sum of the other two, γ^2 is positive and γ is real, resulting in an attenuated wave. However, for high frequencies, the first term outweighs the other two, γ^2 is negative, γ is imaginary, and there is a real wave propagated, without attenuation. Thus the cutoff is given by setting $\gamma^2 = 0$ in (15.15). The relation is most conveniently stated by using the equivalent wave length of the disturbance in empty space, given by

$$\lambda_0 = \frac{v}{f} = \frac{2\pi}{\omega \sqrt{\epsilon\mu}} \tag{15.16}$$

where v is the velocity of the disturbance in the dielectric. Then (15.15) gives us

$$\frac{2}{\lambda_c} = \sqrt{\left(\frac{m}{a}\right)^2 + \left(\frac{n}{b}\right)^2} \tag{15.17}$$

From (15.17) we see that the cutoff frequency is higher, or the wave length shorter, the greater the value of m and n. Thus for propagation of a given frequency wave through a given pipe, a certain number of the lower modes will be propagated, but the higher modes will all be attenuated. Often it is desirable to design a pipe so that for the frequency being employed only one mode, that of lowest frequency, will be propagated. This will be a transverse electric mode, with either m or n equal to unity, the other one equal to zero; clearly the index connected with the smaller of the dimensions a and b must be zero, that connected with the greater must be unity. The transverse magnetic modes all have higher cutoff frequencies, since both m and n must be different from zero for the TM modes. For the lowest TE mode, the electric lines of force run across the guide, from one long side to the other, with maximum intensity in the center, as shown in Fig. 33. If the longer of the two dimensions is a, (15.17) then becomes

$$\frac{\lambda_0}{2} = a \quad \text{for } TE_{1,0} \tag{15.18}$$

as the condition of cutoff. That is, the longest wave that can be transmitted in the pipe has a half wave length equal to the greater

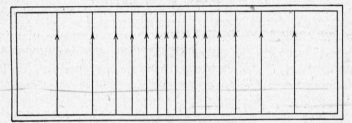

FIG. 33.—Lines of electric force in $TE_{1,0}$ mode, looking along axis of pipe.

of the two dimensions of the pipe. For further diagrams, similar to Fig. 33, showing lines of electric and magnetic force in various modes, the reader is referred for instance to Chu and Barrow.[1] The case shown in Fig. 33 is the most important in practice.

It is interesting to find the velocity of propagation along the z axis, and the impedance, for the various modes of propagation. Let us again take $\sigma = 0$. Then using (15.15), with the substitution (15.16), we have $\gamma = j\beta$, where

$v = \frac{\omega}{\beta}$ $\gamma = j\beta$ $\sigma = 0$

$$\beta = \omega \sqrt{\epsilon\mu} \sqrt{1 - \left(\frac{m\lambda_0}{2a}\right)^2 - \left(\frac{n\lambda_0}{2b}\right)^2} \tag{15.19}$$

from which v, which is equal to ω/β, is

$$v = \frac{1}{\sqrt{\epsilon\mu}} \frac{1}{\sqrt{1 - (m\lambda_0/2a)^2 - (n\lambda_0/2b)^2}} \tag{15.20}$$

[1] Proc. I.R.E., 26, 1520 (1938).

group vel $v_g = 1 / \frac{\partial\beta}{\partial\omega} = \frac{c^2}{v}$ when $v = \infty$ $v_g = 0$ $v_g = c = v$ when λ is small $\ll$ pipe dimensions

λ_g = wavelength in the pipe = $\frac{2\pi}{\beta}$ = $\frac{1}{\sqrt{1 - \left(\frac{m\lambda_0}{2a}\right)^2} \left(\frac{m\lambda_0}{2b}\right)}$

$\lambda_c = \frac{\lambda_0}{\sqrt{\lambda_c^2 - \lambda_0^2}}$

$= \frac{\lambda_0}{\sqrt{1 - (\lambda_0/\lambda_c)^2}}$

$= \lambda_g$

$\lambda_g = \frac{2\pi}{\beta} \sqrt{1 - (\lambda_0/\lambda_c)^2}$ $m = 0, n = 1$

for $TE_{0,1}$ $\beta = $

reducing properly to our previous value (14.12) for the case $m = 0$. We notice that the phase velocity is greater than the value $1/\sqrt{\epsilon\mu}$ characteristic of the dielectric medium, becoming infinity at cutoff but gradually reducing to the limiting value $1/\sqrt{\epsilon\mu}$ as the frequency is increased indefinitely. The impedance Z is different in the TE and the TM case. For the TE case, using (15.3), we have

$$Z = \sqrt{\frac{\mu}{\epsilon}} \frac{1}{\sqrt{1 - (m\lambda_0/2a)^2 - (n\lambda_0/2b)^2}} \qquad (15.21)$$

proportional to the velocity; for the TM case, using (15.13), we have

$$Z = \sqrt{\frac{\mu}{\epsilon}} \sqrt{1 - \left(\frac{m\lambda_0}{2a}\right)^2 - \left(\frac{n\lambda_0}{2b}\right)^2} \qquad (15.22)$$

inversely proportional to the velocity and reducing to zero at cutoff. We note that each separate mode of propagation has its own impedance. A hollow-pipe transmission line has entirely different characteristics for its different modes, so that the best analogy to the simple transmission lines of Chap. I is obtained if we regard one mode of the hollow pipe as being equivalent to a whole transmission line.

16. Attenuation in Rectangular Wave Guides.—In the preceding sections of this chapter, we have considered only the case of hollow pipes with perfectly conducting walls, so that the electric vector could have no tangential component at the surface. Corresponding to this, the propagation constant γ was pure imaginary, above cutoff, corresponding to a wave without attenuation. Now we shall take up the case where the walls have only a finite conductivity and shall ask how much attenuation this introduces. To handle this problem straightforwardly, we should set up a damped wave in the metal walls, of the type discussed in Secs. 12 and 13, and join this properly to a damped wave inside the wave guide, built up as in Sec. 13. We shall however use an approximate method, entirely accurate enough for our purposes, which requires practically no calculation beyond what is already done for the case of perfectly conducting walls. Then we shall describe an exact solution and show that it reduces to the approximation already worked out.

We have seen in Sec. 12 that the propagation constant in a good conductor is given by

$$\gamma_0 = \alpha_0 + j\beta_0 = \sqrt{\frac{\sigma\mu\omega}{2}}\,(1 + j) \qquad (16.1)$$

as shown in (12.9), and the intrinsic impedance is given by

$$Z_0 = \sqrt{\frac{\mu\omega}{2\sigma}}\,(1 + j) \qquad (16.2)$$

as in (12.17). In Sec. 13, we have seen that at a boundary between a good conductor and a dielectric, no matter what may be the angle of incidence in the dielectric, the wave normal in the conductor is almost exactly along the normal to the surface. This is the case with both the vectors k_r and k_i of Fig. 31, representing the vectors perpendicular to the surfaces of constant phase and of constant amplitude respectively. Thus, by the arguments used in deriving Fig. 31, both electric and magnetic field in the metal will be practically tangential to the surface, having no normal component. The ratio of the tangential component of E to the tangential component of H is given by (16.2); the two vectors are at right angles to each other. Since Z_0, as given in (16.2), is very small, as was shown in Sec. 12, the tangential component of E is very small, but it is not zero, as it would be in a perfect conductor. A method now suggests itself for approximating to the solution of our problem. First let us find the tangential component of magnetic field in the dielectric, for the case of perfectly conducting walls. This tangential component ordinarily will be large. It is reasonable to suppose that it will not be much changed if the walls are given a finite rather than an infinite conductivity. By the conditions of continuity, it will equal the tangential component of H just inside the metal. The principal effect of giving the walls a finite conductivity will be to introduce a small tangential electric field, given by Z_0 times the magnetic field, inside the metal, which by continuity must equal a corresponding tangential component of E just outside the surface.

The method just described allows us to estimate the small tangential component of E at the surface of a good but not perfect conductor. This is not the quantity of primary interest, however; we are really interested in the attenuation constant α, the real part of the propagation constant γ connected with propagation of the wave along the z direction in the wave guide. Fortunately we can find α from a knowledge of the tangential components of electric and magnetic field over the conducting surface. To do this, we use the principle that α is determined if we know how rapidly the energy flow diminishes with distance as we go along the wave guide, and the decrease of energy flow is accounted for by flow of energy into the conducting walls, which in turn can be computed by integrating Poynting's vector over the surface of the walls. Poynting's vector and the energy per unit volume both depend on the square of the field and, since both electric and magnetic fields are attenuated according to the exponential $e^{-\alpha z}$ in going along the wave guide, the energy flow must be attenuated according to the exponential $e^{-2\alpha z}$. Thus we have the relation

$$\frac{d \text{ (energy flow)}}{dz} = -2\alpha \text{ (energy flow)} \qquad (16.3)$$

But the energy flow is the integral of Poynting's vector over a cross section of the wave guide, while $-d$ (energy flow)$/dz$ is the energy lost in unit distance or is the integral of Poynting's vector over the part of the metallic surface contained in unit length of the wave guide. Hence we have

$$\alpha = \frac{1}{2}\frac{\int \text{(metallic surface) Re } (E_t \times \bar{H}_t)\, da}{\int \text{(cross section) Re } (E_t \times \bar{H}_t)\, da} \qquad (16.4)$$

The integral in the denominator of (16.4), the total energy flow along the wave guide, has to be computed specially for each mode of oscillation, and there is nothing more to say about it until we come to special cases. The numerator, however, representing the rate of energy flow into the metal, is of considerable interest. The Poynting's vector representing energy flow into the metal has an average value of $\frac{1}{2}$ Re $(E \times \bar{H})$, as we saw in Sec. 11. We are interested only in the component of Poynting's vector normal to the surface, which means that we must use tangential components of E and H in computing it. By (16.2), the tangential component of E, which we may call E_t, equals Z_0 times the tangential component H_t of H. Thus we have

$$S = \frac{1}{2}\text{ Re } (E \times \bar{H}) = \frac{1}{2}\text{ Re } Z_0(H_t\bar{H}_t) \qquad (16.5)$$

The product of any number by its complex conjugate is simply the square of its absolute magnitude and is real. Hence, substituting the real part of Z_0 from (16.2), we have

$$S = \frac{1}{2} \sqrt{\frac{\mu\omega}{2\sigma}} |H_t|^2 \qquad (16.6)$$

Equation (16.6) thus gives a simple formula for the energy loss per unit area of conducting walls of a wave guide, in terms of the tangential component of magnetic field and the magnetic permeability and electrical conductivity of the metal. This formula can be put in an interesting form if we compute the energy flowing into unit area of the metal per cycle of the alternating field. This is found by multiplying (16.6) by $2\pi/\omega$, the period of the oscillation. The result is

$$\frac{2\pi}{\omega} S = \frac{2\pi}{\omega} \frac{1}{2} \sqrt{\frac{\mu\omega}{2\sigma}} |H_t|^2 = \pi \sqrt{\frac{2}{\mu\omega\sigma}} \frac{1}{2} \mu |H_t|^2 \qquad (16.7)$$

We recognize the quantity $\sqrt{2/\mu\omega\sigma}$ as the distance δ defined in (12.13), the distance in which the field inside the metal falls to $1/e$ of its value at the surface; this distance is sometimes called the skin depth. Furthermore, we recognize $\frac{1}{2}\mu|H_t|^2$ as the magnetic energy per unit volume associated with the tangential component of magnetic field. Thus we have the interesting result that the energy dissipated per cycle, in the conductor, equals the magnetic energy contained in a thin sheet of thickness $\pi\delta$, in which the energy density is the same that it is immediately outside the surface. Since as we saw in (12.14) the thickness δ is very small for a good conductor like copper, this means that the energy loss per cycle is a very small fraction of the total energy, from which it follows that the Q value of such a wave guide is large.

To estimate the Q value of a wave guide, we may use an approximation which is interesting in showing the order of magnitude. From our fundamental definition (4.47) we have

$$Q = \frac{\beta}{2\alpha} \qquad (16.8)$$

and we shall use this definition later in making exact calculations of Q values. Using (16.4) and the relation $v = \omega/\beta$, this gives

$$Q = \frac{\omega}{v} \times \frac{\text{energy flow in pipe}/\text{second}}{\text{energy loss per unit length per second}}$$

$$= \frac{2\pi}{v} \times \frac{\text{energy flow in pipe}/\text{second}}{\text{energy loss per unit length per cycle}} \quad (16.9)$$

The energy flow in the pipe equals the average flow per unit area, times the area of the pipe. If we picture the energy as flowing with the velocity v (an assumption which is not really correct and which prevents this argument from being correct except in order of magnitude), we should find that the energy per unit volume, times the velocity of flow, should equal the energy flow per unit area. Thus the energy flow in the pipe, divided by v, which appears in (16.9), should be the energy per unit volume, times the cross-sectional area, or should be the energy contained in unit length of the pipe. In other words, we should conclude that Q equaled 2π times the ratio of energy contained in unit length of the pipe, to the energy lost per unit length per cycle. We have seen that this energy loss equals the magnetic energy contained in a sheet of thickness $\pi\delta$ around the boundary of unit length of the pipe. Thus in order of magnitude Q equals the ratio of the volume of unit length of the pipe, to the volume of a sheet of thickness δ around the area; or it is equal to the ratio of the cross section, to the cross section of a strip of width δ, and length equal to the perimeter of the pipe. This argument, as we have pointed out, is correct to order of magnitude only, but it gives a good way of visualizing the reasons behind the large Q values of wave guides.

Let us now apply our methods to the calculation of attenuation, in some important special cases. First we shall consider the case of two infinite parallel planes, with the electric field and magnetic field both transverse between the two planes, as in Fig. 29, and as in the *TM* case with $\theta = 0$ in (14.13). In this case the magnetic field is tangential to the conducting planes, and the electric field is normal to the planes, equal to $\sqrt{\mu/\epsilon}$ times the magnetic field. We now see, however, that if the planes have only finite conductivity, there must be a small tangential component of electric field at the surface. If, as in Fig. 32, the magnetic field is along x and the normal component of electric field is along y, this tangential component of electric field will be along z. It will point in opposite directions on the two planes, for in each

case Poynting's vector must point into the metal. Thus over the right-hand plate E_z will be along $+z$, and over the negative plate it will be along $-z$. As a matter of fact, an exact expression for the field between the plates can be set up on the basis of Eq. (14.13), treating the problem as a *TM* case, but with k_y no longer zero, as in the case of perfectly conducting plates, but equal instead to a small, complex quantity. If it is small enough, (14.13) indicates that E_z should be proportional to y and thus should be positive on the right-hand plate, negative on the left one, as we have just seen that it is. The magnitude of E_z, from (16.2), is $\sqrt{\mu\omega/2\sigma}\,(1+j)H_x$. The time average of the component of Poynting's vector pointing into the metal is $\mathrm{Re}\,\tfrac{1}{2}E_z\bar{H}_x = \tfrac{1}{2}\sqrt{\mu\omega/2\sigma}\,H_x^2$. Suppose we consider unit width of the conductors, along the x axis. Then for unit length of the line, there will be two conductors, each with unit area of surface, so that the mean energy flow into the walls, or the energy loss per unit length per second, will be $\sqrt{\mu\omega/2\sigma}\,H_x^2$. On the other hand, the average component of Poynting's vector along the z axis, the axis of the line, is $\tfrac{1}{2}\sqrt{\mu_0/\epsilon_0}\,H_x^2$, where μ_0, ϵ_0 represent the values for the dielectric, while μ represented the value for the conductor. If the distance between plates, along the y axis, is b, the cross section of the line will be b, so that the flow of energy along the line will be $b/2\sqrt{\mu_0/\epsilon_0}\,H_x^2$. Then, using (16.4), we have

$$\alpha = \frac{1}{2}\frac{\sqrt{\mu\omega/2\sigma}\,H_x^2}{b/2\sqrt{\mu_0/\epsilon_0}\,H_x^2} = \frac{1}{b}\sqrt{\frac{\epsilon_0}{\mu_0}}\sqrt{\frac{\mu\omega}{2\sigma}} \qquad (16.10)$$

The attenuation constant, we notice, is proportional to the square root of the frequency and inversely proportional to the square root of the conductivity. This behavior is characteristic of skin effect attenuations.

We can understand the variation of α with frequency and conductivity better if we consider the resistance of a strip of conductor of unit width, when the skin effect formulas apply. The quantity H_x, as we saw in Sec. 9, equals the current in the z direction in the conductor. We have just seen that the z component of electric field is $\sqrt{\mu\omega/2\sigma}\,(1+j)H_x$. This is the voltage between two points unit distance apart along the z axis. The real part of the ratio of E_z to H_x, or $\sqrt{\mu\omega/2\sigma}$, is thus the resistance of unit length of a strip of unit width of the conductor. It is easy to understand why this formula is correct. Suppose we consider the current to be confined to a thin sheet of conductor of thickness δ, as defined in (12.13), given by

$$\delta = \sqrt{\frac{2}{\mu\omega\sigma}} \qquad (16.11)$$

Then its resistance would be $1/\delta$ times the resistance of unit cube, or would be $1/\delta\sigma$, which is equal to

$$R = \frac{1}{\delta\sigma} = \sqrt{\frac{\mu\omega}{2\sigma}} \qquad (16.12)$$

just the value we have found above. The reason why the resistance increases with increasing frequency is thus seen to be that the thickness of the skin in which the conduction takes place decreases with increasing frequency. Let us now see what we should expect for the attenuation constant α in this case, by analogy with a transmission line. From Eq. (2.17) we can see easily that a line with series resistance R per unit length, series inductance L, and shunt capacity C should have

$$\alpha = \frac{R}{2} \sqrt{\frac{C}{L}} \qquad (16.13)$$

In the present case, referring back to the arguments of Sec. 9, we see that unit length of the transmission line, formed of unit widths of strips at a distance of b apart, should have a capacity of ϵ_0/b, and an inductance of $b\mu_0$. The resistance of unit length should be twice the value of (16.12), since the current must flow through both conductors in series. Thus we should expect

$$\alpha = \sqrt{\frac{\mu\omega}{2\sigma}} \frac{1}{b} \sqrt{\frac{\epsilon_0}{\mu_0}} \qquad (16.14)$$

which is just the value (16.10). We shall use the value (16.14) as a standard to which to refer the attenuation in other cases. It is usual to refer to this type of wave, in which both electric and magnetic fields are transverse, as a transverse electromagnetic wave, denoted by TEM. Thus we shall use the abbreviation

$$\alpha_{TEM} = \frac{1}{b} \sqrt{\frac{\epsilon_0}{\mu_0}} \sqrt{\frac{\mu\omega}{2\sigma}} \qquad (16.15)$$

as the attenuation of the transverse electromagnetic wave.

Let us write down the formula for the Q of a *TEM* wave. From (16.8) this is $\beta/2\alpha$, where α is given in (16.15). The value of β for a *TEM* wave, from (9.2), is $\omega \sqrt{\epsilon_0\mu_0}$. Thus we have

$$Q = \omega \sqrt{\epsilon_0\mu_0} \frac{b}{2} \sqrt{\frac{\mu_0}{\epsilon_0}} \sqrt{\frac{2\sigma}{\mu\omega}}$$

$$= \frac{b}{\delta}\frac{\mu_0}{\mu} \tag{16.16}$$

where δ is the skin depth, given in (16.11). This value of Q has the order of magnitude of the value given qualitatively by our discussion of Eq. (16.9); there we saw that in order of magnitude it should equal the ratio of the cross section, which here is b, to the cross section of a strip of width δ and length equal to the perimeter of the pipe. Since the present pipe has only two walls, this latter cross section should presumably be taken to be 2δ. Thus the ratio would be $b/2\delta$, which depends on b and δ as the correct formula (16.16) does.

Now let us consider the attenuation of a *TE* wave between parallel conducting planes. We take the planes to be at $y = 0$, $y = b$, as in Fig. 32. For perfect conductivity, the fields are as in (14.5):

$\left(\sqrt{\frac{\mu_0}{\epsilon_0}} \sec\theta = z \right)$

$z = \sqrt{\frac{\mu_0}{\epsilon_0}}\left[\frac{1}{1 - \left(\frac{n\lambda_0}{2b}\right)^2} \right]$

$$E_x = \sqrt{\frac{\mu_0}{\epsilon_0}} \frac{1}{\sqrt{1 - (n\lambda_0/2b)^2}} H_0 \sin k_y y\, e^{j\omega t - \gamma z}$$

$$H_y = H_0 \sin k_y y\, e^{j\omega t - \gamma z}$$

$$H_z = H_0 \frac{-j(n\lambda_0/2b)}{\sqrt{1 - (n\lambda_0/2b)^2}} \cos k_y y\, e^{j\omega t - \gamma z} \tag{16.17}$$

First we find the z component of Poynting's vector. This is $\frac{1}{2}\,\mathrm{Re}\,(E_x\bar{H}_y)$, involving the factor $\sin^2 k_y y$. To integrate Poynting's vector over the area of the line, we note that the average value of $\sin^2 k_y y$ is $\frac{1}{2}$, so that the integral is $\frac{1}{2}$ times the area, or $b/2$, since we assume the dimensions to be unity along x, b along y. Thus for the total flow of energy along the z axis we have

$$\frac{b}{4} \sqrt{\frac{\mu_0}{\epsilon_0}} \frac{H_0^2}{\sqrt{1 - (n\lambda_0/2b)^2}} \tag{16.18}$$

Next we find the energy loss in the walls. As before, we take the tangential component of H at the surface of the wall, as computed on the assumption of perfect conductivity. In the present case,

flow of energy along $z = \frac{1}{2} \times \frac{1}{2}\,\mathrm{Re}\,(E_x\,\bar{H}_y) =$

time av of $\sin^2 k_y y$

this component is H_z. We then assume the time average energy flow per unit area into the metal is $\frac{1}{2}\sqrt{\mu\omega/2\sigma}\, H_z^2$. Taking H_z from (16.17), we note that the term $\cos k_y y$ is unity at each metallic surface. The area of metallic surface concerned is two square units of area, one for each plate. Thus the energy loss to the walls, per meter of line length, is

$$\sqrt{\frac{\mu\omega}{2\sigma}}\, \frac{H_0^2(n\lambda_0/2b)^2}{1 - (n\lambda_0/2b)^2} \tag{16.19}$$

We are now in position to find α. Using (16.4), this is one-half the ratio of (16.19) to (16.18). Thus we have

$$\alpha = \frac{2}{b}\sqrt{\frac{\epsilon_0}{\mu_0}}\sqrt{\frac{\mu\omega}{2\sigma}}\,\frac{(n\lambda_0/2b)^2}{\sqrt{1 - (n\lambda_0/2b)^2}}$$

$$= \alpha_{TEM}\frac{2(n\lambda_0/2b)^2}{\sqrt{1 - (n\lambda_0/2b)^2}} \tag{16.20}$$

where α_{TEM} is defined in (16.15). This result is remarkable, in that the attenuation decreases for increasing frequency, instead of increasing as α_{TEM} does. To see this, we note that the square root becomes equal to unity for high frequencies, or short wave lengths, while the term λ_0^2 in the numerator varies inversely as the square of the frequency, and α_{TEM} is proportional to the square root of the frequency. Thus α varies as the $-\frac{3}{2}$ power of the frequency, reducing to zero for infinite frequency. The reason for this behavior is simple enough. As the frequency increases, the angle θ_1 of Fig. 32 and Eq. (14.8), approaches zero. Thus the wave approaches the *TEM* case and H_z approaches zero. It is only H_z however, that represents a current in the walls of the wave guide and hence that results in energy dissipation. As H_z goes to zero, it is obvious that the attenuation decreases to zero.

In a similar way we can consider the attenuation of a *TM* wave between parallel conducting planes. The fields, from (14.13), are

$$E_y = -\sqrt{\frac{\mu_0}{\epsilon_0}}\sqrt{1 - \left(\frac{n\lambda_0}{2b}\right)^2}\, H_0\cos k_y y\, e^{j\omega t - \gamma z}$$

$$E_z = -j\sqrt{\frac{\mu_0}{\epsilon_0}}\frac{n\lambda_0}{2b} H_0\sin k_y y\, e^{j\omega t - \gamma z}$$

$$H_x = H_0\cos k_y y\, e^{j\omega t - \gamma z} \tag{16.21}$$

The z component of Poynting's vector is $\frac{1}{2}$ Re $(-E_y \bar{H}_x)$. Integrating over the area of the line, as in the TE case, we have as the total flow of energy

$$\frac{b}{4}\sqrt{\frac{\mu_0}{\epsilon_0}}\sqrt{1 - \left(\frac{n\lambda_0}{2b}\right)^2} H_0^2 \tag{16.22}$$

In finding the flow of energy into the walls, H_x is the tangential component of the magnetic field. Remembering that

$$\cos k_y y = 1$$

at the conducting walls and proceeding as before, we find the energy loss per unit length of line is

$$\sqrt{\frac{\mu\omega}{2\sigma}} H_0^2 \tag{16.23}$$

The attenuation is then

$$\alpha = \frac{2}{b}\sqrt{\frac{\epsilon_0}{\mu_0}}\sqrt{\frac{\mu\omega}{2\sigma}}\frac{1}{\sqrt{1 - (n\lambda_0/2b)^2}}$$

$$\alpha_{TM} = \alpha_{TEM}\frac{2}{\sqrt{1 - (n\lambda_0/2b)^2}} \tag{16.24}$$

We see that for the TM mode the attenuation increases with increasing frequency, just as it does for the TEM wave. It does

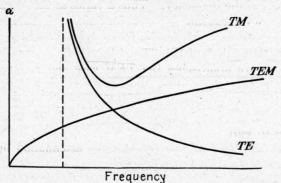

FIG. 34.—Attenuation as function of frequency, for waves between parallel conductors.

not go to zero at zero frequency, however; it becomes infinite at the cutoff frequency of the wave guide, where the square root in the denominator goes to zero, and there is a point of minimum attenuation between the cutoff and infinite frequency. This situation is shown in Fig. 34, where we show the attenuation as a function of frequency for the *TEM*, *TE*, and *TM* modes of the problem of two parallel conductors.

As a next step after the problem of two parallel conducting plates, let us take the $TE_{0,n}$ wave in a rectangular wave guide. The field components are the same as those given in (16.17). There are additional conducting surfaces, however, at $x = 0$ and $x = a$, and these result in two changes. In the first place, the total flow of energy along the z axis is equal to a times the value of (16.18), since the area of the guide is now ab, instead of b. Secondly, there are energy losses not only on the walls perpendicular to y, which are similar to that found in (16.19), but also on the walls perpendicular to x. Both H_y and H_z are tangential to these walls, so that $H_y^2 + H_z^2$ will appear in the expression for energy loss. Both these terms contain terms like $\sin^2 k_y y$ and $\cos^2 k_y y$, which average to $\frac{1}{2}$ over the surface. We then have three terms in the energy loss. The first, similar to (16.19), comes from loss on the walls perpendicular to y. It is

$$a \sqrt{\frac{\mu\omega}{2\sigma}} \frac{H_0^2 (n\lambda_0/2b)^2}{1 - (n\lambda_0/2b)^2} \qquad (16.25)$$

The second comes from the H_z term and from the loss it produces on the walls perpendicular to x. On account of the $\cos^2$ term, there is an extra factor $\frac{1}{2}$, and this term is

$$\frac{b}{2} \sqrt{\frac{\mu\omega}{2\sigma}} \frac{H_0^2 (n\lambda_0/2b)^2}{1 - (n\lambda_0/2b)^2} \qquad (16.26)$$

The third term comes from the term H_y, on the faces perpendicular to x. It is

$$\frac{b}{2} \sqrt{\frac{\mu\omega}{2\sigma}} H_0^2 \qquad (16.27)$$

The two terms (16.26) and (16.27), representing the losses on the faces perpendicular to x, combine to

$$\frac{b}{2} \sqrt{\frac{\mu\omega}{2\sigma}} \frac{H_0^2}{1 - (n\lambda_0/2b)^2} \qquad (16.28)$$

The attenuation constant α is now

$$\alpha = \frac{2}{b} \sqrt{\frac{\epsilon_0}{\mu_0}} \sqrt{\frac{\mu\omega}{2\sigma}} \frac{(n\lambda_0/2b)^2 + (b/2a)}{\sqrt{1 - (n\lambda_0/2b)^2}} \qquad (16.29)$$

The last term, by which (16.29) differs from (16.20), represents the effect of attenuation on the faces perpendicular to x, on which the electric lines of force terminate.

The expression (16.29) behaves quite differently from (16.20). We have seen that the attenuation in (16.20) decreases with increasing frequency or with decreasing wave length. The added term in (16.29), however, approaches $1/a \sqrt{\epsilon_0/\mu_0} \sqrt{\mu\omega/2\sigma}$ at high frequencies, increasing with frequency as the attenuation constant of the *TEM* wave does. As a result, the constant α for the $TE_{0,n}$ modes goes through a minimum at a certain frequency, increasing at high frequencies. To illustrate this, we give in Fig. 35 the attenuation of the $n = 1$ mode, or the $TE_{0,1}$, the mode of lowest frequency. Instead of α, we often use the attenuation in decibels per meter. To get the relation between this quantity and α, we note that attenuation in decibels, by defi-

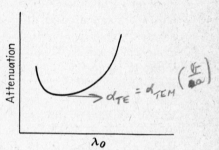

Fig. 35.—Attenuation of $TE_{0,1}$ wave in a pipe, as function of wave length.

nition, is 10 times the logarithm to the base 10 of the ratio of original power to attenuated power. For unit length, remembering that the power goes as the square of the field, this ratio is $e^{2\alpha}$. The logarithm to the base 10 of this quantity is $2\alpha \log_{10} e = 0.8686$. Hence we have

$$\text{Attenuation in decibels} = 8.686\alpha \qquad (16.30)$$

The method that we have used in this section for finding attenuation of the modes in the problem of two parallel conducting planes, and of the $TE_{0,n}$ modes in a rectangular pipe, can be extended in a straightforward way to the general case. Since the $TE_{0,1}$ mode is the important one in practice, however, we shall not carry out the analysis. The formulas are found in references of Schelkunoff and of Chu and Barrow already mentioned, and the qualitative results are similar to what we have found in the $TE_{0,n}$ case, the attenuation going through a minimum between the cutoff and infinite frequency.

It was mentioned at the beginning of this section that the straightforward way to handle the problem of attenuation in rectangular wave guides was to set up a solution of the wave equation within the guide, damped along the z axis, in such a way that exact boundary conditions could be satisfied at the metallic surface. In the case of propagation between two parallel surfaces, this can be carried out exactly, though we shall not carry it through. Referring to Fig. 32, we start with waves propagated along the z' and z'' directions, making an angle of θ with the z axis. At the same time, we wish to have these waves damped. From the principles of Sec. 13, remembering that the medium within the guide is nonabsorbing, we see that the wave must be attenuated in a direction at right angles to the wave normal. That is, for instance, the wave that is propagated along the z' axis in Fig. 32 must be attenuated along a direction in the yz plane at right angles to z', or must contain an attenuation factor $e^{-\alpha_0(z \sin \theta - y \cos \theta)}$. Similarly the wave propagated along z'' must have a factor $e^{-\alpha_0(z \sin \theta + y \cos \theta)}$. Combining these waves, we have a resultant disturbance attenuated along the z axis according to the factor $e^{-\alpha_0 z \sin \theta}$, and at the same time varying with y, not as the sine or cosine of a real constant times y, as in (14.1), for instance, but as the sine or cosine of a complex constant times y. This change, to a complex propagation constant along y, introduces a small tangential component of electric field, proportional to α_0, at the surface of the conductor. We then adjust α_0, which so far is arbitrary, so that the tangential component of electric field satisfies proper conditions of continuity with the field within the conductor, which we have set up according to the principles of Sec. 13. When this is done, the attenuation constant $\alpha_0 \sin \theta$ along the z axis should equal the value α which we have computed in the present section, and it proves to agree with the value we have found. Since this more exact method yields no new result and since it is straightforward though a little tedious to carry out, we shall not reproduce the argument in detail.

CHAPTER IV

THE GENERAL TRANSMISSION LINE PROBLEM

The rectangular hollow-pipe transmission line, which we have taken up so far, is the simplest type from the standpoint of theory, since the waves propagated in such lines are very similar to plane waves in empty space. Now we shall consider more complicated types of transmission lines. The most important of these is the coaxial cable. These lines are more complicated mathematically, in that the metallic surfaces on which boundary conditions must be applied are of less simple shape than in the rectangular pipe, so that the waves that result from the wave equation are of more involved type than plane waves. The fundamental principles, however, are very similar to what we have found with the rectangular case. The general problem which we take up is the following: we imagine the general case of cylindrical conductors, generated by arbitrary cross-sectional curves in the xy plane, moved parallel to the z axis, and find the field and the characteristics of propagation along these conductors, in the z direction. After setting up the general problem, we consider in detail two special cases: the parallel-wire transmission line and the coaxial cable.

17. General Formulation of the Transmission Line Problem.— As with rectangular wave guides, so in the general case we have two types of waves, the transverse electric and the transverse magnetic. At the beginning of Sec. 15 we carried out an analysis for these two types of wave, which was completely general and not limited to the rectangular case. We rewrite the essential equations derived there, taking for convenience only the case where the dielectric has zero conductivity. Then for the TE case we can derive all components of field from H_z. This quantity satisfies the equation

$$\frac{\partial^2 H_z}{\partial x^2} + \frac{\partial^2 H_z}{\partial y^2} + k^2 H_z = 0 \qquad (17.1)$$

where

$$k^2 = \gamma^2 + \epsilon\mu\omega^2 \tag{17.2}$$

and where as usual H_z varies as $e^{j\omega t - \gamma z}$. From H_z we can find the other components of field by the relations

$$H_x = \frac{-\gamma}{k^2}\frac{\partial H_z}{\partial x}, \qquad H_y = \frac{-\gamma}{k^2}\frac{\partial H_z}{\partial y} \tag{17.3}$$

$$E_x = ZH_y, \qquad E_y = -ZH_x, \qquad \text{where} \qquad Z = \frac{\mu j\omega}{\gamma}$$

$$= \sqrt{\frac{\mu}{\epsilon}}\frac{1}{\sqrt{1 - k^2/\epsilon\mu\omega^2}} \tag{17.4}$$

If we regard H_z as a function of the two variables x and y, we see that H_x, H_y form a vector in the xy plane equal to the two-

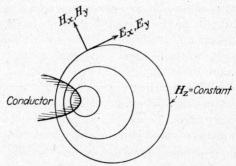

Fig. 36.—Vector relations in xy plane, TE wave.

dimensional gradient of $\frac{-\gamma}{k^2}H_z$, and E_x, E_y form a vector at right angles to H_x, H_y, and equal in magnitude to Z times the magnitude of the vector of components H_x, H_y. The quantity H_z must satisfy the boundary condition that its rate of change along the normal to a conducting surface is zero, provided the conductor has perfect conductivity. These relations are shown more conveniently by a diagram. In Fig. 36 we show the xy plane in an arbitrary problem, with the lines $H_z = $ const. indicated on the diagram. The vector H_x, H_y is at right angles to the lines $H_z = $ const., and the vector E_x, E_y is therefore along the lines $H_z = $ const., so that these lines at the same time form the lines of electric force, while the lines of magnetic force (or rather their projections in the xy plane) are the orthogonal trajectories of the first set of curves.   The surfaces of conductors, like the one shown, must be orthogonal to the lines $H_z = $ const., in order that the electric field may be normal, and the magnetic field tangential, to the perfect conductor.

The situation is similar for the TM waves.   Here it is E_z that is different from zero, and it satisfies an equation just like (17.1). E_x and E_y are determined from it by relations just like (17.3). There is a difference between the two cases, however, in the relations between E and H.   Thus for the TM wave we have

$$H_x = -\frac{1}{Z} E_y, \qquad H_y = \frac{1}{Z} E_x, \qquad \text{where} \qquad Z = \frac{\gamma}{\epsilon j\omega}$$

$$= \sqrt{\frac{\mu}{\epsilon}} \sqrt{1 - \frac{k^2}{\epsilon\mu\omega^2}} \quad (17.5)$$

The boundary conditions at the surface of a perfect conductor are also different in this case from what they are in the TE case.   Here we must have E_z equal to zero at the surface of a conductor.   The situation is then as in Fig. 37. Lines of const. E_z are shown. In this case the conductor must have one of the lines of const. E_z as its boundary.   The vector E_x, E_y is perpendicular to the lines $E_z = $ const., and the vector H_x, H_y is parallel to the lines, so that lines $E_z = $ const. form at the same time magnetic lines of force.

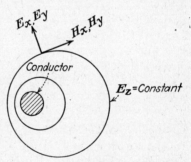

Fig. 37.—Vector relations in xy plane, TM wave.

It is clear from this formulation that any solution of (17.1) furnishes a set of lines which, together with their orthogonal trajectories, provide a solution for either the TE or the TM case. We shall first investigate the special case $k^2 = 0$.   This is the case ordinarily called the principal wave.   In this case, according to (17.2),

$$\gamma = j\omega \sqrt{\epsilon\mu} \quad (17.6)$$

the value which it has for a plane wave in empty space propagated along the z direction; for either the TE or the TM case, Z is given by

$$Z = \sqrt{\frac{\mu}{\epsilon}} \qquad (17.7)$$

also the value characteristic of a plane wave propagated through the medium in the absence of conductors. In this case, we see from (17.3) that $H_z = 0$, in order that the ratio H_z/k^2 may be finite. That is, this wave is a *TEM* wave with no longitudinal component of either H or E. It is convenient then to introduce a quantity, say ϕ, defined by

$$\phi = \frac{\gamma}{k^2} H_z \qquad (17.8)$$

which remains finite in the limit as k goes to zero. In terms of it, we have

$$H_x = -\frac{\partial \phi}{\partial x}, \qquad H_y = -\frac{\partial \phi}{\partial y} \qquad (17.9)$$

with

$$E_x = \sqrt{\frac{\mu}{\epsilon}} H_y; \qquad E_y = -\sqrt{\frac{\mu}{\epsilon}} H_x \qquad (17.10)$$

From (17.1), we see that ϕ satisfies

$$\frac{\partial^2 \phi}{\partial x^2} + \frac{\partial^2 \phi}{\partial y^2} = 0 \qquad (17.11)$$

or the two-dimensional Laplace's equation. Or if we choose, we can proceed from the *TM* case to the limit. In this case we can define a quantity ψ, by the equation

$$\psi = \frac{\gamma}{k^2} E_z \qquad (17.12)$$

from which E_x and E_y are defined by the relations

$$E_x = -\frac{\partial \psi}{\partial x}, \qquad E_y = -\frac{\partial \psi}{\partial y} \qquad (17.13)$$

The relations between E and H are again given by (17.10), and ψ, like ϕ, satisfies Laplace's equation (17.11). Then as a result of conjugate function theory we can obtain a solution of a transmission line problem from any set of orthogonal trajectories set up from a two-dimensional solution of Laplace's equation.

We shall come to special examples later. We can also derive some general conclusions. Thus let us consider waves within a hollow pipe. The cross section of this pipe will form a closed curve in the xy plane. Then we must find a function ψ satisfying Laplace's equation inside the curve and reducing to zero at every point of the boundary. By general function theory, no such continuous function exists, except zero. Thus there can be no principal wave inside a hollow pipe. This is in accordance with what we found in Chap. III. There the *TEM* wave discussed in Sec. 14, the limiting case of the $TM_{m,n}$ wave for $m = 0$, $n = 0$, was found to exist in the space between two parallel infinite conducting planes, but it could not exist in a hollow pipe enclosed on all sides. This wave was essentially the same principal wave that we are now discussing. The fact that it can exist in the space between two parallel planes does not contradict our statement that it cannot exist within a hollow pipe, for the two planes do not enclose a finite area in the xy plane.

Though a principal wave cannot exist in a wave guide in the form of a hollow pipe, nevertheless it does occur in important practical cases, in particular in the coaxial line, in which the propagation takes place in the ring-shaped region between two concentric cylindrical conductors. In this case the cross section consists of the ring between two concentric circles, and it is easily shown that functions exist that satisfy Laplace's equation in the region between two such circles and that satisfy proper boundary conditions on both surfaces. Considering the outer surface as a hollow pipe, the required functions satisfy Laplace's equation everywhere within the pipe and reduce to the proper boundary conditions on the surface of the pipe, but nevertheless are not allowable solutions of the problem of a hollow pipe, for they have singularities within the material of the inner conductor. These singularities make no trouble in the problem of the coaxial line but would make the solution impossible in the case of a pipe. In fact, the general situation is that a principal wave is impossible in any case where the wave travels in a region bounded by a single conductor; but it is possible if the region is bounded by two or more conductors. The coaxial line, the pair of infinite parallel plates, and the line consisting of two parallel wires are examples of problems in which the principal wave is a possible solution. In cases where the principal wave exists, it is ordinarily by far the most important mode of propagation. We shall accordingly start by considering the principal wave in some important actual cases.

18. The Principal Wave in the Parallel-wire Transmission Line.—The case of the parallel-wire transmission line is such a well-known one that it will pay us to see how it works out, even though it is not a type of line suited to microwave propagation. Let the cross section of the line in the xy plane be as given in Fig. 38, the wires having a radius r and a distance d on centers. We recognize at once that there is a well-known electrostatic or magnetic problem that furnishes a mathematical analogy to this case. Thus if we have two parallel cylindrical wires

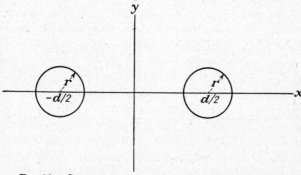

FIG. 38.—Cross section of parallel-wire transmission line.

carrying opposite charges, the equipotentials and lines of force form two sets of orthogonal curves, satisfying Laplace's equation, one set, the equipotentials, being constant over the conducting surfaces. Similarly if two wires carry currents in opposite directions, the magnetic lines of force and their orthogonal trajectories take the form of the same two sets of curves. These curves are shown in Fig. 39. Obviously in the present case the lines going from one wire to the other are lines of electric force; those surrounding a wire are lines of magnetic force. It is a well-known fact that in this problem the lines are all circles. In fact, the problem and the sets of circles are mathematically identical with those met in Fig. 9, in connection with an entirely different problem.

It is hardly worth while to work out the details of this problem, since we are not going to use it in applications. It is easy by analogy with the electrostatic case, to set up the value of ϕ or ψ as a function of x and y, and hence to find the complete field. Since the wave is a principal wave, it is propagated with the velocity of light, and the ratio of components of E and H in the xy plane is the same as for a free wave.   It is interesting to see, however, that in this case the analogy to the type of transmission line considered in Chap. I is very close.   Thus it is well known that the capacity of two parallel wires per unit length, when

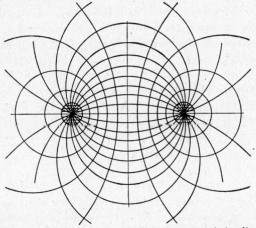

FIG. 39.—Lines of force for parallel-wire transmission line.

the diameter of the wire is small compared to the distance between, is

$$C = \frac{\pi \epsilon}{\ln d/r} \tag{18.1}$$

where d is the axial distance apart, r the radius of a wire, as in Fig. 38.   This result can be easily proved from the electrostatic problem mentioned just above.   Similarly the inductance per unit length of such a pair of wires is

$$L = \frac{\mu}{\pi} \ln \frac{d}{r} \tag{18.2}$$

If we were to use these values, determined from static problems, in Eq. (2.15), which states that the velocity of propagation of a disturbance down a line with inductance L, capacity C per unit length, in the case of no attenuation, is $v = 1/\sqrt{LC}$, we should find

$$v = \frac{1}{\sqrt{\epsilon\mu}} \qquad (18.3)$$

which as a matter of fact is just the velocity of light. Hence we can find the correct velocity of propagation in this case by use of the analogy of lumped transmission lines. We can hardly have much faith in the derivation, however, since the C and L which appear in our formula are determined from static problems, and the problem of wave propagation is certainly not static. The method used in the present section is a much more rigorous way of deriving the results for such a line. When we consider the concept of impedance, we see that the analogy between the present methods and the method of lines is not very close. From Eq. (2.20), the equivalent impedance of the line should be $Z_0 = \sqrt{L/C}$. This gives

$$Z_{eq} = \sqrt{\frac{\mu}{\epsilon}} \frac{\ln d/r}{\pi} \qquad (18.4)$$

which does not agree at all with the value $\sqrt{\mu/\epsilon}$ found in (17.7). This does not indicate an error in either derivation; it merely means that we have meant different things by impedance in the two cases. This is an illustration of the fact that when we deal with wave guides and such problems, the concept of impedance is not a unique and simple one, and it is not obvious what we should mean by impedance. We have so far avoided this question and have used the term "impedance" only to refer to a ratio of the type E/H. In one simple case, the TEM wave between parallel plane electrodes, we saw that this definition of impedance reduced in an obvious way to the ordinary definition as a ratio of a voltage to a current, but we have not tried to push this analogy further, and in fact in general it does not hold. We shall come to this question in more detail in a later section, where we deal with composite lines, and must handle questions of impedance matching between different parts of such a line. Until then, we shall continue referring to ratios of E to H as impedances, in a rather uncritical way.

19. The Principal Wave in the Coaxial Line.—Let us consider an inner circular cylindrical conductor of radius a, surrounded by an outer cylinder of radius b. Then in the principal mode the electric lines of force are obviously radial straight lines, and the magnetic lines of force are circles surrounding the origin. As in (17.13), the electric field must be proportional to the gradient of a scalar function that satisfies Laplace's equation. From one's general knowledge of potential theory, the scalar function, since it depends only on r, the radial distance out from the axis of the cylinders, must be proportional to $\ln r$, and its gradient, the electric field, is proportional to $1/r$. This is the same result that we should have for the electric field in the corresponding electrostatic problem of a uniformly charged infinitely long circular cylinder. If we write our vectors in cylindrical coordinates, r, θ, z, denoting the component along the radius by subscript r, the component along the tangent to a circle surrounding the origin by subscript θ, we then have, using the principles of Sec. 17,

$$E_r = \sqrt{\frac{\mu_0}{\epsilon_0}} \frac{H_0}{r} e^{j\omega t - \gamma z}$$

$$H_\theta = \frac{H_0}{r} e^{j\omega t - \gamma z} \tag{19.1}$$

with

$$\gamma = j\omega \sqrt{\epsilon_0 \mu_0} \tag{19.2}$$

all other components of the fields being zero. By direct substitution in Maxwell's equations it is easy to show that these fields satisfy the field equations, and it is obvious that they satisfy the boundary conditions at the surfaces of the conductors.

From (19.1) we see that a principal wave can be propagated within a coaxial line, a wave traveling with the velocity of light in the dielectric with which the line is filled, and having both transverse electric and magnetic fields. The fields get stronger and stronger as we approach the center of the line, so that they are much stronger at the surface of the inner conductor, at $r = a$, then at the outer conductor at $r = b$. If there were no inner conductor, the field would have a singularity at $r = 0$; this illustrates our previous remark that a principal wave is not possible in a hollow pipe, as for instance a hollow circular cylinder, but becomes possible when there is an inner conductor on which the electric lines of force can terminate. It is to be noted that there is no cutoff frequency for the principal wave. It can be propagated down the coaxial line for any frequency of wave, or any values of the radii of the conductors. This is in contrast to the case of propagation in hollow pipes, as discussed in the preceding chapter, and in contrast to the other modes of propagation in the coaxial line, which we shall discuss later and in which the wave length of the wave must be comparable with or smaller than the dimensions of the line.

We shall now look at the coaxial line a little more closely. First we ask what is the voltage difference between the conductors and the current flowing in the conductors, and compute an equivalent impedance from these values. The z component of surface current in either of the conductors is equal to the tangential component of H at the surface of the conductor, given in (19.1). The total current is the integral of the surface current over the circumference of the circle, or $2\pi r$ times H_θ, as given in (19.1). That is, it is

$$i = 2\pi H_0 e^{j\omega t - \gamma z} \tag{19.3}$$

This of course has opposite signs, but the same magnitude, on the inner and outer conductors. The voltage is the integral of E_r from one conductor to the other, or is

$$V = \sqrt{\frac{\mu_0}{\epsilon_0}} H_0 \ln \frac{b}{a} e^{j\omega t - \gamma z} \tag{19.4}$$

Regarding the coaxial line as a transmission line, with ordinary voltage and current, there would be an equivalent impedance equal to the voltage divided by the current:

$$Z_{eq} = \frac{V}{i} = \sqrt{\frac{\mu_0}{\epsilon_0}} \frac{\ln b/a}{2\pi} \tag{19.5}$$

As in the equivalent impedance of the parallel-wire transmission line, given in (18.4), this quantity is different from the ratio of E to H, which we have also interpreted as an impedance and which is simply equal to $\sqrt{\mu_0/\epsilon_0}$ for any principal wave. Again as in the parallel-wire problem we can set up a capacity and an inductance per unit length of the line, from ordinary static methods, and can compute the velocity of propagation and the equivalent impedance from them. Thus by well-known methods the capacity per unit length in this case is

$$C = \frac{2\pi\epsilon_0}{\ln b/a} \tag{19.6}$$

and the inductance is

$$L = \frac{\mu_0 \ln b/a}{2\pi} \tag{19.7}$$

from which the velocity is

$$v = \frac{1}{\sqrt{LC}} = \frac{1}{\sqrt{\epsilon_0 \mu_0}} \tag{19.8}$$

and the equivalent impedance is

$$Z_{\text{eq}} = \sqrt{\frac{L}{C}} = \sqrt{\frac{\mu_0}{\epsilon_0}} \frac{\ln b/a}{2\pi} \tag{19.9}$$

as in (19.5).

Next we shall consider attenuation in the coaxial line, as a result of the finite conductivity of the walls. We proceed as in Sec. 16. First we find the flow of power down the line, by computing the time average Poynting vector, $\frac{1}{2}$ Re $(E \times \bar{H}) = \frac{1}{2}$ Re $(E_r \bar{H}_\theta)$, and integrating it over the cross section of the line. This is

$$\int_a^b 2\pi r \frac{1}{2} \sqrt{\frac{\mu_0}{\epsilon_0}} \frac{H_0^2}{r^2} \, dr = \pi \sqrt{\frac{\mu_0}{\epsilon_0}} H_0^2 \ln \frac{b}{a} \tag{19.10}$$

We note that this is the same expression for flow of power which we should have got from a conventional transmission line point of view. In that case we should have found the power from the product of voltage and current, and in case voltage and current are given as the real parts of complex quantities, this leads to the relation

$$\text{Power} = \tfrac{1}{2} \text{ Re } V\bar{\imath} \tag{19.11}$$

by Eq. (5.6). If we insert the values of V and i from (19.4) and (19.3), we get just the expression for power already derived from Poynting's vector in (19.10). Having found the flow of power down the line, we next find the power loss to the walls of the coaxial line. To do this, as in (16.6), we must integrate $\frac{1}{2} \sqrt{\mu\omega/2\sigma} H^2$ over the surface of the conductor. The area of unit length of the conductor is $2\pi r$, where r is a or b for the inner or outer conductors. Thus the energy flow into the walls is

$$\frac{1}{2} \sqrt{\frac{\mu\omega}{2\sigma}} 2\pi r \frac{H_0^2}{r^2} = \pi \sqrt{\frac{\mu\omega}{2\sigma}} \frac{H_0^2}{r} \tag{19.12}$$

where r equals a or b, and for the two walls we have the total power loss

$$\pi \sqrt{\frac{\mu\omega}{2\sigma}} H_0^2 \left(\frac{1}{a} + \frac{1}{b}\right) \qquad (19.13)$$

We can now use (16.4) to find α, the attenuation constant; from that equation, α should be $\frac{1}{2}$ times the ratio of (19.13) to (19.10). Hence we have

$$\alpha = \frac{1}{2}\sqrt{\frac{\epsilon_0}{\mu_0}}\sqrt{\frac{\mu\omega}{2\sigma}}\frac{(1/a + 1/b)}{\ln b/a} \qquad (19.14)$$

It is evident that the first term, in $1/a$, is the more important one in determining the attenuation. This means that the larger part of the loss occurs in the small inner conductor, and the smaller this is, the greater is the loss. The reason is that the fields increase rapidly as the conductor is made smaller, resulting in greater energy flow into the conductor. We can at once write down the formula for Q for the principal wave in a coaxial line. Using the definition $Q = \beta/2\alpha$, and remembering that in this case $\beta = \omega\sqrt{\epsilon_0\mu_0}$, we have at once

$$Q = 2\frac{\mu_0}{\mu}\frac{\ln b/a}{\delta/a + \delta/b} \qquad (19.15)$$

where δ is the skin depth, given in (16.11).

20. General Wave Propagation in the Circular Wave Guide and the Coaxial Line.—In the preceding section we have investigated the principal wave in the coaxial line. This was very simple, since the solution could practically be written down by inspection. The general case of propagation in a coaxial line can be easily solved, however, using the well-known solution of the wave equation in cylindrical coordinates. At the same time, the problem of the circular wave guide can be handled by practically identical means. These problems are both taken up, for example, in Stratton,[1] Chap. IX. Since we shall not make much use of the results, we shall not give full mathematical details but shall merely sketch the derivations.

Both the coaxial line and the circular wave guide depend on solutions of the wave equation (17.1) in polar coordinates. For

[1] J. A. Stratton, "Electromagnetic Theory," McGraw-Hill Book Company, Inc.

the coaxial line, boundary conditions must be satisfied on both an inner circle of radius R_0 and an outer circle of radius R_1; for the wave guide, only the outer circle is present.   It is well known that the solution of the wave equation in polar coordinates is the product of a sine or cosine function of the angle, $\sin n\theta$ or $\cos n\theta$, where n is an integer, multiplied by a Bessel function of k times the radius, of order n.   For each value of n, there are two independent solutions of Bessel's equation, generally called Bessel's function, $J_n(x)$, and Neumann's function, $N_n(x)$. These have the general behavior shown in Fig. 40.   They both vary in a more or less sinusoidal way, with an amplitude that

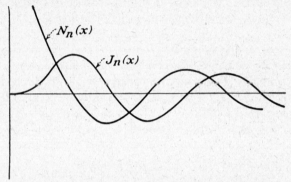

Fig. 40.—$J_n(x)$ and $N_n(x)$ as functions of x (schematic).

decreases roughly as the inverse square root of the value of x. They have a phase relation to each other like the sine and cosine, one having its maxima and minima where the other has its zeros. At $x = 0$, $J_n(x)$ is finite for all values of x, being in fact zero for all cases except for $n = 0$, whereas $N_n(x)$ becomes logarithmically infinite at $x = 0$.   The general solution is an arbitrary linear combination of $J_n(x)$ and $N_n(x)$.   This combination must be chosen to satisfy boundary conditions on the conductors.

In the matter of boundary conditions, the circular wave guide is simpler than the coaxial line.   The function must certainly be continuous at the origin, which means that $N_n(x)$ cannot be used, so that the solution must be simply the Bessel function $J_n(x)$, which remains finite at the origin.   Thus in this case we have

$$H_z \text{ or } E_z = \begin{pmatrix} \sin n\theta \\ \cos n\theta \end{pmatrix} J_n(kr)e^{j\omega t} \qquad (20.1)$$

The boundary conditions are different for *TE* and *TM* waves. In the *TE* case, as we have seen, the normal derivative of H_z must be zero at the boundary; that is, J_n must have a maximum or minimum when r equals the radius of the pipe. By suitable choice of k, we can arrange it so that J_n has its mth maximum or minimum at the radius of the pipe. In this case, we can denote the mode as the $TE_{n,m}$ mode. Similarly in the *TM* case the function E_z must be zero at the boundary. In this case we can choose k so that J_n has its mth zero (not counting the origin) at the radius of the pipe, and we denote this mode as the $TM_{n,m}$ mode. By giving a table of maxima, minima, and zeros of J_n, we can find the value of k for each of these modes. These values are given in the following table:

MAXIMA AND ROOTS OF BESSEL'S FUNCTIONS

$n =$	0	1	2
$J_n' = 0$ (*TE*)	3.832	1.842	3.05
	7.016	5.330	6.71
$J_n = 0$ (*TM*)	2.405	3.832	5.135
	5.520	7.016	8.417

We give values for $m = 1, 2$, in each case. For purposes of notation, we may denote the value of x for the mth maximum or zero of J_n as x_{nm}, where we have one set (marked $J_n' = 0$) for the *TE* waves, another set for the *TM* waves. Thus for instance for the *TE* waves, we have $x_{11} = 1.842$.

From the values given in the table, we can find the value of k occurring in (17.2) and other formulas. We do this simply by the condition

$$kR_1 = x_{nm}, \qquad k = \frac{x_{nm}}{R_1} \qquad (20.2)$$

where R_1 is the radius of the pipe. We can then use (17.2) to find γ, the propagation constant. In the case of real propagation, where $\gamma = j\beta$, this gives

$$\beta = \omega \sqrt{\epsilon\mu} \sqrt{1 - \frac{k^2}{\epsilon\mu\omega^2}} \qquad (20.3)$$

Using the relation

$$\omega \sqrt{\epsilon\mu} = \frac{2\pi}{\lambda_0} \qquad (20.4)$$

where λ_0 is the wave length in empty space, this can be rewritten

$$\beta = \frac{2\pi}{\lambda_0} \sqrt{1 - \left(\frac{x_{nm}\lambda_0}{2\pi R_1}\right)^2} \qquad (20.5)$$

and the pipe wave length, or the wave length of the disturbance in the pipe, is

$$\lambda = \frac{2\pi}{\beta} = \frac{\lambda_0}{\sqrt{1 - \left(\frac{x_{nm}\lambda_0}{2\pi R_1}\right)^2}} \qquad (20.6)$$

We see that the wave length in the pipe is greater than in free space, on account of the fact that the phase velocity in the pipe is greater than in free space.   Furthermore, we see that as in the rectangular pipe there is a cutoff frequency, below which real propagation does not take place.   This comes when the square root in (20.5) becomes zero, or when

$$\lambda_0 = \frac{2\pi R_1}{x_{nm}} \qquad (20.7)$$

From (20.7) we see that the smaller x_{nm} is, the longer is the cutoff wave length, or the lower the cutoff frequency.   From the table, we see that the lowest value of x_{nm} is the value 1.842, coming from the $TE_{1,1}$ wave.   There will then be a considerable range of wave length in which this one mode is propagated, while all other modes are attenuated.   In particular, this range is that for which the circumference $2\pi R_1$ is between 1.842 and 2.405 wave lengths.   It is customary to use a circular wave guide in this range, so as to have only one mode propagated.

In the $TE'_{1,1}$ mode, H_z is given by $\begin{pmatrix} \sin \theta \\ \cos \theta \end{pmatrix} J_1(kr)$.   The function J_1 starts off linearly with x, and then reaches a maximum, which in this mode comes at the wall of the pipe.   On account of the sine or cosine function, H_z itself shows a maximum on one side of the pipe and a minimum on the other.   We remember according to Fig. 36 that the lines $H_z = $ const. are at the same time the electric lines of force in the problem.   Thus the lines of force run as sketched in Fig. 41.   As we see, the lines of force remind us of those shown in Fig. 33, representing the $TE_{1,0}$ mode of a rectangular pipe.   In each case the lines run across from one side of the pipe to the other and are stronger toward the middle of the pipe. In a way these two modes correspond to each other, representing in each case the mode of lowest cutoff frequency. The sizes of pipe required in the two cases are comparable: for the rectangular case, we saw in Sec. 15 that the larger dimension of the pipe must be equal to or greater than a half wave length of the disturbance in empty space; in the circular pipe the diameter $2R_1$ must be at least $1.842/\pi = 0.584$ wave lengths.

In the range where the circumference $2\pi R_1$ is between 2.405 and 3.05 wave lengths, we see from the table that two modes, the $TE_{1,1}$ and the $TM_{0,1}$ waves are possible. It is sometimes desirable to operate circular pipes in the second of these modes, since it has circular symmetry and can thus be used in problems where parts of the apparatus must be allowed to rotate about the axis of symmetry of the pipe. In this mode, E_z is proportional to $J_0(kr)$, as we see from (20.1), a function of r only, reducing to zero at the surface of the pipe. E_r is proportional to the derivative $J_0'(kr)$, having a maximum at the surface of the pipe and reducing to zero at the center, and E_θ is zero, so that in the plane normal to the axis of the pipe E points radially outward. The magnetic field H, which is transverse to the axis, points tangentially, so that the magnetic lines of force are circles surrounding the axis. In the range of wave lengths where this $TM_{0,1}$ wave is used, it is necessary to avoid the $TE_{1,1}$ wave, which is always simultaneously possible, by being careful not to excite the $TE_{1,1}$, by taking advantage of the symmetry of the device used to excite the wave.

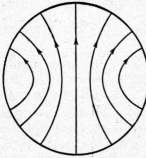

Fig. 41.—Electric lines of force in $TE_{1,1}$ mode of circular pipe.

Now that we have considered the circular hollow pipe, let us see how we should handle the general case of propagation in a coaxial line. In this case, as we have stated before, the function H_z or E_z must be made up of a cosine function of the angle, times a linear combination of $J_n(kr)$ and $N_n(kr)$. Since as we see from Fig. 40 these two functions have the same relation to each other that the sine does to the cosine, we see that by combining them we again get a function of sinusoidal type but with an adjustable phase. We choose this phase so as to satisfy the proper boundary condition at the surface of the inner conductor; that is, to make the combined function have a maximum there in the case of the *TE* waves, or a zero for the *TM* waves. Then we choose k so as to give a correct boundary condition on the outer conductor. Here as with the circular pipe there are an infinite number of ways of satisfying this condition on the outer conductor. Thus for the *TE* waves we have one maximum of the function on the inner conductor. We can have the next minimum on the outer conductor, or the next maximum beyond that, or any one of the infinite number of maxima or minima. We can then denote each mode by two indexes n and m, as before, the first referring to the cosine function, the second one numbering the k value which is used. On account of the fact that both Bessel's and Neumann's functions come into the final result, it is not easy, as it was with the hollow pipe, to derive the cutoff frequencies and pipe wave lengths of the modes in a coaxial line. Qualitatively the situation is the same as before, however: each mode has a cutoff, and the condition for propagation is that the wave length must be smaller than some small numerical factor times the dimensions of the conductor.

The principal mode of the coaxial line, which we have already treated in Sec. 19, can be obtained as a limiting case from the treatment just sketched, but it is easier to investigate it directly, as we have done. To derive it as a special case, we have to write the Bessel and Neumann functions in power series, the Neumann function including also a logarithmic term. We then pass to the limit as k goes to zero, so that only the first term of the power series remains. It then proves to be the case that H_z or E_z goes to a logarithmic function, so that when it is differentiated to give the r and θ components of electric or magnetic field we get functions proportional to $1/r$, as we found in (19.1). We saw in Sec. 19 that the principal mode had no cutoff but could be propagated at arbitrarily long wave length. For this reason, a coaxial line in practice is invariably used in its principal mode. It is used at wave lengths so large that all modes except the principal one will be below cutoff and will not be propagated. In other words, the dimensions of a coaxial line must be considerably smaller than a wave length, to prevent propagation of the other modes. For this reason, a coaxial line is very convenient for transmission of fairly long wave lengths, and it is very commonly used for wave lengths of 10 cm. and upwards. For shorter wave lengths, however, the diameter of the line must become inconveniently small. The main objection to such a small diameter is the large value of the electric field which results around the inner conductor. With large power transmission, this field can easily grow big enough to lead to corona from the conductor. Thus for smaller wave lengths, the hollow pipe, which can have dimensions comparable with the wave length, is much more convenient. In practice, the transition comes between wave lengths of 1 m. and 1 cm. The hollow pipe is by far the more convenient means of propagation at 1 cm., and the coaxial line is better at 1 m.

21. Composite Transmission Lines and Impedance Matching. Our first chapter was devoted to the study of conventional transmission lines. The most important ideas developed in that chapter related to wave propagation, the reflection of waves at discontinuities in the line, and the relation of this reflection to changes in the characteristic impedance of the line. Since then we have taken up the study of Maxwell's equations and their application to wave propagation in rectangular and circular pipes, coaxial lines, and parallel wires. We now come to a question of fundamental importance: to what extent is there an analogy between the conventional transmission lines and our wave guides and coaxial lines? To what extent can we carry over the ideas of impedance and impedance matching to the actual lines we are treating? The question is a difficult and involved one, not a simple and elementary one, and we cannot do more than begin to answer it. Nevertheless it is a very important question, because the engineer, who is used to thinking in terms of transmission line theory, wishes to be guided by this theory in his study of coaxial lines and hollow pipes, and it is most important to know how far these analogies can be safely followed and where they may lead him astray.

The problems that really concern us are those of composite lines, for it is only here that impedance matching and reflection come in. And here, in contrast to conventional transmission line theory, we see that when portions of two uniform lines are joined to form a composite line, there is much more than a mere question of a change in characteristic impedance involved. A real line has many properties, not expressible in a single number. This can be illustrated by examples. The simplest case of the joining of two lines is that in which the two lines are of the same type (both hollow pipes, or both coaxial lines, for example), both of the same dimensions and shape, but differing only in the materials of which they are made. For instance, part of a coaxial line may be filled with air, part with a dielectric material with quite a different dielectric constant. There will be reflection at the surface of separation, and this can be handled easily and completely, as we shall see shortly. A special case of this is the short-circuited line or wave guide, in which the line is terminated by a conducting plate. A next more complicated case of joining is that in which two lines of similar type, as for instance two rectangular wave guides, but of different dimensions, are joined together. Similar to this is the problem of wave guides of uniform properties, but with various obstacles, such as diaphragms, inserted at various points. More complicated still are the cases in which lines of different type are joined together, as for instance a coaxial line inserted into a wave guide to excite it or a coaxial line coupled to a resonant cavity by a coupling loop. Problems of this type border closely on antenna problems, in which a coaxial line or wave guide is coupled to empty space. All these problems have some elements of similarity, and these elements can be tied in qualitatively with properties of transmission lines. But they also possess great and important differences, and it would be a grave mistake to think that all questions relating to them could be solved by transmission line methods. They are, on the contrary, difficult problems in electromagnetic theory, most of which have not yet been solved. Since they have not been solved, our mathematical treatment cannot extend nearly so far as it has in the discussion of the uniform line up to this point. In most respects, the practice of impedance matching has gone much further than the theory, and in many ways it has to be regarded at the present time more as an art than as a science. Fortunately there are some general theoretical ideas which will throw light on the subject, however, even without detailed calculation.

Suppose one has one semi-infinite uniform line extending from the left, joined by some sort of construction to another semi-infinite line of different properties extending indefinitely to the right. These might be a hollow pipe of one cross section, joined by a short tapering region to another pipe of another cross section; or a coaxial line joined by some form of coupling device to a hollow pipe; or two hollow pipes of identical properties, separated by an iris diaphragm, to name only three examples. In each of these lines, there are an infinite number of possible modes of waves possible. (It is this infinite number of modes which makes these real problems so different from the idealized conventional transmission line.) A few of these modes correspond to waves that are really propagated, without attenuation if there are no losses in heating on account of finite conductivity of the walls or leakage in the dielectric, or with small attenuation if these losses must be considered. All the rest of the modes have no real propagation, but instead are attenuated exponentially as we pass along the line, with no real transmission of power if the losses in the walls and dielectric are neglected. So far, we have considered only the really propagated waves, but a general solution of the problem must include the attenuated waves as well. Each type of propagated wave can be propagated either to the left or to the right; each attenuated mode can be attenuated either to the left or to the right.

We now have the mathematical problem of building up solutions of the wave equation in each of the two lines, which will satisfy certain boundary conditions of continuity at the junction between the two lines. The precise nature of these boundary conditions depends on the special problem we are dealing with, but the general principles are the same in each case. In broad outlines, the general solution that we desire is one consisting of an incident and a reflected wave in the line to the left, and a transmitted wave in the line to the right. Let us inquire to what extent this may be possible. Of course, it may be that one type of incident wave, one reflected wave, and one transmitted wave, will by themselves satisfy the necessary boundary conditions. We shall find an important special case where this is true: the case where the cross section and geometrical nature of the line do not change, but only the electrical properties of the materials. But this is a very special case, and in general the boundary conditions cannot be satisfied over the whole cross section of the line in this simple way. The reason is that, if the two lines have different cross sections, a simple elementary wave in one will not vary in the same way across the cross section that a similar wave in the other one would, so that with these waves alone we cannot satisfy boundary conditions at all points of the cross section. We are forced instead to build up a combination of all possible types of waves, propagated and attenuated, and to satisfy the boundary conditions by a combination of them.

We do not need literally all possible types of waves. Our physical intuition tells us, and the mathematics justifies our intuition, that the boundary conditions can be satisfied by superposing a single traveling wave of one type moving to the right in the first line, reflected waves of all the propagated types traveling to the left in the first medium, attenuated waves of all possible types falling off exponentially to the left in the first medium, transmitted waves of all possible types traveling to the right in the second medium, and attenuated waves of all possible types falling off exponentially to the right in the second medium. By sufficiently complicated mathematics we could hope to find the amplitude and phase of each of these waves, in terms of the amplitude and phase of the incident wave. We should then have, not one reflection coefficient, but a variety of reflection coefficients, one giving the ratio of the complex amplitude of each reflected wave to the incident wave, and similarly a variety of transmission coefficients. Almost no problems have actually been carried to the point where all these coefficients can be calculated.

The situation is simplified a good deal if only one type of propagated wave is possible in each line. This is the case usually met in practice, where for instance only the $TE_{0,1}$ wave may be possible in a rectangular wave guide when used at the frequency for which it is designed, or where only the principal wave is possible in a coaxial line. Then we can satisfy the boundary conditions by an incident wave, a single reflected wave, a single transmitted wave, plus all the attenuated waves. At distances from the junction at which the attenuated waves have all been reduced essentially to zero, the situation is really much like that in a conventional transmission line, with only the incident, reflected, and transmitted waves. We may in this case reasonably ask two questions. First, is it possible to set up a formula for the reflection coefficient in terms of the characteristic impedances of the two lines, of the form $(Z_0 - Z_R)/(Z_0 + Z_R)$, such as we met in Chap. I? Secondly, do we need to bother with the attenuated waves, for any ordinary physical application of the problem?

The answer to the first question is that it is a matter of definition. Obviously if the reflection coefficient is known, as a result of exact calculations, we can set it equal to the quantity $(Z_0 - Z_R)/(Z_0 + Z_R)$, and from that can determine the ratio Z_0/Z_R. We can then arbitrarily define Z_0 and Z_R so as to have this ratio, and the reflection coefficient formula will hold. This will do us no good, however, unless the Z's so defined have some simple value in terms of the properties of the lines. We have met at least two quantities that we have treated as impedances, in the present chapter. In the first place, we have the ratio of components of E to H. Secondly we have what we have called an equivalent impedance in coaxial lines, the ratio of the actual voltage between the conductors to the actual current flowing in them. These two quantities did not agree. If either of them would give a reflection coefficient by the simple formula, then the formula would be a very useful thing. One of our tasks in succeeding sections will be to try to get approximate solutions for joining conditions in some actual cases, and see whether either of these values of impedance can be used in the reflection coefficient. In that way we shall get some idea as to what quantities may be usefully called impedances in actual types of transmission lines.

The answer to the second question, as to the usefulness of the attenuated waves, is very definite. In the first place, for an exact mathematical treatment, they must be considered, for it is only by handling the complete problem that we can hope to compute the reflection coefficient from first principles. But secondly, they have a very real physical importance in the case where the finite conductivity of the walls must be considered. These attenuated waves can have very considerable amplitudes in some cases. They then will give rise to large tangential magnetic fields on the surfaces of the conductors near the junction, and thus to large energy loss into the conductors. The general situation at a junction, then, is that the power carried by the transmitted and reflected waves does not equal the incident power but is less by the amount of loss in these attenuated waves. This causes a junction loss, which may be of considerable importance. Such a junction loss is possible even at a junction at which there is no reflection; there still may have to be attenuated waves, to satisfy the boundary conditions.

In a line in which an incident wave approaches a junction and a reflected wave travels back from it, we certainly have the sort of situation met in Chap. I, in which we found the impedance of a line of length l, terminated by an arbitrary terminal impedance. Even though we may have trouble in deciding on the best definition of impedance, the various possible definitions will differ from each other only in numerical factors, so that we can apply the spiral type of diagram discussed in Secs. 4 and 5, with at most an uncertainty as to the scale of the diagram. It may not be possible to give a simple meaning to the terminal impedance Z_R, but at any rate the shape of the diagram and its general characteristics can be carried over quite correctly to the actual line. It is natural to apply the term impedance matching to the process of reducing reflections by suitably combining sections of a composite line, and the fundamental principle of impedance matching in a conventional transmission line applies here too: if we can produce two reflected waves, by means of two discontinuities having equal amplitudes and opposite phases, they will cancel. Furthermore, to secure the proper phase relation, the discontinuities must be a quarter wave length apart. This may not necessarily be exactly true, for the attenuated waves will generally extend more than a quarter wave down the tube and may complicate the exact situation near the discontinuities, resulting in slight corrections, but the principle is correct and shows that we can make impedance-matching devices of real lines, similar to those discussed in Chap. I. Thus even though an exact parallelism with the conventional lines of Chap. I is hardly possible, nevertheless the ideas developed there can be of very wide use with actual lines.

22. Reflections at Changes in Properties of Dielectric.—We shall now proceed to look at a number of types of junction between two transmission lines and find out the relations that hold in each case. By far the simplest case is that in which the line has the same geometrical shape on both sides of the boundary, but in which the properties of the dielectric or other materials concerned in the line change discontinuously on a certain plane, say the plane $z = 0$ (if the line extends along the z axis). Two cases of this type are particularly important in practice. One is the line terminated by a conducting plunger. For tuning purposes, either a hollow pipe or a coaxial line is often closed by a metallic piston, whose position can be adjusted. This case is that in which the line is filled with a dielectric for z less than zero, but by a conductor (which can be approximated by a perfect conductor) for z greater than zero. The other important case is found in the dielectric beads or spacers used in the construction of coaxial lines. For mechanical reasons, the inner conductor of a coaxial line must be supported; this is ordinarily done by slipping dielectric beads or disks over the inner conductor, fitting tightly in the outer conductor. The surface of one of these disks is approximately a surface normal to the z axis, so that reflection at this surface can be handled by the methods of the present section.

The present type of problem is the only one dealing with actual transmission lines in which we have a perfect analogy to the conventional idealized line of Chap. I. The reason is that the boundary conditions at the surface $z = 0$ can be satisfied exactly in this case by the incident, reflected, and transmitted waves alone, without use of attenuated waves. First we shall examine the physical reason for this, and then the mathematical reason. Physically, the reason is that the wave in a wave guide or coaxial line can be considered as made up of a number of plane waves traveling in different directions, chosen so as to satisfy boundary conditions at the surface of the line. In Chap. III we saw how this was done in the special case of transmission between two parallel plane conductors. A similar treatment, with a finite number of waves, is possible in the rectangular wave guide, and a similar treatment with an infinite number of waves in other types of lines. When a discontinuity in properties is assumed at the surface $z = 0$, each of these plane waves effectively meets a plane reflecting surface, and is reflected according to the laws of optics. In Chap. II we have investigated such reflection and have shown that it can be handled according to the impedance equations of a transmission line, provided we use a ratio E/H in place of the intrinsic impedance of the line. The reason was that the boundary conditions at the surface, demanding continuity of tangential components of E and H

and of normal components of B and D, were automatically satisfied if we did two things: first, adjusted angles of incidence and refraction so that incident, reflected, and refracted waves varied in the same way along the surface of discontinuity; and second, arranged that the ratio of tangential components of E and H (which we called the impedance) should be continuous over the boundary. It now proves to be the case that the same situation holds in the wave guide or coaxial line, so that this ratio of E to H is what must be used as the impedance in this case.

To verify these statements, let us now look at the matter from a somewhat more mathematical point of view. Suppose we consider the TE wave. Then, as given in Eqs. (17.1) to (17.4), we first determine H_z by a wave equation, then find H_x and H_y by differentiating H_z, and finally set up E_x and E_y by the condition that the magnitude of E is equal to Z times the magnitude of H, and the vector is at right angles, where Z is given by (17.4). Such a calculation can now be made in each medium, on each side of the boundary at $z = 0$. Referring to Eq. (17.1), we assume the same value of k in each medium. Then automatically H_z satisfies the same equation in each case, and we choose the same solution for each medium, except that we adjust the magnitudes so that μH_z, rather than H_z itself, is continuous at the surface. Next we consider the components of E. Combining (17.2), (17.3), and (17.4), we find that

$$E_x = -\frac{j\omega}{k^2}\mu\frac{\partial H_z}{\partial y}, \qquad E_y = \frac{j\omega}{k^2}\mu\frac{\partial H_z}{\partial x}. \qquad (22.1)$$

Thus on account of the continuity of μH_z and of k, we see that E is automatically continuous over the boundary. If the Z's, as defined by (17.4), are then different for the two media, we see that the tangential component of H cannot be continuous, if we assume only an incident and a transmitted wave. However, if we assume that the disturbance in the first medium is made up of the sum of an incident and reflected wave, we shall find as in Chap. I that Z has opposite signs for the incident and reflected waves. That is, for the same direction of E, we shall have H in opposite directions for the two waves, as we should expect since Poynting's vector is oppositely directed for them. Then, as in Chap. I, we have relations like

$$E_x = Ae^{j\omega t - \gamma_1 z} + Be^{j\omega t + \gamma_1 z}, \qquad H_y = \frac{1}{Z_1}(Ae^{j\omega t - \gamma_1 z} - Be^{j\omega t + \gamma_1 z})$$

$$(22.2)$$

in the first medium, with

$$E_x = Ce^{j\omega t - \gamma_2 z}, \qquad H_y = \frac{1}{Z_2}Ce^{j\omega t - \gamma_2 z} \qquad (22.3)$$

in the second, and for continuity

$$A + B = C, \qquad \frac{1}{Z_1}(A - B) = \frac{1}{Z_2}C \qquad (22.4)$$

from which the reflection coefficient follows as in the derivation of (3.9) in Chap. I:

$$\frac{B}{A} = \frac{Z_2 - Z_1}{Z_2 + Z_1} \qquad (22.5)$$

The coefficient as here written has the sign opposite to that of (3.9), because here our A and B are the coefficients of the voltage rather than of the current.

Thus we see, mathematically as well as physically, why the boundary conditions can be satisfied without attenuated waves and why we are led to the same reflection coefficient as in the case of transmission lines. A derivation entirely parallel to the one we have given can be carried out for the TM case. In either case, as we see, it is simply the ratio of tangential components of E and H which takes the place of an impedance. This does not fix the impedance uniquely, however, for this quantity could be multiplied by any dimensionless function of the geometrical parameters, and we should still have impedance relations as before, since both lines are geometrically similar. Suppose for instance that we are dealing with the principal mode in a coaxial line. The ratio of E to H is simply $\sqrt{\mu/\epsilon}$, the value that we should have for a plane wave in free space. However, in Sec. 19, we saw that for many reasons a quantity called the equivalent impedance, equal by (19.9) to $\sqrt{\mu/\epsilon}\,(\ln b/a)/2\pi$, was a more useful quantity. We remember that it was the ratio of the actual voltage between the conductors, to the actual current flowing in either conductor, and that in terms of it we could correctly compute the flow of power down the line. If now we regard this quantity Z_{eq} as the correct formulation of the impedance for a coaxial line, the arguments of the present section still go through without change. The geometrical factor $(\ln b/a)/2\pi$ is the same for both parts of the line, so that if Z_{eq} has a certain value on one side of the line and another value on the other side, the quantity $\sqrt{\mu/\epsilon}$ will vary in a proportional way. Hence if the formula (22.5) for reflection coefficient can be written in terms of the quantities $\sqrt{\mu/\epsilon}$ in this particular case, it can equally well be written in terms of Z_{eq}. Our present arguments, in other words, would hold equally well whether E/H were chosen as the impedance, or some geometrical factor times E/H, and, although the equivalent impedance is a natural quantity to use for the coaxial line, we have so far not set up a quantity for the wave guide which seems like the natural and obvious definition of the impedance.

Having found that the methods of Chap. I apply to reflections at discontinuities of the medium, we hardly have to go into further detail. A line closed by a perfectly conducting plug is effectively short-circuited. By Eq. (12.17) the intrinsic impedance of a conducting medium is extremely small, and in the limit of perfect conductivity it is zero. Thus a perfectly conducting plug acts like a zero impedance terminating a line, just as we should expect it to, and the whole theory of short-circuited lines, as developed in Sec. 4, applies without change in this case. Similarly the coaxial line with dielectric beads is handled exactly like a transmission line, and the discussion of such problems in Sec. 5 is correct, even though it was handled on the basis of the transmission line analogy. We might reasonably ask, can a hollow pipe open at one end be considered as an open-circuited transmission line, using the methods of Sec. 4? The answer to this question is that we cannot say on the basis of the present section. The open-ended pipe opens into empty space, so that it is not an example of a change of dielectric properties, without change in cross section. In many cases the open end of a pipe is badly matched to empty space and radiates little power, most of the power being reflected. In this case the open pipe would act much like an open-circuited transmission line. But if the pipe were well matched to empty space, which it can be if its dimensions are correct or if it is terminated by a proper horn, there may be very little reflection, and the line will act very differently from an open-circuited transmission line. These problems of open pipes, in other words, are tied up essentially with antenna problems, and we cannot assume at the moment that they can be handled like the analogous transmission line problems.

23. Reflections at Changes of Cross Section with the Principal Mode.—We have seen that in cases where there is a principal mode, as in the coaxial line, the parallel-wire transmission line, and the case of two infinite parallel plates, it is easy to define an

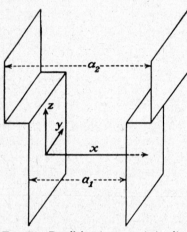

equivalent impedance, the ratio of the actual voltage between the two conductors, to the current flowing in the conductors. In the present section we shall ask whether we are justified in using the transmission line equations in discussing reflection at a sudden change of cross section, using this equivalent impedance in the formulas. It certainly seems at first sight that we should be justified, since at such a change of cross section we should expect voltage and current, and hence

Fig. 42.—Parallel-strip transmission line with sudden change of cross section.

equivalent impedance, to be continuous. We shall find that our intuition in this case is correct, to a first approximation. It is only in this approximation that we can easily get a solution at all; presumably in higher approximations we are not justified in using the simple transmission line equations.

The simplest case of the principal mode mathematically is the propagation of a wave between two parallel perfectly conducting plates, with the electric vector normal to the plates, the magnetic vector tangential. We shall accordingly take up this case first. Let us consider the type of propagation shown in Fig. 29, only now with a sudden change in cross section of the line, as shown in Fig. 42. The conductors are supposed to extend indefinitely along the y direction, but for convenience we may consider a meter width. The distance of separation is supposed to change at $z = 0$ from the value a_1 for negative z, to the value a_2 for positive z.

Let us now set up the problem mathematically. By symmetry, H must be in the y direction, and E may have only x and z components. Furthermore, since propagation is along z, all the vectors must be independent of y. Then Maxwell's equations become

$$\frac{\partial E_x}{\partial z} - \frac{\partial E_z}{\partial x} + j\mu\omega H_y = 0$$

$$\frac{\partial E_x}{\partial x} + \frac{\partial E_z}{\partial z} = 0$$

$$-\frac{\partial H_y}{\partial z} - j\omega\epsilon E_x = 0$$

$$\frac{\partial H_y}{\partial x} - j\omega\epsilon E_z = 0 \qquad (23.1)$$

The third and fourth of Eqs. (23.1) serve to give E_x and E_z in terms of H_y:

$$E_x = -\frac{1}{j\omega\epsilon}\frac{\partial H_y}{\partial z}, \qquad E_z = \frac{1}{j\omega\epsilon}\frac{\partial H_y}{\partial x} \qquad (23.2)$$

The second equation is then automatically satisfied. This leaves only the first, which becomes an equation for H_y:

$$\frac{\partial^2 H_y}{\partial x^2} + \frac{\partial^2 H_y}{\partial z^2} + \epsilon\mu\omega^2 H_y = 0 \qquad (23.3)$$

That is, H_y satisfies a two-dimensional wave equation in the xz plane. The vector E_x, E_z, is perpendicular to the gradient of H_y, from (23.2). That is, it points along the lines $H_y = $ const., or these lines are at the same time electric lines of force. Since the electric lines of force must be normal to the conductors, we see that the lines $H_y = $ const. must also be normal to the conductors, or the normal derivative of H_y must be zero. This then defines our mathematical problem completely.

The boundary value problem which we have just set up does not have a simple, closed solution. In fact, if we try to satisfy it by ordinary means, we shall be led to exactly the problem discussed previously, that of setting up a combination of propagated and attenuated waves in the two sections of the transmission line and of joining them smoothly at the junction. Although this can be done, it is an involved problem, and we shall not try to set it up mathematically. However, there is an important special case in which we can get definite information without complicated mathematics. This is the case in which the wave length is long compared to the distance between the conductors. In this case we may expect the whole disturbance in the region about the junction to take place in much less than a wave length. We can then show easily that the first two terms of (23.3) are large compared to the last, in the region of the junction. To see this, we first note that at a considerable distance from the junction, H_y will vary sinusoidally with z, as the sine or cosine of $2\pi z/\lambda_0$, where

$$\lambda_0 = \frac{1}{\sqrt{\epsilon\mu}} \frac{2\pi}{\omega} \tag{23.4}$$

the wave length of the disturbance in the pipe, which equals that in empty space, since we are dealing with the principal mode. Over a distance short compared to a wave length, this sinusoidal variation can be approximated by a straight line; the second derivative of H_y with respect to z is, in fact, by (23.3), equal to $-(2\pi/\lambda_0)^2 H_y$, and a Taylor expansion of H_y would be of the form

$$H_y = H_{y0} + H'_{y0}(z - z_0) - \frac{1}{2}\left(\frac{2\pi}{\lambda_0}\right)^2 H''_{y0}(z - z_0)^2 \cdots \tag{23.5}$$

where H_{y0}, H'_{y0} are the values of the function and slope at $z = z_0$, about which the expansion is made. From (23.5) we see then that the quadratic term represents a small fraction of H_{y0}, if $(z - z_0)$ is a small fraction of a wave length. In the immediate neighborhood of the junction, however, the slope of H_y will be changing very rapidly. In fact, it may change by a large fraction of itself in a distance comparable to the width a of the transmission line, going from the narrow part of the line to the wide part. This means that in this neighborhood the quadratic term in (23.5) would be of the order of magnitude of $H_{y0}[(z - z_0)/a_1]^2$, rather than of $H_{y0}[(z - z_0)/\lambda_0]^2$, so that $\partial^2 H_y/\partial z^2$ would be greater than $\epsilon\mu\omega^2 H_y$ in the ratio of $(\lambda_0/a_1)^2$, which we have assumed to be large compared to unity. To satisfy (23.3), $\partial^2 H_y/\partial x^2$ must also be large in this region and must approximately cancel $\partial^2 H_y/\partial z^2$. In other words, to a first approximation in the neighborhood of the junction, H_y will satisfy Laplace's equation

$$\frac{\partial^2 H_y}{\partial x^2} + \frac{\partial^2 H_y}{\partial z^2} = 0 \tag{23.6}$$

in place of the wave equation (23.3). This is simply a rather roundabout mathematical way of stating the rather obvious fact: if the wave length is long compared to the dimensions of the junction, the problem of the fields at the junction can be handled to a good approximation as a static problem.

As a result of this argument, we can see that the electric lines of force are just what we should have if the two parallel strips of Fig. 42 were charged to different static electrical potentials.

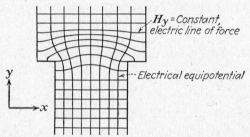

FIG. 43.—Sketch of lines of force at junction of transmission line of Fig. 42.

If we could solve Laplace's equation in this case, we should find a set of lines of constant H_y and a set of orthogonal trajectories, similar to those shown in Fig. 43. As we have seen before, the lines of const. H_y are at the same time the electric lines of force. In this particular problem, to the accuracy to which we are working, the last term of the first equation of (23.1) can be neglected compared to the other two terms; for this equation is just the same as (23.3), in which we could neglect the last term. This equation then states that the curl of E is zero, or that E can be derived from a potential. Thus the orthogonal trajectories to the lines of force are equipotentials, as indicated in Fig. 43. This gives us just the information that we need for our problem of joining. For it states that the two conductors are equipotentials, or that the line integral of E, or the voltage, between them, is constant, equal on both sides of the junction, so long as we are at distances from the junction small compared to the wave length. We have thus verified the result, which seems very natural from an intuitive argument, that the voltage between conductors is continuous across such a junction.

Similarly we can convince ourselves that the current flowing in either conductor is essentially continuous over the junction. From (23.2) we see that the rate of change of H_y along the surface is proportional to the normal component of E. But from Fig. 43 it is obvious that E does not have abnormally large values in the neighborhood of the junction (if it is large near the sharp convex corner of the conductor, in Fig. 43, it is compensatingly small near the sharp concave corner). Thus there is no abnormally large change in H_y as we go from one part of the line to the other, nothing that could be considered as a discontinuity. The changes of H_y are rather just such as we should expect normally in going from one part to another of a continuous line. Since H_y measures the current in the conductor, this means that the current as well as the voltage is continuous across the junction, so that the quantity we have defined as the equivalent imped-ance, the ratio of voltage to current, is continuous, and we can use our transmission line equations in discussing reflection, impedance of composite lines, and other related problems.

If the voltage and current are continuous, this means that the electric field E is, in effect, discontinuous at the junction, though H is continuous, as we have seen. By the discontinuity of E we mean that its approximately constant values inside the two parts of the line, as shown in Fig. 43, are different, so that it changes by a considerable fraction of itself in going through the region of transition. If E_1 is the field in the lower part of the line, E_2 in the upper part, the voltage in the lower part is E_1a_1, and in the upper one E_2a_2. Since these must be equal, we see that E varies inversely as a, decreasing as we pass to the wider part of the line. It is interesting to set up the equivalent imped-ance in this case. If the line has a width b in the y direction (up to now we have assumed b to be unity), the current flowing will be H_yb. Thus the equivalent impedance is

$$Z_{eq} = \frac{V}{i} = \frac{E_x}{H_y}\frac{a}{b} = \sqrt{\frac{\mu}{\epsilon}}\frac{a}{b} \qquad (23.7)$$

differing from the impedance of empty space by the factor a/b. We thus see clearly that though $\sqrt{\mu/\epsilon}$ stays constant going from one size line to another, Z_{eq} changes, thus introducing reflections at the junction.

The simple result just obtained can be generalized. In the first place, we have made no use of the exact shape of the junc-tion. Instead of having square corners, as in Figs. 42 and 43, the junction could be rounded off, without changing the result, so long as our fundamental postulate is satisfied, that the whole change in size of the line, and the whole transition region, is small compared to a wave length. Reflection will not be decreased, in other words, by a small amount of rounding off of the corners. On the other hand, as we shall see in a later section, a gradually tapering junction, extending over several wave lengths, will greatly diminish the reflection, just as we have found in Chap. I that a line of gradually changing properties is practically nonreflecting. A further generalization of our results comes when we consider other types of transmission lines, such as coaxial lines. Intuitively we should expect the same result to hold there: if the dimensions of the line are small compared to a wave length, so that the whole transition region is small compared to a wavelength, the problem of the transition can be handled as a static problem, and we can show that the voltage and current, and hence the equivalent impedance, are continuous at the junction, so that transmission line theory can be applied. A mathematical discussion, similar to what we have given in this section, verifies this intuitive expectation.

As a final remark, it is plain from Fig. 43 and from well-known cases of electrostatic solutions that the region in which the fields are showing large fluctuations, or the transition region, is of small extent, its length along the z axis being comparable to the width of the line. We have here a picture of the sort of disturbance to be expected in every case in the neighborhood of a discontinuity in properties of a transmission line. We have pointed out before that this disturbance can be built up by super-posing attenuated waves, falling off exponentially as we travel away from the junction. In this case too we could describe our transition effects by means of attenuated waves, but the sort of picture given by Fig. 43 is more graphic and gives us an idea of what to expect in the more general case.

24. Reflection at Changes of Cross Section in Hollow Pipes, and Iris Diaphragms.—The problem of reflection at a change of cross section in a hollow pipe is one that has not been handled very completely, theoretically. We have already seen schematically how to solve it: we expand the solution on each side of the discontinuity in incident, reflected, and transmitted propagated waves and in the various possible types of attenuated waves, and apply boundary conditions of continuity at the surface.

One can compute coefficients of the various waves, in practical cases, and not only can find how strong the attenuated waves are but can compute their contribution to the heating loss in case the conducting walls have only finite conductivity. Such specialized calculation, however, does not carry us very far with the important question: how are we to define the impedance of a wave guide, so that the transmission line equations can be used for composite guides? Plainly the case of the wave guide is much less simple than that of the coaxial line; for the coaxial line could have dimensions which were small compared to a wave length, and with a wave guide that is impossible on account of cutoff. Thus it is inherently impossible to treat the junction between two wave guides by electrostatic methods. This can be seen particularly simply from the fact that the electric lines of force start and terminate on parts of the same conductor in a wave guide, showing obviously that we cannot introduce a potential function in terms of which the metal would be an equipotential. Any obvious definition of voltage and current, and of equivalent impedance as their ratio, must then be suspected, and reflection coefficients computed from such a definition cannot be expected to be accurate. Until more calculations are made, it is not possible to say how great the inaccuracies would be expected to be, however.

In spite of these limitations, we can set up in simple cases very plausible expressions for voltage and current and can expect that the impedance defined from them will give at least qualitatively correct answers. Let us consider the $TE_{1,0}$ mode of a rectangular pipe, as shown in Fig. 33. Let a be the longer side, and b the shorter side, of the cross section. Then there is current upward in one of the wide faces, downward in the other, along the axis of the pipe, so that these faces act rather like the two conductors of a transmission line. The electric field runs from one face to the other. If E_1 and H_1 are the values at the center of the pipe, where they have their maximum values, the voltage between conductors at the center is $E_1 b$, decreasing as we go to the edges of the pipe. The current density flowing upward at the center is H_1, and the total current, obtained by integrating the current density across the width of the conductor, is a numerical constant times $H_1 a$. Thus we should expect to have

$$Z_{eq} = \frac{E_1}{H_1} \frac{b}{a} \tag{24.1}$$

except for a numerical constant independent of a and b. This numerical constant is not determined by the theory, but it is not of importance, since it would be the same for two wave guides which were joined together and hence would cancel out in the equations for reflection. Using the value (15.21) for the ratio $Z = E_1/H_1$ we find

$$Z_{eq} = \sqrt{\frac{\mu}{\epsilon}} \frac{1}{\sqrt{1 - (\lambda_0/2a)^2}} \frac{b}{a} \tag{24.2}$$

We observe that as the width b of the wave guide becomes large, the term $(\lambda_0/2a)^2$ can be neglected compared to unity, so that this expression reduces to the value (23.7) found for the principal wave between infinite planes, as we should expect it to do.

As we have already stated, we cannot give anything approaching a proof, as we could for the principal mode, that the impedance as defined in (24.1) or (24.2) can be used in the transmission line equations to calculate reflection coefficients. Nevertheless it is very plausible that it should give a first approximation. We have just seen that when the term $(\lambda_0/2a)$ becomes small, the expression reduces to the correct limiting case. This limit can be reached for short wave length or high frequency. It is possible that in the other limit, as $(\lambda_0/2a)$ approaches unity, or as we approach cutoff, the errors might become more serious. There is some experimental evidence, however, that even in this limit the expression is fairly accurate. It is hardly possible to be sure of the theoretical predictions without further calculation, or to estimate the probable error in the approximations.

It is interesting to consider the conditions for impedance match between two rectangular wave guides of different dimensions, if we assume that Eq. (24.2) is applicable, so that two guides of the same equivalent impedance should match. We may rewrite (24.2) in the form

$$b^2 = \frac{\epsilon}{\mu} Z_{eq}^2 \left[a^2 - \left(\frac{\lambda_0}{2} \right)^2 \right] \tag{24.3}$$

This is the equation of a hyperbola, connecting a and b, if Z_{eq} is kept constant. Any two pairs of points lying on such a hyperbola, then, will represent wave guides whose impedances match. For any value of the longer dimension a of a wave guide, provided only it is longer than a half wave length, Eq. (24.3) determines the shorter dimension b, such that the guide will have a desired impedance. We notice that as a becomes only very slightly greater than a half wave length, b becomes very small; that is, very thin wave guides, slightly greater than half a wave length in their other dimension, can be set up to have any desired imped- ance and to match any desired guide. It would be remarkable if such thin guides could be set up to transmit all the power from a large guide, without reflection, but if Eq. (24.2) is correct, it should be possible. Of course, in such a thin guide the necessary fields become very great, if considerable power is to be trans-

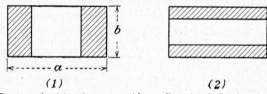

(1)   (2)

Fig. 44.—Rectangular irises in wave guides. Case (1), inductive; (2) capacitive.

mitted, and the loss by resistance in the walls and by corona can be considerable.

A device that is often useful is the diaphragm, a metallic plate closing a wave guide, with a hole cut in it. If this hole is rectangular, we may regard the diaphragm as a short section of wave guide of different size from the main wave guide, and so handle the transmission problem by the principles of Sec. 5. In the first place, we note that the characteristic impedance of the slot in the diaphragm can be made to match that of the wave guide in which it is inserted, by using Eq. (24.3), as we have just described. In that case the diaphragm will transmit radiation without reflection, even if it is a very narrow slot about a half wave length long. On the other hand, if the characteristic impedance of the slot, regarded as a short section of wave guide, is different from that of the wave guide in which it is inserted, there will be reflection. Simple cases are those in which either a or b of the slot equals the value for the wave guide, the other constant being smaller than for the wave guide. Thus suppose the slot has the same small dimension b as the wave guide, but that the large dimension a is smaller (as in Fig. 44,

case 1). Then by Eq. (24.2) the slot will have larger characteristic impedance than the guide. On the other hand, if the
slot has the same value of a as the guide, but a smaller b, its
characteristic impedance will be smaller than that of the guide.

It is often convenient to consider a diaphragm as a reactance
shunted across a transmission line. We can easily derive a
formula for this shunt reactance, in terms of the characteristic
impedance Z_0 of the wave guide, and the characteristic impedance
Z_1 of the guide of which the diaphragm forms a small section.
Let the length of the diaphragm be L, the propagation constant
of the wave in it β_1, and let us assume that $\beta_1 L$ is small compared
to unity, so that the diaphragm is thin. Then, using the reciprocal of Eq. (4.3), the admittance of the section of diaphragm
terminated by the line of characteristic impedance Z_0 is

$$Y = \frac{1}{Z_1} \frac{Z_1 \cos \beta_1 L + jZ_0 \sin \beta_1 L}{jZ_1 \sin \beta_1 L + Z_0 \cos \beta_1 L} \qquad (24.4)$$

Considering $\beta_1 L$ as a small quantity, this may be rewritten

$$Y = \frac{1}{Z_0} \frac{1 + j(Z_0/Z_1)\beta_1 L}{1 + j(Z_1/Z_0)\beta_1 L}$$

$$= \frac{1}{Z_0} + \frac{j\beta_1 L}{Z_1} \left[1 - \left(\frac{Z_1}{Z_0} \right)^2 \right] \qquad (24.5)$$

Equation (24.5) is the admittance of a shunt combination of the
resistance Z_0 and a reactance

$$X = \frac{Z_1}{\beta_1 L [(Z_1/Z_0)^2 - 1]} \qquad (24.6)$$

In Eq. (24.6) we have an expression for the equivalent reactance
which we must assume shunted across a line, to be equivalent
to a diaphragm. We see, then, that a diaphragm of type 1,
Fig. 44, corresponds to a positive or inductive reactance, that a
diaphragm of type 2 is a negative or capacitive reactance, and
that the slot of the same characteristic impedance as the guide
has an infinite reactance or zero admittance or makes no difference in the circuit.

25. Gradual Change of Cross Section with the Principal Mode.
In Chap. I we have given reasons for thinking that reflection at
a change in properties of a transmission line will be very small,
if the change is made gradually, over a length of several wave

lengths. We can handle such a problem analytically, in a number of cases, and show that this is actually the situation. We shall choose as an example the principal wave between parallel conductors, as in Figs. 29 and 42, taking the case where the change in cross section occurs by means of a tapered section with plane walls, as shown in perspective and in cross section in Fig. 45. The tapered section is a simple form of horn, and the theory of electromagnetic horns of sectoral form has been treated quite completely.[1] We shall not treat the general case

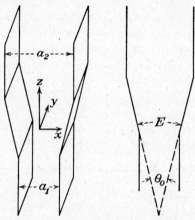

FIG. 45.—Perspective and cross section of tapered section in parallel-strip transmission line.

of horns at present. The particular case needed here is very simple, and we can handle it by methods that are not very difficult. From the cross section shown in Fig. 44 it is clear that the tapered section can be regarded as part of the sectoral region bounded by two planes making an angle θ_0 with each other. We then investigate solutions of Maxwell's equations within such a sectoral horn and ask whether these solutions can be fitted smoothly onto the solutions already investigated in the two plane parallel lines joined by the sectoral sector.

The problem of wave propagation in a sectoral horn is mathematically not unlike that of propagation in the circular wave guide, handled in Sec. 20. Both problems deal with the solution of Maxwell's equations in cylindrical coordinates. In Fig. 44 we can obviously set up polar coordinates, with the pole

[1] See Barrow and Chu, *Proc. I.R.E.*, **27**, 51 (1939).

at the intersection of the two sides of the sectoral horn.   Now, in contrast to the case of Sec. 20, we do not want to consider propagation along the axis of the cylindrical coordinates (in this case, the y axis), but rather we wish propagation out along the radius.   In Sec. 20, we considered a solution which varied sinusoidally along the axis of the cylinder (z in that case, y in this case), sinusoidally with θ, and as a Bessel function J_n or Neumann function N_n of kr, where k was a constant and r the radius.   We chose constants so as to satisfy boundary conditions on one or two cylindrical surfaces, the boundaries of the wave guide or coaxial line.   Here we do not wish our solution to depend on y. On the other hand, we must satisfy boundary conditions on the surfaces at $\theta = 0$, $\theta = \theta_0$, the two surfaces of the sector.   It turns out that in this case there is a very simple solution corresponding to the principal wave. H is everywhere along the y direction and depends on the distance r from the axis, but not on θ; E is along the direction tangential to a circle, so that lines of electric force are segments of circles, and E depends only on r. Solutions of this type are

$$H_y = [AJ_0(kr) + BN_0(kr)]e^{j\omega t}$$
$$E_\theta = \frac{\mu j \omega}{k}[AJ_0'(kr) + BN_0'(kr)]e^{j\omega t} \qquad (25.1)$$

where A and B are constants, J_0 and N_0 are Bessel's and Neumann's functions of order zero, and J_0' and N_0' represent derivatives of the corresponding functions with respect to their arguments kr.   In their computation, a useful relation from the theory of Bessel's functions is

$$J_0'(x) = -J_1(x), \qquad N_0'(x) = -N_1(x) \qquad (25.2)$$

In (25.1), k is given in terms of the frequency by the relation

$$k = \omega \sqrt{\epsilon\mu} \qquad (25.3)$$

The solution (25.1) can be verified by direct substitution in Maxwell's equations, in polar coordinates.

Either the term in A or in B, in (25.1), would represent a standing wave, since it is a product of a function of r times a sinusoidal function of t.   By combining the two, however, we can get a traveling wave, propagated either outward or inward. To see how to do this, we first must remember that J_0 and N_0

vary roughly as the sine or cosine of their argument, times the inverse square root of the argument, as we mentioned in Sec. 20. In fact, for large x, they approach the asymptotic values

$$J_0(x) \rightarrow \sqrt{\frac{2}{\pi x}} \cos \left(x - \frac{\pi}{4} \right)$$

$$N_0(x) \rightarrow \sqrt{\frac{2}{\pi x}} \sin \left(x - \frac{\pi}{4} \right) \qquad (25.4)$$

These asymptotic values are fairly accurate for x greater than about π, corresponding to a half wave length out from the origin of coordinates. We then see that for large r the combination

$$H_y = A[J_0(kr) - jN_0(kr)]e^{j\omega t} \qquad (25.5)$$

would approach the value

$$H_y \rightarrow \sqrt{\frac{2}{\pi kr}} A \left[\cos \left(kr - \frac{\pi}{4} \right) - j \sin \left(kr - \frac{\pi}{4} \right) \right] e^{j\omega t}$$

$$= A \sqrt{\frac{2}{\pi kr}} e^{j(\omega t - kr + \pi/4)} \qquad (25.6)$$

a traveling wave moving outward with velocity

$$v = \frac{\omega}{k} = \frac{1}{\sqrt{\epsilon\mu}} \qquad (25.7)$$

or the velocity of light in empty space. If we had used the positive sign instead of the negative in (25.5) we should have had a wave traveling inward.

Not only does the wave in the horn travel with the velocity of light, so long as we are not too near the apex of the triangle, but also the ratio of E to H has the same value as in empty space. Using the second of Eqs. (25.1) and the approximations (25.4) for J_0 and N_0, we have

$$E_\theta = \frac{\mu j\omega}{\omega \sqrt{\epsilon\mu}} A \sqrt{\frac{2}{\pi kr}} (-j)e^{j(\omega t - kr + \pi/4)}$$

$$= \sqrt{\frac{\mu}{\epsilon}} H_y \qquad (25.8)$$

so that

$$\frac{E_\theta}{H_y} = \sqrt{\frac{\mu}{\epsilon}} \qquad (25.9)$$

as in a free wave in empty space. This ratio, the impedance, naturally does not remain constant down to the apex of the triangle, since the approximations (25.4) do not hold that far; calculation shows, however, that it remains constant to a fairly good approximation to within a half wave length of the apex.

We may now ask how the solution we have found can be joined onto principal wave solutions for the two plane-parallel regions in Fig. 45. If the angle θ_0 giving the taper of the horn is sufficiently small, the joining becomes very accurate. For in that case, in the first place, the arcs of circles, like that shown in Fig. 45, representing lines of force within the horn, will be almost equivalent to straight lines, so that the z component of E in the horn can be practically neglected. Then we can set E_θ in the horn equal to E_x in the plane-parallel region, without any considerable error. In addition, if θ_0 is small, the imaginary dotted part of the horn, shown in Fig. 45, will be long; if it is considerably longer than a wave length, the impedance in the part of the horn actually existing will be practically the same as in empty space and hence practically the same as in the plane-parallel transmission line. Thus if we join E continuously, H will be continuous as well, and the boundary conditions will be exactly satisfied. Such a joining can be carried out at both extremities of the tapered section, so that we have succeeded in setting up a single, nonreflecting solution of the wave equation traveling right through the tapered region of the line. On the other hand, if the angle of flare θ_0 is large, the joining will be poor, both because the circular lines of force will depart considerably from the straight lines and because the impedance of the part of the horn that actually exists will be considerably different from the impedance of empty space. In that case, the boundary conditions cannot be satisfied without the use of reflected and attenuated waves. Obviously in the limiting case where θ_0 approaches 180°, the problem must approach that of Sec. 23, in which we have already seen that there is reflection. Without more elaborate calculation than has been made, it is hard to estimate the way in which the reflection depends on the angle θ_0, but our derivation shows qualitatively the sort of dependence to expect. It is clearly the angle that is significant, rather than the actual length of the tapered section; with a small change of cross section, a relatively short tapered section will be adequate to prevent reflection; with a large change a much longer taper is necessary. In any case, the small end of the horn must be cut off at least a half wave length from the imaginary apex of the sector.

In reflectionless transmission down a tapered line, it is obvious that the same power must be transmitted through each cross section of the line. Through the tapered region, the cross section is proportional to r. Thus the Poynting vector must be inversely proportional to r, and the electric and magnetic field separately must be inversely proportional to the square root of r. This dependence is shown in the solutions (25.6) and (25.8) and arises from the approximate proportionality of the Bessel function to the inverse square root of r. As a result of this, when two sections of line of separation a_1 and a_2, as in Fig. 45, are joined by a nonreflecting tapered section, the fields E_1 and E_2 in the two sections will be in the ratio of $\sqrt{a_2/a_1}$, and the voltages, which are equal to E times the distance a between plates, will be in the ratio of $\sqrt{a_1/a_2}$. The voltage will not be continuous, as it was in the case of a sudden change of cross section discussed in Sec. 23, but instead will be greater in the wider part of the line. We may well ask where the argument of Sec. 23, which was used to prove the continuity of voltage, breaks down in the present case. The argument there was based on the abnormally large values of $\partial^2 H_y/\partial x^2$ and $\partial^2 H_y/\partial z^2$ in the neighborhood of the junction. Those large values arose from the distorted shape of the lines of force near the junction. In the present case, however, with tapered walls, the lines of force will not be greatly distorted, so that the second derivatives will not be large, and the argument used in Sec. 23, by which we reduced the wave equation to Laplace's equation, cannot be used, so that the problem cannot be handled as an electrostatic problem. On the contrary, curl E is of important significance throughout the region of the tapered section in the present case, so that it does not follow by any means that the voltage between the two conductors, computed along different lines of force, must be the same.

We have handled mathematically only a very simple case of tapered transmission lines. There is no reason to doubt, however, that the same sort of result will hold in the general case, that a line of slowly changing properties, changing by only a small fraction of itself in a wave length, will be nonreflecting. This conclusion presumably applies to hollow-pipe transmission lines, as well as to the coaxial line and other types of lines operating in their principal mode.   For rectangular hollow pipes, one can make the same sort of calculation we have used in the present chapter.   The different types of waves are possible in a sectoral horn, just as they are in a hollow pipe, and we can pick out a type that joins fairly smoothly onto each of the hollow-pipe modes. These waves in the horn are discussed in the paper of Barrow and Chu, previously quoted.   The situation with all these modes in the horn is similar to that found in the simple case we have taken up.   Far from the apex of the horn, the velocity of propagation and the impedance approach those of empty space. Closer to the apex, these quantities vary somewhat as the corresponding quantities would for a rectangular pipe of the same cross section.   There are larger and larger departures from this situation as we approach the apex, however, and we have a rather involved field close to the apex, in which there are large fields of the attenuated type, which fall off rapidly as we depart from the apex, and do not carry power.   This means that the joining conditions between a hollow pipe and a horn are not very accurately fulfilled if the joining is near the apex, just as we found in the present section; except that the higher the order of the wave, the farther out these abnormalities persist.   Furthermore, if the walls of the pipe are of finite conductivity, these attenuated parts of the wave can result in considerable power loss in the walls.   In other words, this problem approaches that taken up in the preceding section, where we discussed joining of hollow pipes, and we cannot go much further than we could there in estimating the exact nature of the reflections and losses.   We can be sure in all cases, however, that a sufficiently gradually tapered line will be nonreflecting.

26. Survey of Other Problems of Composite Lines.—There are many other types of discontinuities that can be present in transmission lines, beyond those taken up in this chapter.   In coupling wave guides to concentric lines, and vice versa, it is very common to terminate the concentric line in a small dipole, or coupling loop, or other device, within the wave guide.   We are really not yet equipped to take up many of these problems. The reason is that, if we consider them in detail, most of these problems have a close analogy to radiation from an antenna, or scattering or absorption by an antenna. Coupling loops are obviously like antennas; a concentric line terminated by such a loop inside a wave guide is plainly radiating into the wave guide, or absorbing radiation from the wave guide. Before handling these problems, it is plain that we must understand the radiation and absorption of radiation by antennas, and the diffraction resulting from the limitation of a beam. We shall accordingly go ahead with the study of antennas and radiation. After we have handled them, we shall be equipped to return to problems of transmission lines and to understand more in detail some of the practical devices used in connection with them. Of course, such study as we shall make of antennas, scattering, and like problems will be applied primarily to the propagation of radiation in empty space. In the next chapter we proceed with the problem of radiation and absorption of energy by a simple antenna and then go on to the effect of reflectors and other devices for producing directed beams, with the problems of diffraction associated with them.

CHAPTER V

RADIATION FROM ANTENNAS

All our work so far has dealt with disturbances propagated along one definite direction. An antenna in free space, however, sends out radiation in all directions. Our present problem is to investigate the spherical waves emitted by antennas, including their directional properties. This problem really can be divided into two parts: first, radiation from bare antennas, and secondly, the effect on the radiation of various directive devices, such in particular as dummy antennas and parabolas. At the same time that we are interested in the radiation emitted from the antenna, we must consider the other side of the problem, the antenna as a circuit element. Generally an antenna forms the terminus of a conventional transmission line, in the present case of a coaxial line. It acts, then, as a terminal load on this line, and its impedance must be considered so as to understand how to match it to the line and have the maximum radiated power. In considering this problem, we shall find that it is a very useful, though not entirely accurate, conception to think of the antenna itself as a length of transmission line, starting where the coaxial line impresses voltage on it and terminating at the ends of the antenna. We shall find that in a certain sense we are justified in thinking of the antenna as guiding the wave, just as a coaxial line guides a wave, out to its ends, at which the radiation leaves the guiding members and spreads out into empty space. As a first step in our problem, we shall consider spherical solutions of Maxwell's equations. The solutions that we shall use have singularities, which generally come at the origin; to make them valid, we must assume conductors, the singularities lying inside the conductors. We must then satisfy the ordinary boundary conditions at the surface of each conductor. Our procedure to some extent will be the reverse process, first finding the field, then asking what form of conductor could be used to satisfy suitable boundary conditions with it.

195

27. Maxwell's Equations in Spherical Coordinates.—We shall use conventional spherical polar coordinates, as shown in Fig. 46. The components of a vector can be given in terms of these coordinates, as is indicated in the components E_r, E_θ, E_ϕ in the figure. Then, by well-known methods,[1] Maxwell's equations become

$$\frac{1}{r \sin \theta} \left[\frac{\partial}{\partial \theta} (\sin \theta E_\phi) - \frac{\partial E_\theta}{\partial \phi} \right] + j\omega\mu H_r = 0 \quad (27.1)$$

$$\frac{1}{r \sin \theta} \frac{\partial E_r}{\partial \phi} - \frac{1}{r} \frac{\partial (rE_\phi)}{\partial r} + j\omega\mu H_\theta = 0 \quad (27.2)$$

$$\frac{1}{r} \frac{\partial (rE_\theta)}{\partial r} - \frac{1}{r} \frac{\partial E_r}{\partial \theta} + j\omega\mu H_\phi = 0 \quad (27.3)$$

$$\frac{1}{r^2} \frac{\partial}{\partial r} (r^2 H_r) + \frac{1}{r \sin \theta} \frac{\partial}{\partial \theta} (\sin \theta H_\theta) + \frac{1}{r \sin \theta} \frac{\partial H_\phi}{\partial \phi} = 0 \quad (27.4)$$

$$\frac{1}{r \sin \theta} \left[\frac{\partial}{\partial \theta} (\sin \theta H_\phi) - \frac{\partial H_\theta}{\partial \phi} \right] - j\omega\epsilon E_r = 0 \quad (27.5)$$

$$\frac{1}{r \sin \theta} \frac{\partial H_r}{\partial \phi} - \frac{1}{r} \frac{\partial (rH_\phi)}{\partial r} - j\omega\epsilon E_\theta = 0 \quad (27.6)$$

$$\frac{1}{r} \frac{\partial}{\partial r} (rH_\theta) - \frac{1}{r} \frac{\partial H_r}{\partial \theta} - j\omega\epsilon E_\phi = 0 \quad (27.7)$$

$$\frac{1}{r^2} \frac{\partial}{\partial r} (r^2 E_r) + \frac{1}{r \sin \theta} \frac{\partial}{\partial \theta} (\sin \theta E_\theta) + \frac{1}{r \sin \theta} \frac{\partial E_\phi}{\partial \phi} = 0 \quad (27.8)$$

The solutions of these equations represent, in general, waves propagated outward along the radius. Thus the r direction can be considered the direction of propagation. As with the case of Cartesian coordinates, taken up in Sec. 15, there are two types of waves: transverse electric, or *TE*, in which the longitudinal component of the electric field, E_r, is zero; and transverse magnetic, *TM*, in which H_r is zero. There is also the limiting case of the transverse electromagnetic wave, *TEM*, a principal wave, in which both E_r and H_r are zero.

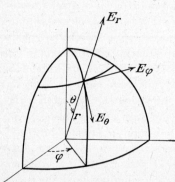

Fig. 46.—Spherical polar coordinates.

---

[1] See, for instance, Slater and Frank, "Introduction to Theoretical Physics," McGraw-Hill Book Company, Inc., New York, or Stratton, "Electromagnetic Theory," McGraw-Hill Book Company, Inc., New York.

This analysis into TE, TM, and TEM waves is brought out particularly clearly, for instance, in a paper by S. A. Schelkunoff.[1]

The problem of Sec. 15 was simplified a great deal because we could assume from the outset that each component of the field varied exponentially along the z axis, the direction of propagation. It cannot be assumed in a corresponding way here that the components vary exponentially with r; as a matter of fact, their variation with r is given by certain Bessel's functions, which approach an exponential form only for large values of r. Therefore we cannot at once carry through derivations like those of (15.3), (15.4), etc., expressing all the field components in the TE case algebraically in terms of H_z, and all the field components in the TM case in terms of E_z. Nevertheless an essentially equivalent discussion can be carried through, except that here the relations are not simply algebraic but involve differentiation. Thus let us start with the TE case. We let H_r be a scalar function of r, θ, ϕ. It is slightly more convenient to operate, not with H_r, but with a quantity which we may denote u, defined by

$$u = rH_r \tag{27.9}$$

It will appear that the equation that must be satisfied by u is the wave equation, which in spherical polar coordinates becomes

$$\frac{1}{r^2}\frac{\partial}{\partial r}\left(r^2\frac{\partial u}{\partial r}\right) + \frac{1}{r^2\sin\theta}\frac{\partial}{\partial\theta}\left(\sin\theta\frac{\partial u}{\partial\theta}\right)$$
$$+ \frac{1}{r^2\sin^2\theta}\frac{\partial^2 u}{\partial\phi^2} + \omega^2\epsilon\mu u = 0 \tag{27.10}$$

It is well known that this equation permits a separation of variables: u can be written as a product

$$u(r,\theta,\phi) = R(r)\Theta(\theta)\Phi(\phi) \tag{27.11}$$

where $R(r)$ satisfies the equation

$$\frac{1}{r^2}\frac{d}{dr}\left(r^2\frac{dR}{dr}\right) + \left[\omega^2\epsilon\mu - \frac{n(n+1)}{r^2}\right]R = 0 \tag{27.12}$$

which can also be written in the form

$$\frac{d^2(rR)}{dr^2} + \left[\omega^2\epsilon\mu - \frac{n(n+1)}{r^2}\right](rR) = 0 \tag{27.13}$$

[1] Transmission Theory of Spherical Waves, *Trans. A.I.E.E.*, **57**, 744 (1938).

The function $\Theta(\theta)$ satisfies

$$\frac{1}{\sin\theta}\frac{d}{d\theta}\left(\sin\theta\frac{d\Theta}{d\theta}\right) + \left[n(n+1) - \frac{m^2}{\sin^2\theta}\right]\Theta = 0 \quad (27.14)$$

and $\Phi(\phi)$ satisfies

$$\frac{d^2\Phi}{d\phi^2} + m^2\Phi = 0 \qquad (27.15)$$

where m, n are constants of separation.

In terms of the function u, we can now set up values of all the other field components. Let us assume, for the *TE* case,

$$H_r = \frac{u}{r}$$

$$H_\theta = \frac{1}{n(n+1)}\frac{1}{r}\frac{\partial}{\partial\theta}\frac{\partial}{\partial r}(ru)$$

$$H_\phi = \frac{1}{n(n+1)}\frac{1}{r\sin\theta}\frac{\partial}{\partial\phi}\frac{\partial}{\partial r}(ru)$$

$$E_r = 0$$

$$E_\theta = \frac{-j\omega\mu}{n(n+1)}\frac{1}{r\sin\theta}\frac{\partial}{\partial\phi}(ru)$$

$$E_\phi = \frac{j\omega\mu}{n(n+1)}\frac{1}{r}\frac{\partial}{\partial\theta}(ru) \qquad (27.16)$$

By direct substitution in Maxwell's equations, (27.1) to (27.8), we can show that these equations are satisfied if u obeys the wave equation (27.10) or its equivalent equations (27.12), (27.14), (27.15). We note that instead of defining H_θ and H_ϕ directly in terms of u, we can instead set up the relations

$$H_\theta = \frac{1}{j\omega\mu}\frac{1}{r}\frac{\partial}{\partial r}(rE_\phi)$$

$$H_\phi = \frac{-1}{j\omega\mu}\frac{1}{r}\frac{\partial}{\partial r}(rE_\theta) \qquad (27.17)$$

These equations are the analogue of (15.3), giving the relation between the tangential components of E and H. We shall soon see the analogy more clearly.

The relations for the transverse magnetic, *TM*, case, are analogous to those just set up. In that case, we have a longitudinal component E_r of electric field, which we write as

$$E_r = \frac{v}{r} \qquad (27.18)$$

where v satisfies the same wave equation (27.10) that u satisfied. In terms of v, we can then write the other components as

$$E_\theta = \frac{1}{n(n+1)} \frac{1}{r} \frac{\partial}{\partial \theta} \frac{\partial}{\partial r} (rv)$$

$$E_\phi = \frac{1}{n(n+1)} \frac{1}{r \sin \theta} \frac{\partial}{\partial \phi} \frac{\partial}{\partial r} (rv)$$

$$H_r = 0$$

$$H_\theta = \frac{j\omega\epsilon}{n(n+1)} \frac{1}{r \sin \theta} \frac{\partial}{\partial \phi} (rv)$$

$$H_\phi = \frac{-j\omega\epsilon}{n(n+1)} \frac{1}{r} \frac{\partial}{\partial \theta} (rv) \qquad (27.19)$$

with

$$E_\theta = \frac{-1}{j\omega\epsilon} \frac{1}{r} \frac{\partial}{\partial r} (rH_\phi)$$

$$E_\phi = \frac{1}{j\omega\epsilon} \frac{1}{r} \frac{\partial}{\partial r} (rH_\theta) \qquad (27.20)$$

We have now written down our formulas. What are their solutions, in terms of well-known functions? Equations (27.12) and (27.13) can be easily transformed into Bessel's equation, and we can show that $R(r)$ must be a linear combination of the spherical Bessel and Neumann functions $j_n(kr)$ and $n_n(kr)$.[1] These functions are defined in terms of the ordinary Bessel and Neumann functions by the relations

$$j_n(x) = \sqrt{\frac{\pi}{2x}} J_{n+\frac{1}{2}}(x), \qquad n_n(x) = \sqrt{\frac{\pi}{2x}} N_{n+\frac{1}{2}}(x) \quad (27.21)$$

The quantity k which appears in $j_n(kr)$ and $n_n(kr)$ is

$$k = \omega \sqrt{\epsilon\mu} \qquad (27.22)$$

In case n is an integer (which it generally is, as we shall see in a moment), j_n and n_n can be expressed in analytic form in terms of algebraic and trigonometric functions. For the first few functions we have

$$j_0(x) = \frac{\sin x}{x}, \qquad n_0(x) = -\frac{\cos x}{x}$$

$$j_1(x) = \frac{\sin x}{x^2} - \frac{\cos x}{x}, \qquad n_1(x) = -\frac{\sin x}{x} - \frac{\cos x}{x^2} \quad (27.23)$$

[1] These are defined in Morse, "Vibration and Sound," p. 246, McGraw-Hill Book Company, Inc., New York, and Stratton, "Electromagnetic Theory," p. 404, McGraw-Hill Book Company, Inc., New York.

At large values of x, the terms in $1/x$ are the leading ones. In the general case, this leading term is given by

$$j_n(x) \rightarrow \frac{1}{x} \cos\left(x - \frac{n+1}{2}\pi\right)$$

$$n_n(x) \rightarrow \frac{1}{x} \sin\left(x - \frac{n+1}{2}\pi\right) \qquad (27.24)$$

In the opposite limit, as x tends to zero, we can expand in power series. In this case the leading term is

$$j_n(x) \rightarrow \frac{x^n}{1 \cdot 3 \cdot 5 \cdots (2n+1)}$$

$$n_n(x) \rightarrow -\frac{1 \cdot 1 \cdot 3 \cdot 5 \cdots (2n-1)}{x^{n+1}} \qquad (27.25)$$

Taking note of (27.24), we see that at large x we can set up two combinations of j_n and n_n, representing respectively waves traveling outward and inward:

$$j_n(x) - jn_n(x) \rightarrow \frac{1}{x} e^{-j\left(x - \frac{n+1}{2}\pi\right)}$$

$$j_n(x) + jn_n(x) \rightarrow \frac{1}{x} e^{j\left(x + \frac{n+1}{2}\pi\right)} \qquad (27.26)$$

These functions are called spherical Hankel functions. We see that the amplitude of the wave falls off as $1/x$; this means that the intensity, being proportional to the square of the amplitude, will fall off as $1/x^2$, giving the inverse square law characteristic of spherical waves. For a wave traveling outward, we shall choose the first of the Hankel functions (27.26) to represent $R(r)$. Then we shall find that the leading term in all transverse components of field depends on r through the function

$$\frac{1}{r} e^{-j\left(kr - \frac{n+1}{2}\pi\right)} \qquad (27.27)$$

at large distances. Thus at large distances quantities like

$$\frac{1}{r}\frac{\partial}{\partial r}(rE_\phi) \qquad (27.28)$$

which appear in (27.17) and (27.20), become equal to $-jkE_\phi$, etc., so that (27.17) and (27.20) become

$$E_\theta = \sqrt{\frac{\mu}{\epsilon}} H_\phi, \qquad E_\phi = -\sqrt{\frac{\mu}{\epsilon}} H_\theta \qquad (27.29)$$

the familiar relations for a *TEM* wave, showing that our spherical waves approach the *TEM* type at large distances.

We have now considered the function of r, which is a solution of (27.12) or (27.13). Next we take up (27.14) and (27.15). In the first place, from (27.15), it is obvious that

$$\Phi = \cos m\phi \text{ or } \sin m\phi \qquad (27.30)$$

If the wave is being propagated in empty space, the function must be a single-valued function of ϕ, so that m must be an integer. On the other hand, we might want to consider the propagation of waves between two planes at angles $\phi = \phi_1$, $\phi = \phi_2$. In that case, we should have to satisfy boundary conditions on those two planes, and m would have to be chosen as nonintegral values. We shall not use that case, however. The equation (27.14) is now recognized as the equation for the associated Legendre polynomials,

$$\Theta(\theta) = P_n^m (\cos \theta) \qquad (27.31)$$

These functions are so well known that we shall not list any of their properties. In order that these functions should be finite at $\theta = 0$ and $\theta = \pi$ (that is, along the axis of the coordinates), it is necessary that n be an integer, and this is the case we usually meet. There is another solution of (27.14), a function related to the associated Legendre polynomial something as the Neumann function is related to the Bessel function, which is infinite both at $\theta = 0$ and π. This solution is clearly inadmissible in the case where we have wave propagation in empty space. For propagation in the biconical horn, however, we imagine conducting cones making angles $\theta = \theta_1$, $\theta = \theta_2$ and consider the propagation of waves between these cones. (We shall consider the principal wave for this case in the next section.) In this case, the angles $\theta = 0$ and π are excluded from the region of the solution, and we must use suitable linear combinations of both P_n^m and of the other solution of Legendre's equation, with a nonintegral value of n chosen so as to satisfy boundary conditions on both cones. We shall describe this case but shall not make calculations with it; for that reason we do not give the necessary formulas here.

We now see the mathematical form of the solutions of Maxwell's equations in spherical coordinates. The general relations are rather formidable, however (we have really given them only

for reference), and we now pass on to several important special
cases, which we shall take up more in detail, with more attention
to their physical significance. We start with the principal wave,
or *TEM* wave. This could be found by a limiting process from
either the *TE* case or the *TM* case, but since it would involve u
or v becoming zero, this is a somewhat inconvenient way to get
at it. Instead, we shall derive the solution directly, by elementary methods.

28. The Principal or TEM Wave.—There are two types of
TEM wave: one in which E_θ and H_ϕ are the only components
different from zero, the other in which E_ϕ and H_θ only are different from zero. Only the first type is of physical importance, for
reasons that we shall see later, and we shall derive it only. We
shall find that E_θ and H_ϕ depend only on r and θ, not on ϕ. Then
the only ones of Maxwell's equations that are not trivial are

$$\frac{1}{r}\frac{\partial}{\partial r}(rE_\theta) + j\omega\mu H_\phi = 0 \qquad (28.1)$$

$$\frac{\partial}{\partial \theta}(\sin\theta H_\phi) = 0 \qquad (28.2)$$

$$\frac{1}{r}\frac{\partial}{\partial r}(rH_\phi) + j\omega\epsilon E_\theta = 0 \qquad (28.3)$$

$$\frac{\partial}{\partial \theta}(\sin\theta E_\theta) = 0 \qquad (28.4)$$

derived from (27.3), (27.5), (27.6), and (27.8) respectively. We
may rewrite (28.1) and (28.3) in the form

$$\frac{\partial}{\partial r}(rH_\phi) = -j\omega\epsilon(rE_\theta)$$

$$\frac{\partial}{\partial r}(rE_\theta) = -j\omega\mu(rH_\phi) \qquad (28.5)$$

two equations of the form of the transmission line equations of
(6.2) and (6.4), with rH_ϕ taking the place of the current and rE_θ
taking the place of the voltage. Differentiating the first of
Eqs. (28.5), and substituting from the second, we have

$$\frac{\partial^2}{\partial r^2}(rH_\phi) + \omega^2\epsilon\mu(rH_\phi) = 0 \qquad (28.6)$$

with an identical equation for rE_θ. Thus we see that rH_ϕ and
rE_θ depend on r as $e^{\pm jkr}$, where $k = \omega\sqrt{\epsilon\mu}$. From (28.2) and

(28.4) we see that the field components vary inversely as sin θ. From (28.5) we can get the relation between the magnitudes of electric and magnetic fields. We then have

$$H_\phi = \sqrt{\frac{\epsilon}{\mu}} E_\theta = \frac{A e^{i(\omega t - kr)}}{r \sin \theta} \tag{28.7}$$

From the solution (28.7) for the *TEM* case, it is obvious that the field components become infinite when θ becomes 0 or π. Thus the solution cannot exist unless the axis is cut out by conducting surfaces. The case[1] in which this solution holds is the biconical horn, shown in Fig. 47, in which there are conducting surfaces at θ_1 and θ_2. Clearly the electric field is normal, and the magnetic field tangential, to the conducting cones, so that the boundary conditions are satisfied by the solution (28.7), no matter what may be the angles of the cones. Since the electric lines of force go from one conductor to another, and the velocity of propagation and other properties are like those of a wave in free space, this solution is a principal mode, in the same sense as the principal modes in transmission lines, which we took up in Secs. 18 and 19. As in those cases, we can define a voltage, a current, and an equivalent impedance, in a unique way.

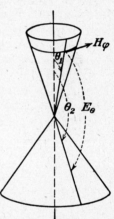

Fig. 47.—The biconical horn.

The voltage is the integral of E_θ from one conductor to the other. Thus it is

$$V = \int_{\theta_1}^{\theta_2} E_\theta r \, d\theta = \sqrt{\frac{\mu}{\epsilon}} A e^{i(\omega t - kr)} \int_{\theta_1}^{\theta_2} \frac{d\theta}{\sin \theta}$$
$$= \sqrt{\frac{\mu}{\epsilon}} A e^{i(\omega t - kr)} \ln \left(\tan \frac{\theta_2}{2} \cot \frac{\theta_1}{2} \right) \tag{28.8}$$

The current is the integral of H_ϕ around a circle, or is $2\pi r \sin \theta H_\phi$. Thus we have

$$i = 2\pi A e^{i(\omega t - kr)} \tag{28.9}$$

[1] This case is treated by Barrow, Chu, and Jansen, *Proc. I.R.E.*, **27**, 769, (1939), as well as by S. S. Schelkunoff, *Trans. A.I.E.E.*, **57**, 744 (1938), and *Proc. I.R.E.*, **29**, 493 (1941).

The equivalent impedance is then

$$Z_{eq} = \frac{V}{i} = \sqrt{\frac{\mu}{\epsilon}} \frac{1}{2\pi} \ln \left(\tan \frac{\theta_2}{2} \cot \frac{\theta_1}{2} \right) \qquad (28.10)$$

This formula simplifies slightly when the cones both have the same angle, so that $\theta_2 = \pi - \theta_1$. Then $\cot \theta_1/2 = \tan \theta_2/2$, so that

$$Z_{eq} = \sqrt{\frac{\mu}{\epsilon}} \frac{1}{\pi} \ln \cot \frac{\theta_1}{2} \qquad (28.11)$$

We notice that as θ_1 approaches zero, so that the cones degenerate to very thin conductors surrounding the axis, Z_{eq} becomes indefinitely large.

The case of very narrow cones, where θ_1 is very small and θ_2 very close to π, is interesting, as Schelkunoff has pointed out, because it approximates a transmission line such as is found in an antenna, two wires or other conductors leading away from an electromotive force at the origin. For very small angle cones, a short segment of the cone approaches a segment of a cylinder, and the field (28.7) actually approaches the field of a principal wave guided by a cylindrical conductor. This field is given in (19.1), where we were discussing coaxial lines; the absence of an outer conductor would not affect the field of (19.1), which is $H = \sqrt{\frac{\epsilon}{\mu}} E = \frac{H_0}{r} e^{j\omega t - \gamma z}$, in the notation used there. We were then using cylindrical coordinates, and the quantity r measured the radial distance out from the axis, or just the same quantity measured by $r \sin \theta$ in spherical coordinates. Thus the fields agree exactly with (28.7), the only difference being that the electric field in the cylindrical case pointed out normal to the axis of the cylinder, and here it points along circles, as shown in Fig. 47. As far as the part of the field near the conductor is concerned, this makes no difference. On account of the factor r, or $r \sin \theta$, respectively, in the denominator of (19.1) or (28.7), the field is very large near the conductor and falls off as we leave it. The case of very narrow cones, then, leads to the propagation of a wave in both directions down the conductor from the electromotive force at the origin, the wave being guided by the conductor much as if it were cylindrical. There is a singularity of voltage at the origin; but it is to be assumed that the wave propagation would be almost the same if there were a large but finite voltage confined to a small region near the origin. This problem, of the propagation of a wave in both directions down a cylindrical conductor as a result of a concentrated electromotive force near the origin, has been discussed by Stratton and Chu.[1] Their solution, however, is in terms of cylindrical rather than spherical coordinates, and it is hard to see from it whether it reduces to something like the present principal wave or not.

29. The Field of an Electric Dipole.—In many ways the most important spherical wave physically is that produced by an electric dipole. This is the simplest *TM* wave. If we consider our solution of Sec. 27, we see that the function v must depend on θ or ϕ, in order that any of the derivatives in (27.19) may be different from zero. Thus we cannot have the case $n = 0$, since the spherical harmonic $P_0(\cos \theta)$ is a constant and does not depend on angles at all. The lowest value that n may have is 1. In this case, m can be 0 or 1. We consider the case $n = 1, m = 0$. This proves to be the simple dipole field. If we choose v to be

$$v = \cos \theta [j_1(kr) - jn_1(kr)] \qquad (29.1)$$

or

$$v = \cos \theta \left[-\frac{1}{kr} + \frac{j}{(kr)^2} \right] e^{-jkr} \qquad (29.2)$$

which is equivalent to it according to (27.23), we find for the field components

$$E_r = ke^{j(\omega t - kr)} \cos \theta \left[-\frac{1}{(kr)^2} + \frac{j}{(kr)^3} \right]$$

$$E_\theta = \frac{k}{2} e^{j(\omega t - kr)} \sin \theta \left[\frac{-j}{kr} - \frac{1}{(kr)^2} + \frac{j}{(kr)^3} \right]$$

$$H_\phi = \frac{k}{2} \sqrt{\frac{\epsilon}{\mu}} e^{j(\omega t - kr)} \sin \theta \left[\frac{-j}{kr} - \frac{1}{(kr)^2} \right] \qquad (29.3)$$

The other field components are zero. These functions, of course, are to be multiplied by an arbitrary amplitude.

To understand the meaning of our solution, let us first consider the terms that are important at small distances, those in the highest inverse powers of r ($1/r^3$ for E_r and E_θ, $1/r^2$ for H_ϕ). We shall show that the terms in the electric force represent the

[1] *J. Applied Phys.*, **12**, 230 (1941).

field of an electric dipole at the origin and that the magnetic field is the field of the corresponding current element, derived from the time rate of change of the dipole moment, as found from the Biot-Savart law. We remember that a dipole of moment $\dot{M}$ consists of two equal and opposite charges, $\pm q$, at a distance d apart, where

$$M = qd \qquad (29.4)$$

Then, as we see in Fig. 48, the electrical potential ψ at an arbitrary point P can be written

$$\psi = \frac{q}{4\pi\epsilon}\left(\frac{1}{r_1} - \frac{1}{r_2}\right) = \frac{q}{4\pi\epsilon}\frac{(r_2 - r_1)}{r_1 r_2}$$
$$= \frac{q}{4\pi\epsilon}\frac{d\cos\theta}{r^2} = \frac{M\cos\theta}{4\pi\epsilon r^2} \qquad (29.5)$$

In this derivation, the 4π comes because we are using rationalized units; and $r_2 - r_1$ becomes equal to $d\cos\theta$, and $r_1 r_2$ to r^2, where

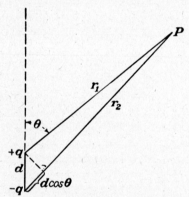

r is the mean distance from P to the dipole, in the limit as d becomes small compared to r. We can now find E_r and E_θ, by electrostatics, for a dipole of moment $Me^{j\omega t}$ by the equations

$$E_r = -\frac{\partial\psi}{\partial r} = \frac{2M}{4\pi\epsilon}e^{j\omega t}\frac{\cos\theta}{r^3}$$
$$E_\theta = -\frac{1}{r}\frac{\partial\psi}{\partial\theta} = \frac{M}{4\pi\epsilon}e^{j\omega t}\frac{\sin\theta}{r^3}$$
$$(29.6)$$

Fig. 48.—Potential of a dipole.

We observe that these two components are in the same ratio as the corresponding components in (29.3), so long as we consider only the terms in $1/r^3$, so that by multiplication by a proper factor we can convert (29.3) into the field of a dipole of moment $Me^{j\omega t}$.

A dipole whose moment was $Me^{j\omega t}$ would carry with it a current equal to its time derivative, or to $j\omega Me^{j\omega t}$. This small current element would have a magnetic field H_ϕ which would be given according to the Biot-Savart law by

$$H_\phi = \frac{j\omega M}{4\pi}e^{j\omega t}\frac{\sin\theta}{r^2} \qquad (29.7)$$

On inserting the value of k, one finds that this is in the same ratio to the H_ϕ of (29.3) that the other two field components of (29.6) are to the corresponding values of (29.3). In other words, all three components of field at short distances can be found from the field of a dipole of moment $Me^{j\omega t}$. Let us now multiply the field components of (29.3) by $-jMk^2/2\pi\epsilon$, so as to reduce them to the values of (29.6) and (29.7) at small distances. We then have

$$E_r = \frac{Mk^3}{4\pi\epsilon} e^{j(\omega t - kr)} \cos \theta \left[\frac{2j}{(kr)^2} + \frac{2}{(kr)^3} \right]$$

$$E_\theta = \frac{Mk^3}{4\pi\epsilon} e^{j(\omega t - kr)} \sin \theta \left[\frac{-1}{kr} + \frac{j}{(kr)^2} + \frac{1}{(kr)^3} \right]$$

$$H_\phi = \frac{j\omega Mk^2}{4\pi} e^{j(\omega t - kr)} \sin \theta \left[\frac{j}{kr} + \frac{1}{(kr)^2} \right] \tag{29.8}$$

The field components of Eq. (29.8) thus represent a solution of Maxwell's equations reducing to the field of a dipole of moment $Me^{j\omega t}$ at sufficiently small distances, and thus are the complete solution for the field of such a dipole.

Let us now consider the behavior of our solution at large values of r. As we see from (29.3) or (29.8), E_r is proportional to $1/r^2$ at large distances, and E_θ and H_ϕ are proportional to $1/r$ and hence become indefinitely greater than E_r as r becomes great enough. In other words, the field becomes transverse in the limit of large r. At the same time the ratio of E_θ to H_ϕ approaches the value $\sqrt{\mu/\epsilon}$ characteristic of *TEM* waves, as we see particularly easily from (29.3). Let us compute Poynting's vector and its integral. We have

$$S = \tfrac{1}{2} \operatorname{Re} E_\theta \bar{H}_\phi$$

$$= \tfrac{1}{2} \operatorname{Re} \frac{\omega M^2 k^5}{16\pi^2\epsilon} \sin^2 \theta \left[\frac{1}{(kr)^2} - \frac{j}{(kr)^5} \right]$$

$$= \frac{\mu \sqrt{\epsilon\mu} \; \omega^4 M^2 \sin^2 \theta}{32\pi^2 r^2} \tag{29.9}$$

where we have used (29.8). We see that the intensity of radiation varies as $1/r^2$, the inverse square law. To find the total radiation, we must integrate over all directions, by multiplying by the element of area $2\pi r^2 \sin \theta \, d\theta$ and integrating from 0 to π. We then have

$$\int S \, da = \frac{\mu \sqrt{\epsilon\mu} \, \omega^4 M^2}{32\pi^2} \, 2\pi \int_0^\pi \sin^3 \theta \, d\theta$$

$$= \frac{\mu \sqrt{\epsilon\mu}\omega^4 M^2}{12\pi} \tag{29.10}$$

The total radiation is independent of r, as it must be, since the same energy must be radiated through every sphere concentric with the origin. The radiation is most intense at right angles to the axis of the dipole, the intensity being given by the formula $\sin^2 \theta$, as we see from (29.9).

It is interesting to compute the ratio E_θ/H_ϕ for short distances, as well as long distances; we find that this ratio shows a behavior characteristic of the impedance of an antenna, as we should expect from general considerations. Using (29.3), we have

$$\frac{E_\theta}{H_\phi} = \sqrt{\frac{\mu}{\epsilon}} \frac{j/(kr)^3 - 1/(kr)^2 - j/kr}{-1/(kr)^2 - j/kr}$$

$$= \sqrt{\frac{\mu}{\epsilon}} \frac{1}{jkr} [1 + jkr - (kr)^2][1 - jkr + (jkr)^2 - (jkr)^3 \cdots]$$

$$= \sqrt{\frac{\mu}{\epsilon}} \left[\frac{1}{jkr} + jkr + (kr)^2 \cdots \right]$$

$$= \frac{1}{j\omega\epsilon r} + j\omega\mu r + \sqrt{\frac{\mu}{\epsilon}} (kr)^2 \cdots \tag{29.11}$$

The first term, as we see, is a capacitive reactance, the second an inductive reactance, and the third a resistance. We shall see later that the impedance of an antenna has very similar terms, and furthermore that an antenna of linear dimensions r has a capacity and inductance which are essentially proportional to r, while the resistance is proportional to r^2, for small sizes of antennas, just as we have in the expression of (29.11). As a result, a very short antenna has a large capacitive reactance, which as the antenna is increased in length (or as the frequency is increased) is more and more counteracted by the inductance, leading to zero reactance at a resonance point, which for an actual antenna comes when the antenna is approximately half a wave length long. (In this approximation, it would come for $kr = 1$, or $2\pi r/\lambda = 1$, or $\pi r = \lambda/2$.) At this resonance point, the impedance is a pure resistance, which for an actual antenna is of the order of magnitude of 70 ohms, though this crude approximation would give $\sqrt{\mu/\epsilon}$, or 376 ohms. This resistance is called the radiation resistance. It does not result from any energy loss in heating the conductor of which the antenna is constructed, but rather from energy loss in radiation. We shall discuss the value of the impedance of actual antennas in a later section. It is interesting to see, however, that a simplified model for the actual behavior is provided by the simple formula (29.11).

30. The Field of a Finite Antenna.—In the preceding section, we have seen how one of the simplest solutions of Maxwell's equations for the TM case, as tabulated in (27.16), reduces to the field of an electric dipole. In a later section we shall consider the corresponding solution for the TE case, showing that it corresponds to a magnetic dipole. In the present section, however, we shall inquire how to solve the general problem of finding the field of a finite antenna. As with any electrical problem involving conductors, there are two types of problem that we may consider. First, and simpler, is the problem of finding the field, given the distribution of charge and current. Second, and much more difficult, is that of finding a field which reduces to the correct boundary conditions at the metallic surface of the antenna. The first type of problem can be completely solved; the second has been worked out in only one or two special cases. Fortunately, it turns out either by experiment or by a result of calculations of the second type, that the current distribution in actual antennas is often closely approximated by a simple function, in particular by a sinusoidal distribution along the antenna. Consequently a calculation of the field of such a current distribution gives a good approximation to the actual field of the antenna, and the total radiation of power from the antenna can be found with rather good accuracy from such a calculation. Such a calculation for the half wave antenna, which is very nearly at resonance, is particularly well known.

Let us first ask how to find the field of an arbitrary current distribution. This field, of course, could be expanded outside the distribution in a series of functions like those of (27.16). This, however, is not ordinarily the simplest way to do it. If we chose to carry such a calculation through, we should first have to expand the current distribution in a series of multipoles, beginning with electric and magnetic dipoles and including all higher multipoles, in a way familiar to physicists. We should then find by examination of (27.16) and (27.19), that each solution of the type we have set up represents the field of a particular multipole, just as we have found one solution to represent the field of an electric dipole. We then superpose these fields, with suitable coefficients derived from the expansion of the arbitrary current distribution in terms of multipoles, and the resulting sum of fields is the field of the antenna. This method is satisfactory if the dimensions of the antenna are small compared to the wave length. If they are not, however, the series proves to be very slowly convergent, or not convergent at all, so that the method is not practicable.

A substitute method of expansion can be set up, using the solution (29.8) for the field of a dipole. This is the field of a small element of current, of magnitude qd, where q and d are as in (29.4), located at the origin. We can now consider the whole current distribution to be made up of many infinitesimal current elements, located at different points of space. The field can then be made up by superposing fields like (29.8), each one radiating from a different point of space, and each one with an amplitude and phase appropriate to the current element that happens to be located at that point. This method of expansion converges very much better than the expansion in multipoles, and if we are interested only in the field at a large distance, it can be carried out by quite elementary methods. Even the field close to the antenna can be found exactly, in simple cases. This method is often set up in terms of the Hertz vector, but this is not necessary; it comes down exactly to a superposition of fields like (29.8), with different origins and amplitudes.

Let us use this method to find the limiting value of the field at large distances for a linear antenna half a wave length long, in which there is a sinusoidal distribution of current. Let the antenna extend from $z = -\lambda/4$ to $z = \lambda/4$, where its length is $\lambda/2$. Let the current at a point z be $u(z)e^{i\omega t}$, where

$$u(z) = i \cos \frac{2\pi z}{\lambda} = i \cos kz \qquad (30.1)$$

which equals i at the center of the antenna and reduces to zero at the ends. We then consider a length dz of the antenna. If this were polarized to form a dipole, the dipole moment would be

$dM\ e^{j\omega t}$, where

$$dM = q\ dz = \frac{u(z)}{j\omega}\ dz \qquad (30.2)$$

using the fact that the charge is the integral of the current. The field of this current element dz is then given by (29.8), substituting dM for the M that appears in that formula. We find the field at a point P which is so far from the dipole that only the term in $1/r$ in the field needs to be considered, and so far that the variation of θ and of $1/r$ from one part of the antenna to another can be neglected. We cannot, however, neglect the

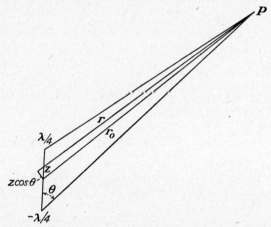

Fig. 49.—Geometrical arrangement for a half-wave antenna.

variation of phase in the fields emitted by different parts of the antenna, for this variation of phase is the essential part of the problem; it results in interference effects that are important in the final answer. From Fig. 49, we see that the distance r from a point at coordinate z, to the point P, can be approximately written

$$r = r_0 - z \cos \theta \qquad (30.3)$$

where r_0 is the distance from the center. Using (29.8), we then have for the total value of E_θ at P the value

$$E_\theta = \int_{-\lambda/4}^{\lambda/4} i \cos \frac{2\pi z}{\lambda} \frac{\sin \theta}{j\omega} \frac{k^3}{4\pi\epsilon} e^{j(\omega t - kr_0 + kz \cos \theta)} \left(\frac{-1}{kr_0}\right) dz$$

$$= \frac{j}{4\pi} \sqrt{\frac{\mu}{\epsilon}} \frac{i}{r_0} \sin \theta\ e^{j(\omega t - kr_0)} \int_{-\lambda/4}^{\lambda/4} \cos kz\ e^{jkz \cos \theta}\ k\ dz \qquad (30.4)$$

where we have used the relation $k = 2\pi/\lambda$. Writing the exponential in terms of the cosine and sine, the integral can be carried out by elementary means, and the result is

$$E_\theta = \frac{j}{2\pi} \sqrt{\frac{\mu}{\epsilon}} \frac{i}{r_0} e^{j(\omega t - kr_0)} \frac{\cos(\pi/2 \cos\theta)}{\sin\theta} \qquad (30.5)$$

It is interesting to compare this field with the one that we should have from an infinitesimal dipole of the same dipole moment as our antenna. The dipole moment of a finite distribution of charge is by definition the sum of qz for all the elements of charge, where q is the amount of charge and z its z coordinate. If ρ represents the charge per unit length along the antenna, we can then find ρ from $u(z)$ by the equation of continuity,

$$\frac{\partial\rho}{\partial t} = j\omega\rho = -e^{j\omega t}\frac{\partial u}{\partial z} = ik \sin kz e^{j\omega t} \qquad (30.6)$$

The dipole moment is then the integral of $\rho z \, dz$, or is

$$M = -jie^{j\omega t}\sqrt{\epsilon\mu}\int_{-\lambda/4}^{\lambda/4} z \sin kz \, dz$$

$$= -\frac{2jie^{j\omega t}}{\omega^2\sqrt{\epsilon\mu}} \qquad (30.7)$$

When we now substitute this value in (29.8), we find

$$E_\theta \text{ (dipole)} = \frac{j}{2\pi}\sqrt{\frac{\mu}{\epsilon}}\frac{i}{r_0}e^{j(\omega t - kr_0)}\sin\theta \qquad (30.8)$$

differing from the value (30.5) for the half wave antenna only in the function of the angle. When $\theta = \pi/2$ or is at right angles to the antenna, both functions of the angle equal unity, and the expressions (30.5) and (30.8) agree. At other angles, however, the function in (30.5) is smaller than $\sin\theta$, so that the half wave antenna radiates less than the corresponding infinitesimal dipole of the same dipole moment. This is shown in Fig. 50, where the squares of E_θ, proportional to the radiated intensity, are plotted in a polar diagram. The reason why the two cases give equal intensity at right angles, but why the half wave intenna has less intensity at other angles, is easy to see. At right angles all parts of the half wave antenna are radiating in the same phase, and there is no interference effect. At other angles, however, different parts of the half wave antenna are partly out of phase with each other, and there is an interference effect, which is responsible for the difference between the two cases.

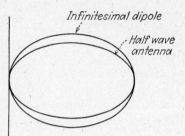

We have now found the field of our half wave antenna at distant points, and we can next calculate Poynting's vector and the total radiation from the antenna. Since $E_\theta / H_\phi = \sqrt{\mu/\epsilon}$,

Fig. 50.—Polar diagram of intensity as function of angle, for infinitesimal dipole and half-wave antenna.

the average Poynting vector in the direction θ, using (30.5), is

$$S = \frac{1}{2} \operatorname{Re} \sqrt{\frac{\epsilon}{\mu}} \, |E_\theta|^2$$

$$= \frac{i^2}{8\pi^2 r_0^2} \sqrt{\frac{\mu}{\epsilon}} \left[\frac{\cos\left(\pi/2 \cos\theta\right)}{\sin\theta} \right]^2 \qquad (30.9)$$

We may rewrite this

$$S = \frac{i^2}{8\pi^2 r_0^2} \sqrt{\frac{\mu}{\epsilon}} \, F^2(\theta) \qquad (30.10)$$

where

$$F(\theta) = \left[\frac{\cos\left(\pi/2 \cos\theta\right)}{\sin\theta} \right] \qquad (30.11)$$

Then the total radiation, found by integrating over the surface of a sphere of radius r_0, is

$$\text{Radiation} = 4\pi r_0^2 \frac{i^2}{8\pi^2 r_0^2} \sqrt{\frac{\mu}{\epsilon}} \, \overline{F^2(\theta)}$$

$$= \frac{1}{2} i^2 \frac{1}{\pi} \sqrt{\frac{\mu}{\epsilon}} \, \overline{F^2(\theta)} \qquad (30.12)$$

We remember that, if a current equal to the real part of $ie^{j\omega t}$ flows in a resistance R, the power dissipated in the resistance equals $\frac{1}{2} i^2 R$. This suggests rewriting (30.12) in the form

$$\text{Radiation} = \tfrac{1}{2} i^2 R \qquad (30.13)$$

where

$$R = \frac{1}{\pi} \sqrt{\frac{\mu}{\epsilon}} \, \overline{F^2(\theta)} \qquad (30.14)$$

Using the relations (7.24), (7.25), (7.27), we see that the quantity $1/\pi \sqrt{\mu/\epsilon}$ can be written as $376/\pi = 120$ ohms, or as $4c \times 10^{-7} = 4 \times 3 \times 10^{8} \times 10^{-7}$. Thus we have

$$R = 120\overline{F^2(\theta)} \qquad (30.15)$$

The quantity R may be called the radiation resistance of the antenna. In a later section we shall see what relation it has to the resistive component of the actual input impedance of an antenna, the quantity that is experimentally called the radiation resistance. We shall see that there are reasons to expect the two quantities to agree fairly closely, though not exactly. To find our radiation resistance, then, we must evaluate the average value $\overline{F^2(\theta)}$, where $F(\theta)$ is given in (30.11). This is a somewhat complicated integral, which cannot be evaluated by elementary means. It is discussed in Stratton.[1] Using the method described there, we find approximately

$$\overline{F^2(\theta)} = 0.612 \qquad (30.16)$$

Thus we have

$$R = 73.5 \text{ ohms} \qquad (30.17)$$

for the half wave antenna. It is interesting to note that if we had had the infinitesimal dipole, as in (30.8), the distribution of intensity in angle would have been given by a function F^2, where

$$F(\theta) = \sin \theta \qquad (30.18)$$

instead of the value of (30.11). If we find the corresponding average in that case, we have

$$\overline{\sin^2 \theta} = \tfrac{2}{3} \qquad (30.19)$$

and

$$R = 80 \text{ ohms} \qquad (30.20)$$

The value 80 ohms just derived does not actually represent the radiation resistance of an infinitesimal dipole; it is only the value that would be found for a half wave antenna, if its directional properties were like an infinitesimal dipole. It is of interest, however, to calculate the total radiation and radiation

---

[1] *Op. cit.*, p. 444. Chapter VIII of Stratton contains a more complete discussion of the antenna problem than we have given here and is an excellent résumé of what has been done, together with references to the literature.

resistance of a dipole of arbitrary length l, and sinusoidal current distribution,

$$u(z) = i \cos \frac{\pi z}{l} \tag{30.21}$$

going to a maximum in the middle, reducing to zero at the ends at $z = \pm \frac{1}{2}$. This might represent a very rough approximation to the actual behavior of a short antenna, since in that case the current would presumably have to go to zero at the ends and to a maximum in the middle. We can easily carry through with this current distribution a derivation just like that given in the preceding pages and find that the value of $F(\theta)$ is

$$\frac{2l}{\lambda} \sin \theta \frac{\cos \left(\frac{\pi}{2} \frac{2l}{\lambda} \cos \theta \right)}{1 - (2l/\lambda)^2 \cos^2 \theta} \tag{30.22}$$

For the half wave antenna, $2l/\lambda = 1$, and (30.22) reduces to the value (30.11). On the other hand, for an antenna short compared to a half wave length, (30.22) reduces to

$$F(\theta) = \frac{2l}{\lambda} \sin \theta \tag{30.23}$$

Using (30.19), we then find

$$R = \left(\frac{2l}{\lambda} \right)^2 80 \text{ ohms} \tag{30.24}$$

for the radiation resistance of an antenna of length l. This quantity, as we see, is proportional to the square of the antenna length, as we mentioned in connection with our discussion of a similar term in (29.11).

In considering the directional properties of an antenna, it is convenient to introduce a quantity called the gain. This will be particularly appropriate in later sections, where we speak of antenna systems that concentrate most of their energy in a beam surrounding a particular direction. The object of such a system is to concentrate as much of the intensity in the preferred direction as possible, with as little as possible in other directions, like a searchlight. We can define the gain of such an antenna system as the ratio of the intensity of radiation in the direction of maximum intensity, to the intensity that we should have if

the antenna emitted the same total power, but if it were uniformly distributed over all directions.   That is, it is the ratio
of the Poynting's vector in the direction of maximum intensity,
to the average Poynting's vector.   In our cases of the linear
antenna, the maximum intensity comes at $\theta = 90°$.   Thus the
gain in such cases is

$$\frac{F^2(90°)}{\overline{F^2(\theta)}} = \frac{1}{\overline{F^2(\theta)}} \qquad (30.25)$$

since in these cases $F(90°) = 1$.   For the infinitesimal dipole,
using (30.23) and (30.19), the gain is $\frac{3}{2}$; for the half wave antenna,
it is $1/0.612 = 1.63$.   Of course, these antennas are hardly
directional at all, compared to really directional systems, in
which the gain can be of the order of magnitude of several
hundred.

A final interesting problem is that of an antenna more than
a half wave length long, but with the same sinusoidal current
distribution $u(z) = i \cos 2\pi z/\lambda$ which we have assumed in (30.1)
for the half wave antenna.   This is different from the case we
have just taken up; in that one, the current distribution (30.21)
did not correspond to the wave length λ of the disturbance in
empty space but instead was shorter, in proportion to the length
of the dipole.   Such a current distribution could only be set
up in a quite artificial way.   The present case is assumed, however, to be one with the same wave length λ that we assumed in
(30.1).   For the current to be zero at the end of the antenna, we
must then have the antenna a whole number of half wave lengths
long.   If the length is m half wave lengths and m is odd, we can
use just the current distribution (30.1); if m is even, the current
must be given by the sine rather than the cosine.   When we
carry out this problem, we must carry out just the same steps as
those of (30.3) to (30.5), only with different ranges of integration.
The calculation is given by Stratton.   We find that

$$F(\theta) = \frac{\cos\left(\dfrac{m\pi}{2}\cos\theta\right)}{\sin\theta} \qquad \text{for } m \text{ odd}$$

$$= \frac{\sin\left(\dfrac{m\pi}{2}\cos\theta\right)}{\sin\theta} \qquad \text{for } m \text{ even} \qquad (30.26)$$

Polar diagrams of F^2 for various cases of m are given by Stratton. Instead of having only one loop, the polar diagram has m loops, as shown in Fig. 51, where for illustration we reproduce the case $m = 4$.   The zeros of intensity come for directions for which

$$\frac{m\pi}{2}\cos\theta = \frac{\pi}{2}, \frac{3\pi}{2}, \cdots$$

or

$$\cos\theta = \frac{1}{m}, \frac{3}{m}, \cdots \qquad \text{for } m \text{ odd}$$

$$\cos\theta = 0, \frac{2}{m}, \cdots \qquad \text{for } m \text{ even} \quad (30.27)$$

Fig. 51.
Radiation pattern of antenna four half wave lengths long.

with the maxima approximately halfway between. It is easy to show that these zeros of intensity result from interference.   At $\theta = 0$, each half wave length of the antenna radiates a wave which is 180° out of phase with the next half wave length.   At another angle, however, there will be a path difference of $(\lambda/2)\cos\theta$ between successive half wave lengths, so that the phase difference will be $2\pi(\frac{1}{2} + \frac{1}{2}\cos\theta) = \pi(1 + \cos\theta)$.   In a vector diagram, then, each half wave length of the antenna will send out a wave that can be represented by a vector of fixed length and phase $\pi(1 + \cos\theta)$.   In Fig. 52, for instance, we show the case of $m = 4$, in which we have four vectors to be added together to give the resultant disturbance, represented

Fig. 52.—Vector diagram for interference in four half wave antennas.

in the left-hand figure by the dotted line. If the figure closes, as in the square in Fig. 52, the vector sum is zero, and there is no intensity in the corresponding direction.   This comes when m times the phase difference $\pi(1 + \cos\theta)$ equals a whole multiple of 2π.   That is, it comes when

$$m(1 + \cos\theta) = 2s \qquad (30.28)$$

if s is an integer, or when

$$\cos\theta = -1 + \frac{2s}{m} \qquad (30.29)$$

This leads to the same condition as (30.27).

It has been shown by various writers[1] that the field of a finite linear antenna with a sinusoidal current distribution can be computed exactly not only at large distances, as we have done in this section, but at small distances as well. We shall not reproduce the calculation, which is somewhat involved. This allows us, however, to find the field of such an antenna on the surface of the antenna, assuming it to be a cylinder of small but finite radius. The magnetic field and the component of electric field pointing radially out from the cylinder prove to be just what we should expect them to be. Thus we know the current at each point of the cylinder, from our fundamental assumption (30.1); and the magnetic field proves to be just such as to give the correct surface current density, by the condition of continuity of H. Similarly we know the charge in each part of the cylinder from (30.6), and the normal component of E is just what we should find from the resulting surface charge. In addition to these components, however, there is also a tangential component of E, E_z, pointing along the axis of the antenna. This component proves to be given by the following formula for the half wave antenna

$$E_z = - \frac{2}{\pi \lambda} \sqrt{\frac{\mu}{\epsilon}} \, i e^{j\omega t} \frac{\cos kz + j(2kz/\pi) \sin kz}{1 - (2kz/\pi)^2} \qquad (30.30)$$

We notice that E_z has components in phase with the current (the

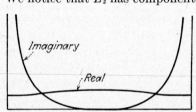

real part) and out of phase (the imaginary part). When z approaches the end of the antenna, we have $kz = \pi/2$. The denominator then goes to zero, as does $\cos kz$, and the numerator of the imaginary component stays finite. Thus the real part of E_z stays finite over the whole antenna, and

Fig. 53.—Real and imaginary parts of E_z at surface of cylindrical half wave antenna, as functions of distance along antenna.

the imaginary part becomes infinite at the ends. These components are shown in Fig. 53.

Knowing E and H at the surface of the antenna, we can compute Poynting's vector there and integrate over the surface. When we do this, we find the following result:

$$\tfrac{1}{2}\int E \times \bar{H} \, da = \tfrac{1}{2}i^2(73.5 + j42.5) \qquad (30.31)$$

[1] See Stratton, op. cit., Secs. 8.11, 8.12 for these results.

The first term is exactly the same as the radiation found earlier from the calculation at large distances. Thus the real part of (30.31), which should give the total radiation, agrees with our previous value. This must be the case, since no energy accumulates between the surface of the antenna and the large sphere on which our previous integration was made. The last term of (30.31) is not present at large distances, and this does not contradict anything. The imaginary term in Poynting's vector, or in an expression representing a power, gives the pulsating part of the energy flow, which averages to zero over a cycle. There is no reason why this has to give the same answer irrespective of where the energy flow is computed. We may, if we choose, regard the quantity 42.5 ohms in (30.31) as a reactance, since we should have $\frac{1}{2}V\bar{\imath} = \frac{1}{2}i^2Z = \frac{1}{2}i^2(R + jX)$ as the complex rate of energy production, corresponding to the quantity (30.31). We must be very suspicious of the correctness of identifying this reactance with the input reactance of the antenna, however, particularly when we remember that this quantity, unlike R, depends on the exact field in the neighborhood of the antenna, which is not accurately given by the assumptions of the present section. We merely mention these points here and shall come back to them in much more detail in the next section.

31. The Field of Metallic Antennas.—In the preceding section, we have discussed the problem of finding the radiation field of an arbitrary distribution of current, and in particular the field of a sinusoidal distribution of current in a region half a wave length long. This problem was solved correctly; but there is no reason, as far as the arguments of that section went, to suppose that it had anything to do with the field of a real metallic antenna. For in a metallic antenna, as in any conductor in electromagnetic theory, we are not at liberty to assign the currents at pleasure. Instead, we must satisfy certain boundary conditions at the surface of the conductor. We have seen that if the conductor has perfect conductivity, these conditions are very simple: E must be normal to the surface and H tangential. If the conductivity is finite, we have seen that there are small changes in these conditions, which can be neglected for a first approximation. We can now see, by reference to the preceding section, that the fields set up on the assumption of a sinusoidal current distribution certainly cannot be correct. For they led to a tangential component of electric field, E_z, as we saw in Eq. (30.30) and Fig.

53, and this definitely contradicts the boundary conditions. The contradiction is not very serious. The field of Eq. (30.30) equals $(2/\pi\lambda)\sqrt{\mu/\epsilon}\, ie^{j\omega t}$ times a geometrical factor of the order of magnitude of unity. On the other hand, the radial component of field proves to be $-j(1/2\pi r_0)\sqrt{\mu/\epsilon}\, ie^{j\omega t}$ times a geometrical factor, where r_0 is the radius of the cylindrical antenna. If r_0 is small compared to the wave length, it is clear that the normal component of field is large compared to the tangential component. Thus presumably the error in our current distribution, and hence in the magnetic field and the normal component of the electric field, is not very large in proportion; presumably it gets smaller in proportion as the antenna becomes thinner and thinner, vanishing altogether as it degenerates to a line.

How, then, can we correct our calculations? The method in principle is clear. We should solve Maxwell's equations subject

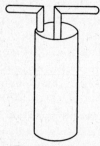

to suitable boundary conditions over the surface of the antenna, and as a result we should find both the radiation field and the current distribution. If we chose, we could take the current distribution so found and compute a radiation field by the methods of the preceding section, and the result would have to agree exactly with the radiation field found directly from Maxwell's equations. If the final, correct, current distribution differed only slightly from the sinusoidal distribution we assumed in the preceding section, the field would presumably differ only slightly also, so that our calculation of total radiation would be approximately correct, though the field would differ just enough from our calculation so that E_z would be zero.

Fig. 54.—Sketch of antenna fed by coaxial line.

Before we get far with this type of argument, we must have one thing clearly in mind: the place of the impressed electromotive force in the calculations. We can visualize things more clearly if we have an actual case in mind. Let us therefore think of an antenna fed by a coaxial transmission line. This is shown in a schematic way in Fig. 54. There are two conductors, one fixed to the center conductor and the other to the outer wall of a coaxial line. There is, of course, a large electric field between the two conductors of the coaxial line, which results in a large field between the two conductors of the antenna. As far as the fields are concerned, one can then replace the actual antenna .by a simplified model, as shown in Fig. 55. In this model, we have eliminated the coaxial line and show only the conductors making up the antenna. Electric lines of force must pass from one terminal to the other, as shown in (*a*); but at the same time it must be possible for current to flow from one terminal to the other, as it actually flows through the mechanism of the coaxial line. This can be described as in (*b*), where we have shown the conductor as extending from one terminal to the other, so as to carry current. At the same time, however, we must allow the electric lines of force to pass from one conductor to the other, just as we did in (*a*), and this means that we must

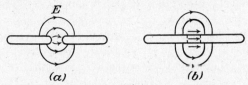

FIG. 55.—Two simplified models of antenna.

allow E to be tangential to the conductor, in the small region symbolizing the junction between the two terminals. We may, if we choose, follow the procedure of Stratton and Chu[1] and assume that there is an applied electromotive force in the small central region of (*b*), a tangential nonelectrical force just equal and opposite to the tangential component of E, and we may interpret the boundary conditions as being that the sum of E and the applied electromotive force must be normal to the surface. It is not necessary to make this interpretation, however. If we keep in mind the way in which our model of Fig. 55(*a*) or (*b*) approximates the actual situation of Fig. 54, we see that all we must do is to find a solution of Maxwell's equations that gives no tangential component of E over the actual terminals of the antenna but gives a predetermined value of tangential component over the region between the two terminals. Clearly the integral of this tangential E, from one terminal to the other, must be numerically equal to the voltage difference between the two conductors of the coaxial line of Fig. 54 and must be the voltage impressed on the antenna. Similarly the current flowing in the region between the two terminals, in Fig. 55, which of

[1] *J. Applied Phys.*, **12**, 230 (1941).

course could be measured from the tangential component of H, must be equivalent to the current flowing in the coaxial line of Fig. 54, the current flowing into one terminal and out the other. The ratio of this voltage to current is then the input impedance of the antenna, the impedance that it would have if it were regarded as a terminal impedance for the coaxial line.

Since the tangential component of E is zero over the surface of the antenna, except in the region where the impressed electromotive force is located, it is obvious that the normal component of Poynting's vector must likewise be zero except in this region. That is, no power flows out of the antenna into space, in marked contrast to the approximate solution, in which we have seen, as in Eq. (30.31), that the normal component of Poynting's vector integrates to a quite definite value. We naturally ask then, does this result of (30.31) have any physical significance, and if so, why? This contrast between the approximate solution and the correct one, in the matter of Poynting's vector, is one which has been understood only recently. It is brought out clearly, for instance, in the papers previously quoted.[1] These papers handle the problem by various essentially correct methods, which we shall describe presently. The results, however, are not very different from (30.31), and it becomes a question of much interest to ask why that approximate treatment works as well as it does, whether there is a fundamental reason behind it, or whether it is pure coincidence.

There seems every reason to believe that the resistance component of the impedance, as found in (30.31), should really represent the input resistance of a real antenna, to a better and better approximation as the antenna becomes thinner and thinner, approaching the ideal linear antenna assumed in the derivation of (30.31). The reason is simple. If i is the input current into an antenna (peak value), then the power input, which must equal the radiated power, has the average value of $\frac{1}{2}i^2R$, where R by definition is the radiation resistance. We could find this radiated power by integrating the normal component of Poynting's vector over any closed surface surrounding the antenna. If the surface coincided with the surface of the antenna, Poynting's vector would be zero except in the short

[1] Stratton and Chu, *J. Applied Phys.*, **12**, 230 (1941); Schelkunoff, *Proc. I.R.E.*, **29**, 493 (1941).

region of the electromotive force, where the tangential component of E was not zero. In that region, the tangential component of E would be connected with the voltage, and the tangential component of H with the current, in an obvious way, so that the integral would come out to give $\frac{1}{2}$ Re $V\bar{\imath}$ directly, which would equal $\frac{1}{2}i^2R$. The same answer would have to be obtained from any other surface, however, and in particular for a surface at a large distance from the antenna. Now (30.17) was found by just such an integration over a very large sphere, on the assumption of a sinusoidal current in the antenna. We have seen that, although this assumption is not right, as we observe from the fact that it incorrectly gives a tangential component of E along the whole surface of the antenna instead of a large tangential component in the center section of the antenna and none elsewhere, still it is not very wrong, in that the tangential component is not very large anyway and becomes smaller in proportion to the normal component as the antenna becomes thinner and thinner. The correct current, then, will depart from the sinusoidal value by a smaller and smaller amount as the antenna becomes thinner. The difference between the actual current distribution and a sinusoidal distribution must give a field which, on the surface of the antenna, just cancels the tangential component of E given in (30.30) and replaces it by the correct value, concentrated in a small region about the center of the antenna. This is not a very big change, in proportion to the field as a whole, and it seems reasonable to think that at large distances this additional current would make only a small correction to the field, and hence to the integral of Poynting's vector.

This argument makes it plausible, then, that the calculation of radiated power made in (30.31) for the sinusoidal current should be a fairly good approximation to the value for a real antenna, so that the radiation resistance of 73.5 ohms for the half wave antenna should be a good approximation to the real value. This of course is not a really valid demonstration of the value, or anything of that sort; it is intended merely to make it reasonable if the correct calculations give values in this neighborhood, as they do, rather than making it look like a pure coincidence. When it comes to the reactive part of the input impedance of a half wave antenna, however, the argument for the value 42.5 ohms of (30.31) is much weaker. The term in the integrated Poynting vector corresponding to this represents the pulsating power, flowing out of the antenna for a half cycle, back during the other half cycle. The corresponding energy is located in the immediate neighborhood of the antenna, so that this term cannot be found by integrating over a large sphere; the value of the integral is different for each possible surface of integration. Since the field close up will presumably be decidedly different in the actual case from what it is in the case of the sinusoidal current distribution, we might expect this pulsating energy to be decidedly different in the two cases, so that the value 42.5 ohms for the reactance of a half wave dipole might be rather seriously in error. As a matter of fact, values of this quantity determined by accurate methods are not very different from the value of 42.5 ohms, so that our misgivings are not too well justified.

Now that we have gone into the relations between a correct calculation and the approximation based on the sinusoidal current distribution, let us look at the various methods of getting exact results. The two most successful methods are those of Stratton and Chu, and of Schelkunoff, whose papers have already been quoted. The method of Stratton and Chu approximates an actual antenna by a thin spheroidal conductor, which can become thinner and thinner, approximating more and more closely to the linear case. They solve the wave equation in spheroidal coordinates, in which a whole family of solutions is possible, in analogy to the family of solutions that we found in Sec. 27 in the case of spherical coordinates. By superposing a series of such solutions, they can satisfy boundary conditions on the surface of the spheroidal conductor, and they choose the coefficients of this series in such a way as to give a vanishing tangential component of electric field everywhere except in the region where the electromotive force is located. By integrating Poynting's vector over the surface of the conductor, they can then find both the radiated and the reactive power, and hence both real and imaginary components of the radiation impedance of the antennas. This represents an exact solution of the problem they have attacked, accurate to the extent to which the series converge. They find curves for resistance and reactance as a function of impressed frequency, or as a function of antenna size for a fixed frequency, for spheroids of arbitrary eccentricity. These results are thus very valuable in that they give exact solutions of a problem similar to the one actually met in practice. Of course, real antennas are not ordinarily of spheroidal shape; certainly the antenna of Fig. 55 is not. Nevertheless, it is probable that the approximations involved in replacing an actual antenna by a spheroid of comparable size, and using the solution of Stratton and Chu, are no greater than approximations met in other ways in the other types of attack on the problem. One drawback in the solution of Stratton and Chu is that the calculations have to be entirely numerical, and it is hard to visualize the results and get any further understanding of the problem from them. For this reason, we shall take up first the method of Schelkunoff, which is easier to understand, though probably less accurate. Then we shall come back later to a comparison of the numerical results of the two theories.

Schelkunoff's fundamental idea is to replace the two branches of an antenna like that shown in Figs. 54 and 55, by the two segments of a biconical horn, like that of Fig. 47, cut off at a finite length. The angular openings of the two segments of the horn are made small, so as to approximate the thin cylinders that often form an antenna. As we see from (28.7), there is a singularity of electric field at the origin, resulting in a finite voltage, given by (28.8), between the two conductors, at the origin. This singularity takes the place of the tangential field that we have interpreted as an electromotive force in Fig. 55. The two cones then form a transmission line, fed at the center and leading to propagation outward of a wave along both conductors, as we saw in Sec. 28. The equivalent characteristic impedance of this transmission line, as we see in (28.11), has a value depending on the flare angle of the cone, becoming infinite as the cone becomes infinitely narrow.

An actual antenna differs from the transmission line of Sec. 28 in that it is of finite rather than infinite length. Thus the principal wave by itself will not satisfy the boundary conditions in all parts of space, and we must instead superpose many types of spherical waves to solve the problem. Schelkunoff imagines a sphere drawn about the antenna, as in Fig. 56, such that the cones and sections of the sphere bound the antenna. He then considers that the sphere forms essentially a junction between two transmission lines of different properties: within the sphere we have the cone and essentially the principal wave; outside the sphere there is no conductor and the principal wave is impossible. He then builds up a solution as follows:

1. Inside the sphere, he assumes not only a principal wave traveling outward, but also a reflected principal wave of adjustable phase and amplitude, traveling inward from the sphere, which is regarded as a reflecting surface. At the same time, he assumes a superposition of all other types of wave that can be set up satisfying the boundary conditions at the surface of the cone.

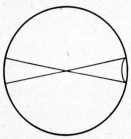

These other waves decrease in amplitude very rapidly, as we pass in from the sphere toward the origin, and take the place of the attenuated reflected waves which, as we have seen in Sec. 24, must be assumed in the problem of reflection at a discontinuity in properties of a hollow pipe. Over most of the length of the antenna, then, the disturbance consists of a direct and a reflected principal wave, but these attenuated waves build up to a considerable importance near the spherical surface.

Fig. 56.—Sphere bounding conical antenna.

2. Outside the sphere, there is no principal wave. Schelkunoff then superposes all types of spherical waves of the suitable symmetry, the field of an electric dipole being a leading term. He then applies joining conditions to make the fields inside and outside the sphere join smoothly at the spherical surface. It is not practicable to apply these conditions entirely rigorously; as a result of this, the whole calculation is not exact, though it forms a good approximation.

As far as the principal wave is concerned, the antenna behaves like a transmission line terminated by some definite impedance; one must use this impedance and the characteristic impedance of the line in the reflection equations to find the amplitude and phase of the reflected wave. When this reflected wave is known, we can then find the impedance of the line at the input end, using the ordinary transmission line equations for impedance at an arbitrary point. This gives us both input resistance and reactance of the antenna. Schelkunoff's calculation finds the terminal impedance that must be assumed to get the correct results from such a transmission line theory. The terminal impedance, unlike the situation in simple lines, is not independent of the length of line. Rather it is a function varying in a more or less periodic fashion with the length of line. That this variation does not change the general characteristics of the problem is shown, however, by the curve of Fig. 57, where we show a resistance-reactance curve for a particular cone angle, as a function of the length of the antenna. We see that, for lengths greater than a half wave length, the curve is much like the circles found in Chap. I for the resistance-reactance diagram of an attenuationless line. The principal difference is that the circle

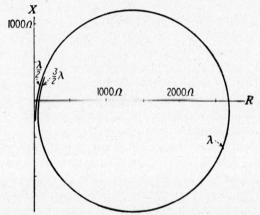

FIG. 57.—Resistance and reactance curve for conical antenna of characteristic resistance 750 ohms, as function of length; taken from Schelkunoff's curves of *R* and *X* as functions of length.

is displaced downward, so that its center lies below the real axis. Increase of length of the antenna by a half wave length corresponds to increase of the transmission line by a quarter wave length, and carries us halfway around the circle.

It would seem plausible at first sight that the effective terminal impedance that should be used to terminate the line should be infinite, resulting in zero current at the end of the antenna. There are several ways of seeing that this is wrong, however. In the first place, it would give a reflection coefficient of unity. Then the reflected principal wave would carry back all the power carried out in the direct principal wave, and there would be no radiated power. Actually, the reflected wave must have smaller amplitude than the direct wave, the difference accounting for the radiation. We see immediately that the current distribution in the antenna cannot be sinusoidal, in the half wave case, with a current node at the end, as is assumed in Sec. 30. For the sinusoidal distribution would be obtained by superposing a direct and reflected wave of equal amplitude and proper phase relation. As a matter of fact, since the reflected wave has a smaller amplitude than the direct wave, the total disturbance is not a pure standing wave at all.

If the direct and reflected waves do not have equal amplitudes, there will not be a current node at the end of the antenna. At first sight this seems paradoxical. One naturally asks where the current goes to. The answer is simple, however. Toward the end of the antenna, the attenuated waves come in, and they furnish components of the current, which add to the current carried by the principal waves, to give a total current of zero. This is the condition assumed by Schelkunoff; it is not obvious, however, that it is correct, though at first sight it would seem to be. The reason is that the end of the antenna is a circular area, which has a certain capacity. Charge will then flow to and away from this end, resulting in a current at the end of the conical part of the antenna, though of course not at the center of the circular end. This effect, which can be considerable with a conical antenna of wide flare angle, or in the corresponding case of a rather thick cylindrical antenna, is very difficult to compute directly. The only antenna calculation in which it seems to be correctly taken into account is that of Stratton and Chu on the spheroidal antenna, in which there is no sharp boundary between the sides and ends of the antenna, and the current reduces to zero only at the center of the end.

In addition to the arguments we have already used, we can see that the effective terminal impedance of the antenna is finite rather than infinite by looking directly at the resistance-reactance curve of Fig. 57. The part of this curve for lengths less than a half wave length is quite different in character from the circular part of the curve, representing greater lengths. Let us consider this circular portion. At the point marked λ in Fig. 57, the antenna is a wave length long, or the equivalent transmission line is a half wave length. Thus by ordinary transmission line theory the input impedance of such a transmission line should, neglecting attenuation, equal its output impedance. The impedance at the point marked λ, then, gives an idea of the order of magnitude of the output impedance of the antenna (only an idea of order of magnitude, for as we have mentioned we must assume the output impedance to be a periodic function of line length, rather than a constant). As we see, the output impedance is large, but by no means infinite.

Other features of Fig. 57 are of interest. First let us consider the case where the antenna length is less than a half wave length. Then, as Fig. 57 shows, the impedance starts for very short antennas as a very large capacitive reactance. With increasing length the reactance becomes more inductive, becoming zero at a length slightly less than a half wave length, the resonant point. At the same time the resistive component is increasing with the length of the antenna. We saw in Eq. (29.11) that even the very simple model of the electric dipole showed a behavior of impedance as a function of dimensions, which was qualitatively of this form. Next let us see how the impedance behaves for approximately a half wave dipole. From Schelkunoff's curves one can find the resistance and reactance of a half wave dipole, and the values prove to be not very far from the values $73.5 + j42.5$ ohms of Eq. (30.31), though by no means exactly equal to them. The values of course depend on the characteristic impedance of the line, or the flare angle of the cone, though at a half wave length the variation with flare angle is less than at most other lengths. From Fig. 57 it is clear that if it is desired to have the input impedance of the antenna a pure resistance, its length must be slightly less than a half wave length. At this value, the admittance of the antenna (the reciprocal of the length of the radius vector from the origin to the resistance-reactance curve of Fig. 57) is very close to its maximum value, so that an antenna should be made of about this length to develop maximum power in an antenna fed with a given voltage. In microwave work, antennas are almost always designed to operate with this resonant wave length. This is in partial contrast to long wave work, where a half wave dipole can sometimes become inconveniently large, and a shorter antenna is used. In that case the capacitive reactance of the antenna must be balanced out by some lumped circuit-tuning device, if it is desired to have a high admittance.

We note that the approximately half wave resonant antenna is a selective device, tuned for the frequency for which it is designed but not for other frequencies.   It is interesting to see how the Q value of the antenna is to be determined from the curve of Fig. 57. Q is the ratio of the frequency difference between the two points where the power has half its maximum value, to the resonant frequency.   This plainly depends on the behavior of the admittance as a function of frequency at constant antenna length (or, what is essentially the same thing, the admittance as a function of antenna length at constant frequency).   This in turn depends greatly on the flare angle of the cones, or on the thickness of the conductors of the antenna. For a very thin antenna, the characteristic impedance is very high, and the circular pattern of Fig. 57 is on a very large scale, extending out thousands of ohms along the real axis, as in the case shown in Fig. 57.   On the other hand, for a large flare angle, or a thick antenna, such as is more common in microwave work, the characteristic impedance is low and the circle is much smaller than shown in Fig. 57.   The curves for different thicknesses of antennas, however, all have their first resonance in the same neighborhood, with the resistance not very far from 73.5 ohms, and the length not much less than a half wave length.   We now see that for a thin antenna, a given proportional change of frequency will carry us the same fraction of the distance around the circle as for a thick antenna.   This means a much greater absolute distance, however.   The square of the admittance, which gives the resonance curve whose width is used to find the Q value, equals $1/(R^2 + X^2)$.   In the neighborhood of the first resonance, we see from Fig. 57 that R changes rather slowly with frequency and that X is zero at resonance and changes much more rapidly with frequency.   The half maximum of the curve, then, comes approximately when X equals R.   We have just seen that for a very thin antenna, this will come about with a relatively small frequency change from resonance; with a thick antenna the frequency change must be much greater.   In other words, a thin antenna has a high Q value, a thick antenna a relatively small Q value, so that a thick antenna is not nearly so selective as a thin one.   For antennas as thick as those used in microwave work, the Q value may be as low as 10, so that the selectivity of such an antenna is not serious, if it is to be used for frequencies that do not differ a great deal fractionally from the value for which the antenna was designed.

We have been speaking mostly about Schelkunoff's theory of the conical antenna. In his paper he also gives formulas for antennas of cylindrical and other forms, handled as transmission lines of slowly varying constants. Although these formulas are useful for computation, they do not indicate any striking qualitative difference from the conical case, and for that reason we shall not discuss them here. The reader is referred to Schelkunoff's paper for the details. Similarly the work of Stratton and Chu on spheroidal antennas, previously referred to, leads

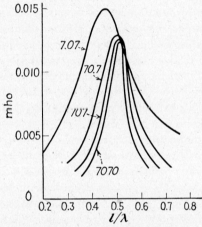

Fig. 58.—Input admittance of spheroidal antennas as function of ratio of antenna length to wave length. Numbers 7.07, etc., give ratio of length of antenna to maximum diameter. (*From Stratton and Chu.*)

to results qualitatively similar to the results we have just been discussing. Since their results are only numerical, without much possibility of qualitative understanding, it is hard to give anything more in an account of this sort than a statement that qualitatively the agreement with the theory we have just discussed is good, and there are few conspicuous qualitative features that are new in the discussion. One interesting qualitative point is that as the spheroid becomes thicker and thicker, more and more like a sphere, the circlelike figure of Fig. 57 not only becomes smaller, as it would for the conical antenna, but also becomes more and more depressed, so that for the sphere itself the curve never cuts the real axis. The reactance stays capacitive for all frequencies, or all antenna sizes, and there is no true resonance at all. In spite of this, of course the admittance goes through a maximum value, so that there is a preferred size of antenna for maximum power output. As for numerical results of Stratton and Chu's theory, they are tabulated graphically in their paper in a convenient form. We give in Fig. 58 one quantity which they do not plot, though it can be found easily from their curves. This is the magnitude of the admittance, as a function of the length of the antenna. Curves for different thicknesses of antenna are given in Fig. 58. It is seen that the maximum admittance comes in each case for slightly less than a half wave length, but the resonant length is considerably smaller for the very thick antennas. This feature is also found in Schelkunoff's theory. It is of interest in microwave antenna design, since they are usually thick, and the length for maximum admittance can well be as small as 0.45 wave lengths. We also notice in Fig. 58 how much sharper the curves become for the thinner antennas, checking our previous statement that thin antennas had higher Q values than thick ones.

32. The Magnetic Dipole Antenna.—In the preceding sections we have been speaking of antennas whose field to a first approximation was not very different from the electric dipole discussed in Sec. 29. This is the most important type of antenna for most purposes. However, there are cases where we are interested in radiation or absorption by wire loops. The most familiar example of this is the coupling loop used to introduce energy into or remove it from resonant cavities. Although such a loop behaves rather differently in a cavity from its behavior in empty space, still it is worth while understanding its behavior as a radiator. A current loop acts like a small solenoid and produces at neighboring points a field like a small magnetic dipole. Thus we may expect that the field of such a loop will resemble the field of an electric dipole, as given in (29.3), but with the magnetic and electric fields interchanged. This is in fact the case. Our electric dipole solution was the simplest TM wave; similarly the magnetic dipole is the simplest TE wave. By methods similar to those of Sec. 29, we can give the field components in terms of the magnetic dipole moment.

By methods like those used in deriving Eq. (29.8), we find that the field of a magnetic dipole of moment $Me^{j\omega t}$ is

$$H_r = \frac{Mk^3}{4\pi} e^{j(\omega t - kr)} \cos\theta \left(\frac{2j}{(kr)^2} + \frac{2}{(kr)^3} \right)$$

$$H_\theta = \frac{Mk^3}{4\pi} e^{j(\omega t - kr)} \sin\theta \left(\frac{-1}{kr} + \frac{j}{(kr)^2} + \frac{1}{(kr)^3} \right)$$

$$E_\phi = -\frac{j\omega\mu Mk^2}{4\pi} e^{j(\omega t - kr)} \sin\theta \left(\frac{j}{kr} + \frac{1}{(kr)^2} \right) \tag{32.1}$$

As in (29.11), it is interesting to find the ratio of transverse components of E and H, since this quantity has some resemblance to the actual input impedance of an antenna. Proceeding as in the derivation of (29.11), we have

$$-\frac{E_\phi}{H_\theta} = j\omega\mu r + \sqrt{\frac{\mu}{\epsilon}} (kr)^4 \cdots \tag{32.2}$$

The first term is an ordinary inductive type of reactance, proportional to the frequency and to the linear dimension, as the inductance of a loop would be. The second term is the radiation resistance term, which is here proportional to the fourth power of frequency and linear dimensions, rather than to the square of these quantities as in the electric dipole case. There is no capacitive reactance in this simple case. Actually a coupling loop would not have capacitive reactance, except for the fact that it is ordinarily fed from some form of transmission line, and the sharp changes in direction

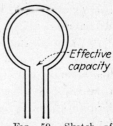

Fig. 59.—Sketch of magnetic dipole antenna.

of the conductors, as indicated in Fig. 59, would act somewhat like a condenser.

There does not seem to have been nearly so much work devoted to the theory of the finite loop antenna as to the electric dipole antenna. For coupling loops, however, this is hardly necessary, since such loops are generally made small compared to the wave length. Even for this problem, as far as the writer knows, there has not been any good investigation of the reactive part of the input impedance of such an antenna in free space. As would be suggested by Eq. (32.2), we should expect the reactive impedance to be an inductive reactance, which would reduce at low frequencies to the inductive reactance of the loop as computed by ordinary quasi-stationary arguments. We should probably not be too much in error in extrapolating this inductance up to the frequencies actually used in coupling loops. As far as the radiation resistance is concerned, a value can be easily found by computing the energy loss by integrating Poynting's vector over a very large sphere, as was done in Sec. 30 in the electric case. Suppose we have a loop of radius R_0, carrying a current i in the wire. Then the equivalent magnetic moment is

$$M = \pi R_0^2 i \qquad (32.3)$$

the current times the area, or the strength of the equivalent magnetic shell. We can substitute this in (32.1) and find the field in terms of the current. We then compute the radial component of Poynting's vector, integrate over a sphere, and find for the power dissipated per second

$$W = \frac{\pi}{12} \sqrt{\frac{\mu}{\epsilon}} (kR_0)^4 i^2 \qquad (32.4)$$

Setting this equal to $\frac{1}{2} i^2 R$, where R is the radiation resistance, we have

$$R = \frac{\pi}{6} \sqrt{\frac{\mu}{\epsilon}} (kR_0)^4 \qquad (32.5)$$

The resemblance of this formula to the simple one (32.2) derived from the ratio of E to H is obvious. If we wish to express k in terms of the wave length and use the value 376 ohms for $\sqrt{\mu/\epsilon}$, we find

$$R = 3.075 \times 10^5 \left(\frac{R_0}{\lambda}\right)^4 \text{ ohms} \qquad (32.6)$$

For small loops, this gives a fairly small resistance; thus for R_0 equal to about a tenth wave length, R would be 30 ohms. Presumably at high enough frequencies there would be a resonance, the capacitive reactance indicated in Fig. 59 canceling the inductive reactance of the loop. With loops small compared to a wave length, however, we are far from this situation, and it is not necessary to consider resonance in the same way that it is for an electric dipole. For the magnetic dipole, unlike the electric dipole, the impedance is low and the admittance high, at low frequencies or for small antennas. Thus small loops can be effectively used, whereas electric dipoles shorter than the resonant value near a half wave length have such small admittance that they cannot be used without some sort of tuning device, as we mentioned in the preceding section.

CHAPTER VI

DIRECTIVE DEVICES FOR ANTENNAS

In the preceding chapter we were treating the radiation from simple antennas. This radiation was not very directive. For a half wave antenna, we saw in Fig. 50, that radiation was intense in all directions except in the neighborhood of the axis of the antenna; even for longer antennas, as we illustrated in Fig. 51, although the radiation pattern is more complicated, the energy is not concentrated in a single direction. One of the principal advantages of microwaves is, however, the fact that the waves can be directed in a rather sharp beam. In this chapter we shall take up some ways of accomplishing this purpose. The possibility of directing short waves depends on their resemblance to optical waves. A source of light placed at the focus of a parabolic mirror, for instance, forms a parallel beam and can be used like a searchlight. The width of this beam is limited among other things by diffraction. The parabolic mirror has a finite aperture, and the radiation reflected from it is effectively transmitted through an aperture of the size of the mirror. It is known from optics that if the aperture is many wave lengths in diameter diffraction is unimportant; if the aperture is of the same order of magnitude as the wave length, the beam will spread out broadly. Short microwaves become short enough so that it is practicable to have parabolic reflectors a number of wave lengths across and hence practicable to reduce the diffraction effects to reasonable magnitude. The present chapter deals with the problem of setting up directive devices of desired character, to take the radiation from a simple antenna and transform it into a concentrated beam.

33. Absorption and Scattering by a Dipole.—We shall begin our discussion by taking up a problem which at first sight might seem unrelated to our main interest. We shall consider a plane wave falling on a dipole and setting it into vibration, so that it both absorbs and scatters energy. This problem is interesting in one way: it furnishes a simple model for the behavior of a real

235

antenna as an absorber of energy, rather than as an emitter. But it also has close connection with our problem of directive devices. Most such devices, such as dummy antennas and reflectors, consist of conductors placed near the antenna and not directly fed with any source of power. They serve to scatter the radiation reaching them from the antenna, and the scattered radiation interferes with the direct radiation from the antenna to form the radiation pattern.

Our present problem is the simplest one in scattering. We assume a plane wave to fall on a dipole; later, in the director problem, we shall have to take a spherical wave from one source, falling on a conductor and making it into a source on its own account. We next ask how the dipole behaves under the action of the field. This is a problem that cannot be solved without making assumptions about the dynamical behavior of a dipole. It must act like a resonant circuit, if we use electrical analogies, or like a mechanical particle held by linear restoring forces, if we use mechanical analogies, so that when it is acted on by a sinusoidal force, it is set into forced vibrations with a definite amplitude and phase, determined by the effective inductance, resistance, and capacity of the dipole. Finally we must take the oscillating dipole and consider the radiation emitted by it, and the energy balance, as determined by Poynting's vector. Before going through the analysis, it will be helpful if we describe in words just what the situation is.

FIG. 60.— Model of simplified dipole.

Suppose for the sake of definiteness we imagine a small dipole built as in Fig. 60. It is assumed to consist of conductors at top and bottom, forming a condenser of capacity C, and a wire connecting them, with inductance L and resistance R. The length of the dipole is assumed to be d. We shall assume this length to be small compared to the wave length. The incident wave is assumed to have an electric vector along the axis of the dipole, which we may take to be the x axis. The direction of propagation of the incident wave must be at right angles to x, say along the z axis. The frequency of the incident wave is assumed to be arbitrary. We are interested in the frequency variation of the scattering and absorption. The dipole, since it forms an oscillating circuit, has a natural frequency, at which it resonates. As the external frequency approaches this natural frequency, the amplitude of the oscillating dipole increases, becoming large at the natural frequency. The dipole, on account of this oscillation, itself emits a spherical wave, as described in the preceding chapter. It is now interesting to consider Poynting's vector. The field consists of two parts: the incident plane wave and the spherical wave. Since Poynting's vector is a quadratic expression, there will be three sorts of terms in it. There are the terms in which the E and H of the plane wave both appear, those in which the E and H of the spherical wave both appear, and finally cross terms, the product of the E of the plane wave by the H of the spherical wave, or vice versa.

To investigate energy flow, we should integrate each type of term from Poynting's vector over a sphere or other closed surface

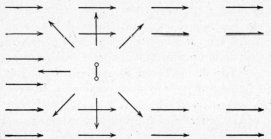

Fig. 61.—Schematic diagram of scattering and absorption of energy by a dipole.

surrounding the dipole. The plane wave terms will integrate to zero. As much energy flows out of the far side of the sphere as flows in the near side. The spherical wave terms will give an outflow of energy, just as if the dipole were radiating on account of any other form of excitation. The interesting and new terms are the cross terms between plane wave and spherical wave. We shall find that these terms give a net inflow of energy into the dipole, more than enough to compensate the energy lost in its own spherical radiation. The excess of energy inflow over outflow of course supplies the energy used up in heat in the resistance of the dipole. It is interesting not only to find the amount of this inflow of energy into the dipole but to see where the flow is located in space. The easiest way to describe it is to say that the dipole casts a shadow. In Fig. 61, we show schematically the way Poynting's vector behaves in this case. The plane wave is supposed to approach from the left, as is indicated by the horizontal arrows. Superposed on this incident wave is the outward spherical wave, indicated by the arrows pointing out from the dipole. But in the direction to the right of the dipole, the shadow, the incident plane wave, and the scattered wave travel in the same direction. In this case, interference effects are possible; and these effects prove to be just such as to cancel the effect of the incident radiation, the scattered wave being of opposite phase to the incident wave. The cancellation is not complete, and there is no sharply defined shadow. Nevertheless the cross terms in Poynting's vector represent a decrease of intensity compared to the sum of the intensities in the incident and scattered waves, and located in the region that we have described as the shadow.

We can then describe the situation in the following way. The incident plane wave strikes the dipole, and a certain amount of the energy is stopped by the dipole and removed from the incident beam. We can describe the amount stopped by giving the dipole a fictitious cross-sectional area, such that the amount of energy removed from the beam would be the amount that we should find falling on the cross-sectional area, if we calculated according to geometrical optics. We shall find this effective area to be of the order of magnitude of the square of the wave length. The energy removed from the beam is divided into two parts. One part is reradiated or scattered, in a spherical wave. The other part is absorbed, going into the heating of the resistance.

It is natural to ask next, what determines the relative amounts of energy scattered and absorbed. We shall find that in the equation of motion of the dipole, we must assume as a resistance the sum of two terms: the ordinary ohmic resistance of the conductor and the radiation resistance, computed as in the preceding chapter. Let us call these R_0 and R_r respectively, so that R, the total resistance, will be the sum of R_0 and R_r. The power input into the dipole from the external wave, which acts as an applied e.m.f., will be $\frac{1}{2}i^2(R_0 + R_r)$, of which the part $\frac{1}{2}i^2R_0$ goes into absorption, and $\frac{1}{2}i^2R_r$ into scattering. Thus the relative amount of absorption and scattering depends on the relative values of R_0 and R_r. For different purposes we wish to adjust these relative values in different ways. Thus if we are using the dipole as an absorbing antenna, we wish the absorption to have the maximum possible value, for a given input voltage. We shall find easily that this is accomplished when R_0 equals R_r. In this case, of course, R_0 is to represent the input impedance of the line inserted into the antenna and coupling it to the receiving apparatus; we assume actual ohmic resistance in the antenna to be negligible. For maximum power absorption by the antenna, in other words, the antenna should be matched to the line, each having a resistance R_r equal to the radiation resistance of the antenna. On the other hand, if we are using the dipole as a dummy antenna in a directive array, we are interested only in the scattering and wish to minimize absorption. In this case obviously the ohmic resistance R_0 should be made as small as possible. For the absorbing dipole, since R_0 equals R_r, the absorbed energy and scattered energy will be equal, while for the scattering dummy antenna, the absorption will be negligible compared to the scattering. The scattering cannot be made to vanish under any conditions.

With this qualitative description of the results, we can now go on to the mathematical treatment. As a first step, let us take a dipole at the origin, with dipole moment $Me^{i\omega t}$ in the x direction, and a plane wave with field components equal to

$$E_x = E_0 e^{i(\omega t - kz)}, \qquad H_y = \sqrt{\frac{\epsilon}{\mu}}\, E_0 e^{i(\omega t - kz)} \qquad (33.1)$$

and investigate Poynting's vector for this field. Later we shall find what M must be equal to, if the dipole is acted on by the plane wave, regarded as an impressed e.m.f. It is obvious without proof that the integral of the normal component of Poynting's vector over a closed surface, for the plane wave alone, is zero; the proof is not difficult, if one wants to give it. For the spherical wave alone, the integral has been computed in Eq. (29.10). This leaves only the cross terms to be computed. We shall find these terms on the surface of a sphere of radius r large compared to the wave length. On this sphere, using Eq. (29.8), we may take the leading terms of the field components, finding

$$E_\theta = -\frac{Mk^2}{4\pi\epsilon} \frac{e^{i(\omega t - kr)}}{r} \sin\theta$$

$$H_\phi = -\sqrt{\frac{\epsilon}{\mu}} \frac{Mk^2}{4\pi\epsilon} \frac{e^{i(\omega t - kr)}}{r} \sin\theta \qquad (33.2)$$

We shall now find that the essential contributions to the cross term of Poynting's vector all come from a small region of the sphere surrounding the point where the z axis cuts it; that is, they come from the region of the shadow, as shown in Fig. 61. It is convenient to introduce new coordinates on the surface of the sphere, near this point. These are shown in Fig. 62. They amount to a set of polar coordinates on the surface of the sphere. The angles θ, ϕ are the ordinary polar coordinate angles for the spherical polar coordinates having x as the axis, and suitable for considering the radiation from the dipole. We have indicated another set of polar coordinates, however, with the z axis as axis, and they are the ones that we shall use. In place of the usual

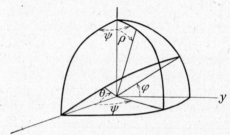

Fig. 62.—Polar coordinates for scattering problem.

colatitude angle like θ, we shall use the distance ρ, measured along the surface of the sphere; this quantity equals r times the colatitude angle. The azimuth angle of these coordinates will be denoted by ψ. We shall find that the essential region is in the immediate neighborhood of the pole, or for small values of ρ, and for these values the curvature of the sphere is unimportant, so that we can approximately consider ρ and ψ to be polar coordinates in the tangent plane to the sphere.

In the immediate neighborhood of $\rho = 0$, we have $\sin \theta = 1$, and E_θ becomes equivalent to $-E_x$, H_ϕ to $-H_y$. Thus the field components of the dipole, which we may call E_1 and H_1, become in this neighborhood

$$E_{x1} = \frac{Mk^2}{4\pi\epsilon} \frac{e^{j(\omega t - kr)}}{r}, \qquad H_{y1} = \sqrt{\frac{\epsilon}{\mu}} \frac{Mk^2}{4\pi\epsilon} \frac{e^{j(\omega t - kr)}}{r} \qquad (33.3)$$

To find the field components of the plane wave, which we may denote by subscript zero, we must find z in terms of our polar coordinates. We have at once

$$z = r\left(1 - \cos\frac{\rho}{r}\right) = r\left[1 - \frac{1}{2}\left(\frac{\rho}{r}\right)^2 \cdots\right]$$

$$= r - \frac{1}{2}\frac{\rho^2}{r} \cdots \tag{33.4}$$

for small values of ρ. Thus the field components of the plane wave are

$$E_{x0} = E_0 e^{j(\omega t - kr)} e^{jk\rho^2/2r}$$

$$H_{y0} = \sqrt{\frac{\epsilon}{\mu}}\, E_0 e^{j(\omega t - kr)} e^{jk\rho^2/2r} \tag{33.5}$$

The cross terms of Poynting's vector are then

$$S_{01} = \frac{1}{2}\,\text{Re}\,(E_{x0}\bar{H}_{y1} + E_{x1}\bar{H}_{y0})$$

$$= \frac{1}{2}\,\text{Re}\,\sqrt{\frac{\epsilon}{\mu}}\,\frac{k^2}{4\pi\epsilon}\,\frac{1}{r}\,(E_0\bar{M}e^{jk\rho^2/2r} + \bar{E}_0 M e^{-jk\rho^2/2r}) \tag{33.6}$$

To get the integrated Poynting's vector, we must integrate this quantity over the surface of the sphere. For small ρ, the surface element is the area between circles of radius ρ and $\rho + d\rho$, or is $2\pi\rho\, d\rho$. We wish, then, integrals of the form

$$2\pi\int e^{\pm jk\rho^2/2r}\rho\, d\rho \tag{33.7}$$

We note that this can be rewritten

$$\frac{2\pi}{2}\int e^{\pm jk\rho^2/2r}d(\rho^2) = \mp\frac{2\pi jr}{k}\,e^{\pm jk\rho^2/2r} \tag{33.8}$$

taken between suitable limits. The lower limit is $\rho = 0$. We must consider the upper limit, however. We have made a number of approximations which are good only for small ρ. For this region, as we see from (33.8), the integral varies sinusoidally with ρ^2. As ρ^2 becomes very large, it does not approach any definite limit. However, actually the terms we have neglected in the integrand have the effect of making the oscillations of the function $e^{jk\rho^2/2r}$ gradually decrease, as if for instance there were a small factor $e^{-a\rho^2}$ multiplying the complex exponential. If there were such a term, it would also appear in the integral, leaving the same value as in (33.8) at the lower limit but giving zero for the upper limit. More careful examination of the problem shows that the upper limit of the integral really should be set equal to zero, as this suggests. The integral then becomes

$$\pm\frac{2\pi jr}{k} \tag{33.9}$$

so that we have

$$\int S_{01}\, da = \frac{1}{2} \operatorname{Re} \sqrt{\frac{\epsilon}{\mu}} \frac{k^2}{4\pi\epsilon} \frac{1}{r} \frac{2\pi j r}{k} (E_0 \bar{M} - \bar{E}_0 M) \quad (33.10)$$

We may without loss of generality take E_0 to be real.   Then this becomes

$$\int S_{01}\, da = \tfrac{1}{2}\omega E_0 M_i \quad\quad (33.11)$$

where M_i represents the imaginary part of M, the part out of phase with E_0.

We have taken a rather involved, though interesting, method for computing the energy flow out of the dipole on account of the cross terms in Poynting's vector.   We can now show very simply that this result is just what we should have expected from ordinary conceptions of impressed e.m.f.'s.   The dipole moment $Me^{j\omega t}$ is the product of d, the distance between the two conductors in Fig. 60, and the charge on either conductor.   If $ie^{j\omega t}$ is the current flowing between the conductors, the charge is $ie^{j\omega t}/j\omega$.   Thus we have

$$M = \frac{id}{j\omega} \quad\quad (33.12)$$

Hence we have

$$\int S_{01}\, da = -\tfrac{1}{2}E_0 d(ij)_i$$
$$= -\tfrac{1}{2}E_0\, di_r \quad\quad (33.13)$$

where i_r is the real part, i_i the imaginary part, of i.   Putting it otherwise, we have

$$-\int S_{01}\, da = \tfrac{1}{2} \operatorname{Re} V\bar{\imath} \quad\quad (33.14)$$

where

$$V = E_0 d \quad\quad (33.15)$$

The quantity $-\int S_{01}\, da$ is the power input to the dipole on account of the cross terms in Poynting's vector, and V is the voltage between the conductors, as a result of the external field E_0 acting through the distance d.   Thus this most elementary method gives the correct value for the power input.

Once we understand the situation regarding the flow of energy, the rest of the analysis follows very simply.   Obviously the power input given by (33.14) must be equal to the sum of the power dissipated in the resistance and the power reradiated. If the ohmic resistance is R_0, the first part is

$$\tfrac{1}{2}i^2 R_0 \quad\quad (33.16)$$

If the radiation resistance is R_r, the second part is

$$\tfrac{1}{2}i^2R_r \tag{33.17}$$

On the other hand, if

$$V = iZ = i(R + jX) \tag{33.18}$$

then the total power input from (33.14) can be rewritten

$$\tfrac{1}{2}i^2R \tag{33.19}$$

It is then obvious that the total resistance R of the dipole is

$$R = R_0 + R_r \tag{33.20}$$

and that its impedance is

$$Z = R_0 + R_r + j\left(L\omega - \frac{1}{C\omega}\right) \tag{33.21}$$

The radiation resistance for this particular type of dipole can be easily found from the expression (29.10) for the radiated energy. We have

$$\frac{1}{2}\,i^2R_r = \frac{1}{2}\,\frac{M^2\omega^2}{d^2}\,R_r = \frac{\mu\,\sqrt{\epsilon\mu}\,\omega^4 M^2}{12\pi} \tag{33.22}$$

$$R_r = \frac{1}{6\pi}\,\sqrt{\frac{\mu}{\epsilon}}\,(kd)^2 = \frac{2\pi}{3}\,\sqrt{\frac{\mu}{\epsilon}}\left(\frac{d}{\lambda}\right)^2 \tag{33.23}$$

This value may be compared with the value of (30.24), which was computed under somewhat different assumptions and hence should not agree with (33.23).

Using the expression (33.21) for the impedance, the power absorbed in the ohmic resistance can be written

$$\frac{1}{2}\,\frac{V^2R_0}{(L\omega - 1/C\omega)^2 + (R_0 + R_r)^2} \tag{33.24}$$

and the power reradiated is

$$\frac{1}{2}\,\frac{V^2R_r}{(L\omega - 1/C\omega)^2 + (R_0 + R_r)^2} \tag{33.25}$$

Keeping V constant and differentiating with respect to R_0, we can show immediately that the expression (33.24) has a maximum when $R_0 = R_r$, verifying our earlier statement that the maximum power absorption comes when the series resistance in the absorbing dipole equals the radiation resistance. Obviously both absorption and scattering are at a maximum at resonance, when the reactive term in the denominator of (33.24) and (33.25) vanishes. It is interesting to consider the breadth of the resonance curve, or the value of Q. By (4.48), we have

$$\frac{1}{Q} = \frac{R_0 + R_r}{\omega L} \qquad (33.26)$$

Thus both types of resistance, the ohmic resistance and the radiation resistance, act in series to diminish the value of Q. It is also interesting to compute the effective cross section of the antenna, the area from which energy would have to be absorbed from the incident beam, to equal the actual energy removed from the beam on account of absorption and reradiation. We can write $V^2 = E_0^2 d = \sqrt{\mu/\epsilon}\, E_0 H_0 d$. Using this, the expressions (33.24) and (33.25) can be rewritten respectively as

$$\tfrac{1}{2} E_0 H_0 A_0 \text{ and } \tfrac{1}{2} E_0 H_0 A_r \qquad (33.27)$$

where A_0 and A_r are effective cross sections for absorption and reradiation and are given by

$$A_0 = \frac{d^2 R_0 \sqrt{\mu/\epsilon}}{(L\omega - 1/C\omega)^2 + (R_0 + R_r)^2}$$

$$A_r{}' = \frac{d^2 R_r \sqrt{\mu/\epsilon}}{(L\omega - 1/C\omega)^2 + (R_0 + R_r)^2} \qquad (33.28)$$

It is interesting to find the maximum value which the absorption cross section A_0 can have. It attains this value at resonance, when the resistance R_0 is matched to the radiation resistance R_r. It is thus equal to

$$A_{0\text{max}} = \frac{d^2 \sqrt{\mu/\epsilon}}{4R_r} = \frac{3}{8\pi} \lambda^2 \qquad (33.29)$$

where we have used (33.23). This value, as we stated earlier, is of the order of magnitude of the square of the wave length. A somewhat simpler expression is obtained if we consider different possible orientations of the dipole. We have taken up only the case where the dipole is parallel to the electric field in the incident wave. If it is at an angle θ to the incident electric field, the absorbed power will be only $\sin^2 \theta$ times as great as we have found, so that if we wish to consider the average absorption of dipoles oriented at random, we must multiply the value above by the average of $\sin^2 \theta$ over all directions, which is $\frac{2}{3}$. Then we have

$$A_{0av} = \frac{1}{4\pi} \lambda^2 = \pi \left(\frac{\lambda}{2\pi}\right)^2 \qquad (33.30)$$

the area of a circle whose circumference is the wave length. We then obtain a correct physical picture of the amount of absorption by assuming that all the energy falling on such a circle is absorbed, the rest being transmitted. An equal amount, of course, is scattered, in addition to the absorption.

The arguments of the present section have dealt with a particular sort of infinitesimal dipole. However, most of the results hold for arbitrary types of antennas. It is quite clear that our analysis of the antenna as a resonant circuit, with a resistance which is the sum of the ohmic resistance R_0 and the radiation resistance R_r, should be much more general than this special case. Of course, the reactance of an antenna cannot be written exactly as the reactance of a simple series circuit, but as we saw in the preceding chapter it really is a complicated quantity. Nevertheless in the neighborhood of resonance an effective L and C could be found such that the series circuit formula (33.21) would give a good approximation to the impedance. Our conclusions would still stand that the energy removed from the incident plane wave equaled the energy absorbed plus the energy reradiated or scattered. These two quantities would still be determined from the ohmic and the radiation resistance respectively. And for maximum absorption it would still be true that we should have to make the ohmic resistance equal to the radiation resistance or should have to match the line to the antenna, and we should still find that the total scattered energy equaled the absorbed energy. It is only the special results of this section, such as the value of the radiation resistance of the particular sort of dipole we have assumed and the angular variation of the reradiation, that apply only to the special case we have taken up.

34. Directional Properties of a Finite Antenna in Emission and Absorption.—In the preceding section we have considered the relations between emission and absorption for an infinitesimal dipole. Now we extend the same sort of argument to a finite antenna, paying particular attention to the directional properties of this antenna both in emission and absorption. We have already considered the emission from a finite antenna in Sec. 30, and we need to make only a slight generalization of the formulas of that section to get results correct for any antenna or antenna system in emission.   Let us suppose that in emission the antenna system has a current density $J(x,y,z)e^{i\omega t}$ at the point x, y, z, so that we assume a current distributed in space.   The quantity J in general can be complex, so that the current at different points of space may be in different phases.   This will not be true in a simple standing wave system of currents but must be true if we are to have the type of phase relation necessary to give one-sided propagation of radiation, as we shall see in a later section.   It is always convenient in speaking of antennas to have a single quantity that we can call the current.   There is no unique way of defining this current.   In special cases there may be obvious ways, as for instance to define it as the current flowing into the antenna system from a line which supplies the power, but in other cases it may not be so obvious.   In any case we shall assume that a definition has been given.   Since the definition is arbitrary, it cannot affect our final results.   It does, however, affect the values that we find for voltage and for impedance, since these are arbitrary too; but it does not affect the value we find for power, since that can be defined in a unique manner. Assuming a current i, we find of course that the current density J is everywhere proportional to i, the constant of proportionality being a complex function of x, y, z.   We shall call this function f and shall thus have

$$J = if(x,y,z) \qquad (34.1)$$

We note that, since J is a vector and i a scalar, f must be a vector. In a complicated antenna system, there is no reason why f must everywhere point in the same direction, though it does in a simple dipole.

Each small element of volume will now contain an infinitesimal current element, which will generate a dipole radiation field, as described in Sec. 29.   We shall consider this field only at a large distance from the antenna.   Let us try to find the total field in a particular direction from the antenna, at a distance r_0, and for convenience let us take the z axis along this direction.   The field at the point P will then be perpendicular to z, having x and y components.   Let us find one component of the field, choosing the

x direction to be in the direction of that component. This component of field will be determined by the x component of current, as we can see by (29.8), where E_θ, for $\theta = 90°$, represents the component of E opposite to the x direction. In fact, using (29.8) and (30.2), as we did to find (30.4), we find that the infinitesimal field dE_x coming from the current in dv is

$$dE_x = \frac{if_x(xyz)k^2}{4\pi\epsilon j\omega r_0} e^{j[\omega t - k(r_0 - z)]}$$

$$= \frac{if_x(xyz)k^2}{4\pi\epsilon j\omega r_0} e^{j(\omega t - kr_0 + kz)} \qquad (34.2)$$

where we have used the relation that r, the distance from the volume element at xyz to the point P, at $0, 0, r_0$, was approximately equal to $r_0 - z$. The whole field E_x is then

$$E_x = \frac{ik^2 e^{j(\omega t - kr_0)}}{4\pi\epsilon j\omega r_0} \int f_x(xyz)e^{jkz} dv \qquad (34.3)$$

We shall define

$$F_x = \frac{k}{2} \int f_x(xyz)e^{jkz} dv \qquad (34.4)$$

The definition is set up in just this way so as to get agreement with the function $F(\theta)$ of Sec. 30. We then have

$$E_x = \frac{-jike^{j(\omega t - kr_0)}}{2\pi\epsilon\omega r_0} F_x$$

$$= \frac{-j}{2\pi} \sqrt{\frac{\mu}{\epsilon}} \frac{i}{r_\theta} F_x e^{j(\omega t - kr_0)} \qquad (34.5)$$

Remembering that E_x corresponds to $-E_\phi$ of Sec. 30, we can see by comparison with (30.5), (30.8), (30.11), (30.18), that the F defined here agrees with the F of Sec. 30.

As in Sec. 30, we can easily find the total radiation and the radiation resistance of the antenna. The part of Poynting's vector along the z axis associated with E_x and H_y is

$$\frac{1}{2} i^2 \frac{1}{4\pi r_0^2} \frac{1}{\pi} \sqrt{\frac{\mu}{\epsilon}} |F_x|^2 \qquad (34.6)$$

Similarly the part of Poynting's vector associated with E_y and $-H_z$ is an expression like (34.6), only with F_y substituted for F_x, where F_y is defined by analogy with (34.4). To find the total radiation, we multiply the expression like (34.6), only with terms in both F_x and F_y, by the element of area $r_0^2 \, d\Omega$, where $d\Omega$ is an element of solid angle, and carry out an integration over all solid angles. This integration is properly over different directions of the wave normal of the radiation. We have set up our problem, however, in such a way that it is more convenient to keep the wave normal along the z axis and consider different orientations of the antenna. Let

$$\overline{F^2} = \text{average of } |F_x|^2 + |F_y|^2 \tag{34.7}$$

averaged over all orientations of the antenna. Then we may substitute $\overline{F^2}$ for the $|F_x|^2 + |F_y|^2$, encountered in Poynting's vector, and multiply by 4π in place of integrating over solid angles, obtaining

$$\text{Radiated power} = \tfrac{1}{2} i^2 R_r$$
$$R_r = \frac{1}{\pi} \sqrt{\frac{\mu}{\epsilon}} \, \overline{F^2} \tag{34.8}$$

Equation (34.8) is the obvious extension of Eq. (30.14) to the general case of an arbitrary antenna. At the same time, we see the general way to get the polar diagram of intensity of radiation from an antenna as a function of angle: the intensity of radiation in a given direction is proportional to the quantity $|F_x|^2 + |F_y|^2$, where F_x and F_y are defined as in (34.4), the z axis being chosen along the desired direction.

Now we are ready to reverse our problem and consider the effect of an external plane wave on the antenna. We shall find that there is a reciprocal relation: the intensity of radiation emitted in a given direction by an antenna is proportional to the absorption of radiation coming from that same direction. Thus we expect a relation between radiation along the z axis, as we have just set it up, and absorption of a plane wave traveling along the negative z axis. Let us then set up such a wave and ask how much power is absorbed from the wave by the antenna. To find this, we can proceed exactly as in Sec. 33, as far as we are concerned with the antenna as an electric circuit. We can take over Eqs. (33.24) and (33.25) for the power absorbed in the ohmic resistance and the power reradiated, without change, if only we define the voltage V correctly. To find V in an arbitrary case, we can proceed as follows. By definition, the total power absorbed must be $\frac{1}{2}V\bar{\imath}$, where i is the current flowing in the antenna. On the other hand, the power absorbed can also be written in terms of the integral over the volume of the antenna of the power absorbed per unit volume. Thus we have

$$\tfrac{1}{2}V\bar{\imath} = \tfrac{1}{2}\int E \cdot \bar{J}\, dv \qquad (34.9)$$

where E is the electric field and J the current density, in dv. To compute the integral on the right-hand side, we assume the E of a plane wave and make assumptions that will be described at once for J. The integral can then be carried out, and V can be determined from the equation.

At first sight, it would be supposed that J would be given by the expression (34.1), as in emission. In a simple antenna like the dipole of Sec. 33, it is certainly true that the current distribution in emission and absorption will be the same. In the general case, this simple assumption must be changed for the following reason. If the phase of the current in the antenna differs from point to point (in other words, if the current is not a simple standing wave), it is clear that the phase relations must be different in absorption from what they are in emission. If there are differences of phase, the antenna behaves to some extent like a transmission line. There may be actual transmission lines of different lengths feeding different parts of the antenna array in different phases, or the phasing may be taken care of by having some parts of the array consisting of dummy antennas, fed only by radiation from a primary antenna, in which case the distance between the primary antenna and the dummy acts to some extent like a transmission line. In any case, in absorption the energy is flowing in the opposite direction through this transmission line from what it is in emission. Now in the simplest case of a transmission line, a direct wave varies as $e^{j(\omega t - kz)}$, if z is the coordinate along the line, a wave in the opposite direction varies as $e^{j(\omega t - kz)}$, the space part of the function being the conjugate of its value in the other case. This simple case is an example of the general situation, that to reverse the direction of the energy flow in a finite, closed system like a transmission line or an antenna array, we replace the space parts of the various functions by their conjugates. Thus we must expect that the current density J in a volume element of the antenna in absorption will be the conjugate of the corresponding quantity for emission. We then assume that for absorption

$$J = \bar{i}\bar{f}e^{i\omega t} \tag{34.10}$$

It is not perfectly obvious, and probably is not exactly correct, that the current density should be given by (34.10). The reason is that in emission the antenna is fed by a concentrated voltage applied for instance at the point where the transmission line feeds the antenna (as we saw in Sec. 31); in absorption it is fed by a distributed voltage of a plane wave, exerted all over the antenna. It is not at all obvious that the current distributions will be exactly the same in both cases; but the differences are probably slight, and we shall find reason later to suppose that they are such that their effects are felt only at small distances, and not at large distances where we shall compute Poynting's vector.

We are now in position to compute the power absorption (34.9). Before doing this, we note that we could equally well find it, as we did in Sec. 33, by integrating the cross term in Poynting's vector between the plane wave and the scattered wave, and as in Sec. 33 the two calculations give exactly the same answer. Without carrying this calculation through, it is interesting to see how it explains the fact that the intensity patterns of a given antenna for emission and absorption are the same. Suppose for the sake of illustration that we have a highly directional array, sending out most of its energy in approximately a given direction. Let us choose this direction as the z axis. Then we expect it to absorb highly the radiation coming along the negative z direction. The current distribution (34.10) which we find in absorption is the conjugate of what we find in emission, and the resulting scattered wave is the reflection in the origin of the emitted wave. That is, in our particular case it is intense along the negative z axis. A plane wave traveling along the negative z axis will then have particularly large cross terms in Poynting's vector, since these terms come from interference between the plane wave and the parts of the scattered wave traveling in almost the same direction. Thus the large absorption of this wave is understood. If we investigated the whole radiation pattern, plane wave plus scattered wave, in this case, as in Fig. 61 for the simple dipole, we should find that the large scattered beam along the negative z axis was largely canceled by interference, leaving a shadow behind the antenna as before, and the remaining part of the scattered wave would form the diffraction pattern around the edge of this shadow.

Now let us find the absorbed power, by (34.9), and hence the voltage V. Let us assume a plane wave with its electric field along x, traveling along the negative z direction. That is, we assume

$$E_x = E_{0x}e^{j(\omega t+kz)} \tag{34.11}$$

Using (34.10), we have

$$\tfrac{1}{2}V\bar{i} = \tfrac{1}{2}E_{0x}\bar{i}\int\!\!\int f_x(x,y,z)e^{jkz}\,dv \tag{34.12}$$

Referring to (34.4), this gives us

$$V = \frac{2}{k}\,E_{0x}F_x \tag{34.13}$$

for the voltage developed in the antenna by the wave whose electric vector is (34.11). The mean square voltage is then

$$\frac{1}{2}\,V^2 = \frac{1}{2}\,\frac{4}{k^2}\,E_{0x}^2\,|F_x|^2 \tag{34.14}$$

It is this quantity which should appear in Eqs. (33.24) and (33.25). It will be easily verified that the value (33.15) for the voltage for the short dipole follows from (34.13) as a special case. We now observe that the absorption of a plane wave polarized with the electric vector in the x direction, traveling along $-z$, depends on the same factor $|F_x|^2$ that we found in (34.6) determines the intensity of radiation with the same polarization in the $+z$ direction, in emission. This is the origin of our earlier statement that the radiation and absorption patterns of the same antenna should be the same.

The theorem that radiation and absorption patterns should be the same is often proved by the reciprocity theorem.[1] This theorem essentially states the following: if there is a four-terminal network, which may include radiation as part of its elements, and a given voltage impressed on two of the terminals produces a given current at the other two, then the same voltage impressed on the second set of terminals will produce the same current on the first set. This theorem is used to discuss a system of two

---

[1] See, for instance, J. R. Carson, *Bell System Tech. J.*, **3**, 393 (1924); **9**, 325 (1930).

antennas, each with its two terminals, and is used to compare the radiation from the first antenna toward the second, and the radiation from the second toward the first. If the antennas are far enough apart, the second antenna impresses practically a plane wave on the first. If then the first antenna, which is the one we are interested in, is given various different orientations with respect to the second, we can compare the current induced in the second antenna by the first when in various orientations (thus measuring the radiation pattern from the first) with the current induced in the first antenna in various orientations by the second (thus measuring the absorption pattern of the first antenna). When the argument is carried through in detail, it is found, as this discussion would suggest, that the radiation patterns of the same antenna in emission and absorption must be the same. This theorem appears to be based on sounder foundation than our discussion of the preceding paragraphs, for it is not based on the assumption that we have had to make of the relation between the current distribution in the antenna in absorption and emission. Since it leads to the same result that we have found, however, we shall not go into details about it, merely quoting it as a verification of our results. It is on account of this verification that it seems likely, as we stated earlier, that though the real current distribution in absorption is probably not just the conjugate of that in emission, still the difference is probably only one that is felt at short distances and is inappreciable in the radiation part of the field.

There is another relation between emission and absorption of antennas which is not so well known as the reciprocity theorem, but which is just as fundamental and again verifies the results of the preceding paragraphs. This is based on thermodynamics and the theory of black-body radiation. On account of its intrinsic interest we shall describe it, though we shall not go into very great detail regarding the thermodynamic side of the argument. It is a fundamental principle of thermodynamics that at thermal equilibrium at temperature T, space is filled with radiation of a certain type, characteristic only of the temperature, called black-body radiation. Every body immersed in this radiation naturally absorbs a certain amount of it, and at the same time every body must radiate energy on its own account. For thermal equilibrium it is obvious that these two processes should balance, so that each body emits as much radiation as it absorbs. By the use of this fact, one can often derive relations between the rate of emission and absorption of radiation, and this relation can be set up for antennas. We first consider absorption. It is easy, from the discussion we have given already, to find how much energy an antenna will absorb from an arbitrary plane wave. We may then consider the black-body radiation to be made up of a great many plane waves and can find the total rate of absorption at temperature T. Next we consider emission. From the thermodynamic theory of noise in electric circuits, it is shown that at temperature T, as a result of fluctuations, currents and voltages are automatically set up in any conductors. As a result of these voltages, the antenna is automatically excited, so that it must emit energy. For a verification of our ideas, we should prove that this rate of emission equals the rate of absorption. We shall now give this proof.

From (34.14) we find the mean square voltage developed in an antenna as a result of a single plane wave of amplitude E_{0x}. From the theory of black-body radiation, we find that if the radiation is confined in unit volume, we can consider it to consist of a finite number of plane waves, of various frequencies, directions of wave normal, and directions of polarization. In a range of frequency df and with the wave normal in a solid angle $d\Omega$, we find that there are

$$\frac{f^2}{c^3}\, df\, d\Omega \qquad (34.15)$$

different waves of one type of polarization and an equal number of the other polarization. For orientation, we note that the mean energy of each of these waves at temperature T is kT, where k is Boltzmann's constant (not to be confused with the propagation constant k), or more accurately is $hf/(e^{hf/kT} - 1)$, where h is Planck's constant. The second expression, coming from the quantum theory, reduces to the first in the case where hf is small compared to kT, which is always the case if f is a microwave frequency and T is of the order of magnitude of room temperature. Using the one or the other of these expressions and replacing the solid angle $d\Omega$ by 4π, we find that the total radiation energy in the frequency range df, and in unit volume, is

$$\frac{8\pi f^2 kT}{c^3} \, df \quad \text{or} \quad \frac{8\pi h f^3 \, df}{c^3(e^{hf/kT} - 1)} \tag{34.16}$$

respectively, the first being the so-called Rayleigh-Jeans law of black-body radiation, the second being the Planck law.

For the calculation of the mean square voltage, from (34.14), we need the quantity E_{0x}^2, the square of the electric field in a single plane wave. We can get this for one of our waves constituting the black-body radiation, from the fact that its energy is kT. If E_{0x}, H_{0y} represent peak values, as usual, the energy in unit volume is

$$\frac{1}{2}\left(\frac{\epsilon E_{0x}^2 + \mu H_{0y}^2}{2}\right) = \frac{1}{2}\,\epsilon E_{0x}^2 \tag{34.17}$$

the last step following because the electric and magnetic energies per unit volume are equal, as we see from the relation between E_{0x} and H_{0y}. Thus, since the energy (34.17) equals kT, we have

$$E_{0x}^2 = \frac{2kT}{\epsilon} \tag{34.18}$$

The mean square voltage developed by a single wave is then, combining (34.18) and (34.14),

$$\frac{1}{2}\,V^2 = \frac{4kT}{k^2\epsilon}\,|F_x|^2 \tag{34.19}$$

For a single wave polarized along y, we have a similar expression with F_y substituted for F_x. For all the waves in the frequency range df, with wave normal in the solid angle $d\Omega$, using (34.15), the total mean square voltage is

$$\frac{1}{2}\,V^2 = \frac{4f^2}{k^2 c^3}\,\frac{kT}{\epsilon}\,(|F_x|^2 + |F_y|^2)\,df\,d\Omega \tag{34.20}$$

Next we must integrate over solid angles. To do this, as in the derivation of (34.8), we may replace $|F_x|^2 + |F_y|^2$ by its average value $\overline{F^2}$ and multiply by 4π. Thus we have

$$\frac{1}{2}\,V^2 \text{ total} = \frac{4}{k^2}\,\frac{4\pi f^2}{c^3}\,\frac{kT}{\epsilon}\,\overline{F^2}\,df = 4R_r kT\,df \tag{34.21}$$

where we have used Eq. (34.8) for R_r. It is hoped that in the preceding formulas k, Boltzmann's constant, which always occurs in the combination kT, will not be confused with k, the propagation constant.

We have found in (34.21) a simple formula for the mean square voltage connected with the power absorbed in an antenna of radiation resistance R_r, at temperature T, in the frequency range df. From Eqs. (33.24) and (33.25) we could now compute the power absorbed and the power reradiated by the antenna. Next we must find the power radiated by the antenna on account of the voltages resulting from thermal fluctuations and show that it equals the absorbed power. To find this radiated power involves considerable study of the theory of fluctuations in transmission lines. We shall not give this discussion here, but shall direct the reader to some references.[1] In these references, particularly in that of Nyquist, it is shown that every resistance in a circuit may be considered a source of power, resulting from fluctuations. Instead of computing the power output, which depends on the constants of the rest of the circuit, it is convenient to give the mean square voltage developed by the resistance. Thermodynamics shows that this mean square voltage is

$$\tfrac{1}{2}V^2 = 4RkT\,df \qquad (34.22)$$

where R is the resistance we are considering, at frequency f. We now note that this result is the same as that of (34.21). The meanings are different, however. Equation (34.21) gives the mean square voltage associated with the absorption of power from the radiation field; (34.22) gives the mean square voltage associated with emission of power. Since they are equal, we have verified our statement that our values for emission and absorption by an antenna were correct to lead to thermodynamic equilibrium, to balance between emission and absorption. In this way, since the thermodynamic result must be exact, we have a valuable check on our calculation of absorption. This check is really only a verification of the over-all emission and absorption averaged over all directions. We observe, however, that we can draw conclusions about the relation between emission and absorption in a particular direction. In (34.6), supplemented by a term in F_y, we have found the emission in a particular

[1] Schottky, *Ann. Physik*, **57**, 541 (1918); J. B. Johnson, *Phys. Rev.*, **32**, 97 (1928); H. Nyquist, *Phys. Rev.*, **34**, 110 (1928); R. B. Barnes and S. Silverman, *Rev. Modern Phys.*, **6**, 162 (1934).

direction, and in (34.20) we have the absorption of radiation in the same direction, from black-body radiation. We observe that both quantities show the same dependence on direction. Thus, since the total emission and absorption balance and since both show the same directional properties, we see that the emission of radiation in a given infinitesimal solid angle balances the absorption in the same solid angle. This is an example of the so-called principle of detailed balancing in statistical mechanics, according to which in thermal equilibrium each infinitesimal process must be balanced by its inverse process. Often this principle of detailed balancing is taken as a postulate; it can be proved directly from general statistical principles.[1] If we wish to assume this principle of detailed balancing, then, we may reverse our argument of the present section and derive the formula (34.14) for the mean square voltage induced by absorption of waves in a particular direction directly from the formula for emission. This gives an additional justification of our formula (34.14) and adds to our assurance, which we have obtained from the reciprocity theorem, that this formula is correct, even though our direct derivation of it involved possibly unjustified assumptions about the current distribution in absorption.

35. Directional Patterns of Current Distributions.—We now have investigated the general relations between emission, absorption, and directional patterns of antennas and are ready to go ahead to the study of the directive patterns of particular types of antennas. We have found that the essential quantity in studying these patterns is the integral F_x, of (34.4), obtained by multiplying the current density in the antenna by a plane wave function e^{ikz} and integrating over the antenna. There are now two parts to our problem. First we may ask, what sort of patterns do we get from typical current distributions? Secondly, how do we go about getting these current distributions experimentally? In the present section we shall take up the first of these questions, later passing on to the second. We have already made a start on both questions in Sec. 30, where we considered the radiation pattern of a linear antenna with a sinusoidal current distribution. Much more complicated distributions are

---

[1] See for instance J. C. Slater, "Introduction to Chemical Physics," p. 91, McGraw-Hill Book Company, Inc., New York.

necessary for highly directive antennas, however, and we shall consider a few such distributions in the present section. Obviously a great many different types of distribution might be of interest, and we shall consider only a few. However, the general methods that we use will illustrate the proper procedure for studying the general case.

The first problem we shall take up is the one in which we have a current distributed according to an arbitrary law in the xy plane. We shall assume that the current is all along the x axis, and that it is confined to a relatively small finite region. This region may be large compared to a wave length (it must be, in fact, if the antenna is to be very directive), but still it must be

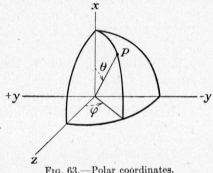

Fig. 63.—Polar coordinates.

small enough so that we can investigate the radiation pattern at distances large compared to the dimensions of the antenna. We shall take the origin somewhere within the antenna. According to our assumption the antenna is small enough so that the exact spot we choose for the origin is not significant. For our present purposes it is more convenient to use coordinates fixed in the antenna, rather than to choose the z axis along the direction of propagation, as we did in Sec. 34. For that reason we shall have to rewrite the quantity F, which gives the directional pattern, in terms of the new coordinates. In Fig. 63, we show a set of polar coordinates, with the x axis as the pole and the angle ϕ measured from the normal to the xy plane. Since the current is assumed to be along the x axis, the electric field at the point P will be along the θ direction. Thus, referring to (34.4), we wish to find F_θ, a component associated with fields in this direction. The corresponding quantity f_θ, associated with the component of current in the direction parallel to the field, will be sin θ times the surface current density. Thus there will be a factor sin θ coming into F, leading to a vanishing intensity along the x axis, since the current points along this axis. In (34.4), we need to write the exponential e^{jkz} in terms of our new coordinates, where z measured the displacement along the wave normal. Plainly we must make the substitution

$$z \to x \cos (n,x) + y \cos (n,y) + z \cos (n,z)$$
$$= x \cos \theta - y \sin \theta \sin \phi + z \sin \theta \cos \phi \quad (35.1)$$

where cos (n,x) represents the cosine of the angle between the wave normal and the x axis, etc. Remembering that the current is assumed to be all located in the xy plane, so that $z = 0$ for all elements of current in (34.4), the exponential becomes

$$e^{jk(x \cos \theta - y \sin \theta \sin \phi)} \quad (35.2)$$

To define the factor f of (34.1) and (34.4) uniquely, we must decide on the value of i. Since for the present purpose we are more interested in the radiation pattern than in the impedance, we shall choose i so as to make F come out unity along the z axis. This is bound to be the maximum value of F in this case, since there is no interference between waves emitted by different parts of the charge. In this direction the exponential of (35.2) reduces to unity, so that by (34.4) F becomes $k/2$ times the integral of f over the plane. Let us choose a quantity ψ proportional to f, in such a way that ψ is a function of x and y (proportional, then, to the surface current density), with the constant of proportionality so chosen that the integral of ψ over the complete plane equals unity. Then we shall have

$$F = \sin \theta \int \psi e^{jk(x \cos \theta - y \sin \theta \sin \phi)} \, da \quad (35.3)$$

This represents the form that (34.4) takes, with our choice of axes and of current density.

As a first example, we shall assume that current is uniformly distributed over a rectangular area of dimension a along the x axis, b along the y axis, and is zero outside this rectangle. We must then take ψ to equal $1/ab$ within the rectangle, zero outside. If the origin is at the center of the rectangle, we have

$$F = \frac{\sin \theta}{ab} \int_{-a/2}^{a/2} e^{jkx \cos \theta} \, dx \int_{-b/2}^{b/2} e^{-jky \sin \theta \sin \phi} \, dy$$

$$= \sin \theta \, \frac{\sin (ka \cos \theta/2)}{(ka \cos \theta)/2} \, \frac{\sin (kb \sin \theta \sin \phi/2)}{(kb \sin \theta \sin \phi)/2}$$

$$= \sin \theta \, \frac{\sin [(\pi a/\lambda) \cos \theta]}{(\pi a/\lambda) \cos \theta} \, \frac{\sin [(\pi b/\lambda) \sin \theta \sin \phi]}{(\pi b/\lambda) \sin \theta \sin \phi} \quad (35.4)$$

where in the last form we have used $k = 2\pi/\lambda$. We note that (35.4) has two factors of the form $\sin w/w$. This function, as shown in Fig. 64, equals unity when $w = 0$ and oscillates with

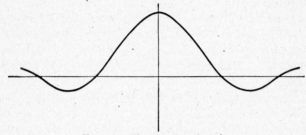

Fig. 64.—The function $\sin w/w$.

decreasing amplitude as w increases, reaching its first zero at $w = \pi$, its first minimum approximately at $w = 3\pi/2$, at which its value is $-2/3\pi = -0.212$, and having its second zero at $w = 2\pi$. The square of this function, which is needed for the intensity of the radiation, has zeros at π and 2π, with a maximum of height $(2/3\pi)^2 = 0.045$ at about $3\pi/2$. We see that the maximum value of F, when both factors $\sin w/w$ equal unity, comes when $\theta = 90°$, $\phi = 0$, or along the z axis, as we should expect. The first zeros of intensity come for

$$\cos \theta = \pm \frac{\lambda}{a}, \qquad \sin \theta \sin \phi = \pm \frac{\lambda}{b} \quad (35.5)$$

If λ/a and λ/b are small or if both dimensions of the rectangle are large compared to a wave length, this can be rewritten

$$\theta = \frac{\pi}{2} \pm \frac{\lambda}{a}, \qquad \phi = \pm \frac{\lambda}{b} \quad (35.6)$$

The main radiated beam lies within these limits, as we see from Fig. 64. Looked at on the surface of a sphere, the limits mark off an approximately rectangular area, whose dimensions in each direction are inversely proportional to the dimension of the slit in the same direction. This behavior is characteristic of all diffraction problems, of which this is a characteristic example. In order to have the beam fill a small angle, the area over which current is distributed must be large compared to a wave length, in each of its dimensions. Outside the main beam, as we can also see from Fig. 64, are small side lobes, containing a few per cent of the energy of the main beam

It is interesting to find the gain, defined as in Sec. 30, Eq. (30.25), as the ratio of F^2 in the direction of maximum intensity, to the average F^2. To find the average F^2, we must square (35.4) and integrate over all solid angles, dividing by 4π. This integration is unmanageable in the general case but becomes simple if the pattern is concentrated, so that sines and cosines can be approximated by their angles, as we have done in (35.6). In this case, we can replace $\sin \theta$ by unity, $\cos \theta$ by $\pi/2 - \theta$, $\sin \phi$ by ϕ. The element of solid angle $\sin \theta \, d\theta \, d\phi$ can be rewritten $-d(\pi/2 - \theta) \, d\phi$. Since the pattern falls to zero rapidly as we depart from its region of maximum intensity, we can carry our integration with respect to $(\pi/2 - \theta)$ and ϕ from $-\infty$ to ∞, in place of the usual limits. Then we have

$$\overline{F^2} = \frac{1}{4\pi} \int_{-\infty}^{\infty} \frac{\sin^2 (\pi a/\lambda)(\pi/2 - \theta)}{[(\pi a/\lambda)(\pi/2 - \theta)]^2} \, d\left(\frac{\pi}{2} - \theta\right)$$
$$\int_{-\infty}^{\infty} \frac{\sin^2 (\pi b/\lambda)\phi}{[(\pi b/\lambda)\phi]^2} \, d\phi$$
$$= \frac{\lambda^2}{4\pi ab} \tag{35.7}$$

Since the maximum value of F^2 is unity, we then have

$$\text{Gain} = \frac{4\pi ab}{\lambda^2} = \frac{ab}{\pi(\lambda/2\pi)^2} \tag{35.8}$$

or the ratio of the area of the emitting region, to the area of a circle whose circumference is the wave length. Large gains are plainly possible according to (35.8). Thus if a and b are each 10 wave lengths, the gain is 400π. It is to be remembered that (35.8), by its derivation, is correct only in cases where the gain is large. If a and b became of the order of magnitude of the wave length, the gain would not go to zero, as (35.8) would indicate, but to a finite value greater than unity, as with the dipole antennas of Sec. 30. Thus the correct formula, to be substituted for (35.8), would be to a first approximation

$$\text{Gain} = \frac{ab + \text{const.}}{\pi(\lambda/2\pi)^2} \qquad (35.9)$$

where the constant presumably should be $\frac{3}{2}\pi(\lambda/2\pi)^2$, so as to reduce properly to the value $\frac{3}{2}$ giving the gain of an infinitesimal dipole, as found in Sec. 30. The resulting formula,

$$\text{Gain} = \frac{ab}{\pi(\lambda/2\pi)^2} + \frac{3}{2} \qquad (35.10)$$

of course, is only an interpolation between the correct limiting values but presumably would be good enough for practical use.

Our next problem will be that of a uniform distribution of current over a circle of radius R, rather than a rectangular area. In this case, except for the factor $\sin \theta$ of (35.3), the pattern will show circular symmetry. We shall consider it only for the case of a narrow pattern with large gain, which as in the rectangular case will come when R is large compared to a wave length. In this case, as before, we can replace $\sin \theta$ by unity, $\cos \theta$ by $\pi/2 - \theta$, $\sin \phi$ by ϕ. On account of the circular symmetry, we do not need to find the pattern for all combinations of values of θ and ϕ. We may, for instance, set ϕ equal to zero and shall then find the pattern as a function of $\pi/2 - \theta$, giving the radial distribution of intensity in the pattern. Let us set

$$\frac{\pi}{2} - \theta = \xi \qquad (35.11)$$

Further, let us introduce polar coordinates in the xy plane, denoting them by r and η. Then, taking ψ of (35.3) as $1/\pi R^2$, we have

$$F = \frac{1}{\pi R^2} \int e^{jk\,\xi r \cos \eta}\, da$$
$$= \frac{1}{\pi R^2} \int_0^{2\pi} d\eta \int_0^R r e^{jk\,\xi \cos \eta}\, dr \qquad (35.12)$$

The integral can be carried out in terms of Bessel's functions, giving

$$F = \frac{2J_1(k\xi R)}{k\xi R} \qquad (35.13)$$

An elementary discussion of this integral is given by Slater and Frank.[1] If well-known formulas involving Bessel's functions are assumed, the integral can be carried out as follows. We integrate first with respect to η. Using the formula

$$\int_0^{2\pi} e^{jz \cos \psi} \, d\psi = 2\pi J_0(z) \tag{35.14}$$

we have

$$F = \frac{1}{\pi R^2} \int_0^R 2\pi r J_0(k\xi r) \, dr \tag{35.15}$$

Using the formula

$$\int_0^z J_0(z) z \, dz = z J_1(z) \tag{35.16}$$

we then have

$$F = \frac{2}{R^2} \left(\frac{1}{k\xi} \right)^2 (k\xi R) J_1(k\xi R) \tag{35.17}$$

reducing at once to the value (35.13).

The function $2J_1(z)/z$ has an appearance much like the function $\sin w/w$ plotted in Fig. 64. It equals unity when $z = 0$, has its first zero when $z = 3.832$, then passes through a minimum, and again reaches zero. Its square then has its first minimum when $z = 3.832$. This square represents the intensity as a function of radius, in the radiated pattern. Most of the intensity is contained in the circle within the first minimum. The angular radius of this circle is given by

$$k\xi R = 3.832, \qquad \xi = \frac{3.832}{kR} = \frac{3.832}{2\pi} \frac{\lambda}{R} = 0.61 \frac{\lambda}{R} \tag{35.18}$$

It is interesting to compare this with the corresponding quantity in the rectangular case. If we had a square distribution of current of the same area as our circle, so that

$$ab = a^2 = \pi R^2 \tag{35.19}$$

we should find from (35.6) that the angular distance out to the first minimum was $\lambda/a = (1/\sqrt{\pi})(\lambda/R) = 0.56 \, \lambda/R$. The close agreement with (35.18) is obvious.

We can easily find the gain of the circular current distribution, as we have earlier found it for the rectangular distribution.

[1] "Introduction to Theoretical Physics," p. 325, McGraw-Hill Book Company, Inc., New York.

As before, we must find $\overline{F^2}$. From (35.13), F depends on ξ, the angle measured out from the center of the pattern. Since we are considering only small patterns, we may introduce polar coordinates in the pattern, setting the element of solid angle between ξ and $\xi + d\xi$ equal to $2\pi\xi \, d\xi$. Then we have

$$\overline{F^2} = \frac{1}{4\pi} \int_0^\infty 2\pi\xi F^2 \, d\xi = 2 \int_0^\infty \frac{J_1^2(k\xi R)}{(k\xi R)^2} \, \xi \, d\xi$$

$$= \frac{2}{(kR)^2} \int_0^\infty \frac{J_1^2(z)}{z} \, dz$$

$$= \frac{1}{(kR)^2} = \frac{(\lambda/2\pi)^2}{R^2} = \frac{\pi(\lambda/2\pi)^2}{\pi R^2} \qquad (35.20)$$

where we have used the result[1] that $\displaystyle\int_0^\infty \frac{J_1^2(z)}{z} \, dz = \frac{1}{2}$. Since the maximum value of F^2 is unity, this gives us

$$\text{Gain} - \frac{\pi R^2}{\pi(\lambda/2\pi)^2} \qquad (35.21)$$

As in the formula for the rectangular antenna (35.8), this holds only for an antenna large compared to the wave length, and a first order correction for smaller antennas could be made by adding a constant, as in (35.9) and (35.10).

We notice the close similarity between (35.21) and (35.8), in that in each case the gain equals the area of the surface covered with current, divided by the quantity $\pi(\lambda/2\pi)^2$, the area of a circle whose circumference is the wave length. This suggests that this should be a general formula in such cases, and we can show easily that it is. We can do this best by going back to the idea of the effective cross section of the antenna for absorption, which was introduced in Sec. 33. In Eq. (33.27) we defined this effective cross section in such a way that it was proportional to the absorption in a given direction. In (33.30) we found that the average absorption cross section of a dipole antenna, at resonance and matched to its line, averaged over all directions, was $\pi(\lambda/2\pi)^2$. We shall shortly prove that this result is general for any type of antenna. On the other hand, for a distribution of current on a plane, like that under discussion, the maximum emission will be along the normal to the surface; consequently

[1] See for instance Watson, "Bessel Functions," Cambridge University Press, 1922, p. 405.

the maximum absorption will be in the same direction.   It seems most plausible that the absorption cross section in this case will be just the area of the current distribution.   The gain, by definition, will be the ratio of maximum absorption cross section to average cross section (that is, it is the ratio of maximum emission to average emission), so that it will be the ratio of the area of the current distribution, to the quantity $\pi(\lambda/2\pi)^2$, which is just the value found in (35.8) and (35.21).   We may expect the same result, then, in any case in which the current distribution is large enough compared to the wave length so that its absorption cross section may be set equal to its actual area.

The result that we have just stated rests on the fact that the average absorption cross section of a matched resonating antenna is $\pi(\lambda/2\pi)^2$, independent of the type of antenna.   This important result is easily proved.   From (33.24), inserting the case of resonance and assuming that R_0, the ohmic resistance of the antenna, is matched to R_r, the radiation resistance, we find that the absorbed power is

$$\frac{1}{2}\frac{V^2}{4R_r} \qquad (35.22)$$

From (33.27) we can rewrite this as

$$\frac{1}{2}E_0H_0A_0 = \frac{1}{2}E_0^2\sqrt{\frac{\epsilon}{\mu}}A_0 \qquad (35.23)$$

From (34.14) we have

$$\frac{1}{2}V^2 = \frac{1}{2}\frac{4}{k^2}E_0^2F^2 \qquad (35.24)$$

To find the average absorbed power, we must average V^2 in (35.22) and (35.24) and average A_0 in (35.23).   We then use $\overline{F^2}$ in (35.24) and write it in terms of the radiated resistance by the use of (34.8).   Combining these, we have

$$\overline{A_r} = \pi\left(\frac{\lambda}{2\pi}\right)^2, \qquad (35.25)$$

the result that we wished to prove.

The rectangular and circular arrays, which we have just discussed, can be made to have as high gains and as directional patterns as desired, by making them large enough, as we have just seen.   However, as we saw in Fig. 64, the intensity does not fall entirely within a single beam but, instead, has side peaks or lobes of appreciable intensity. For some purposes it is desirable to eliminate these side lobes. This cannot be done with any arrangement in which we have a uniform current distribution over a certain area, with no current outside that area. The larger the area is made, the narrower is the main beam, and the farther in the side lobes move, but they remain of the same intensity proportionally to the main beam. It turns out to be the case that it is the sudden discontinuity in current density that is responsible for the side lobes, and that by having the current density gradually fall off to zero, the side lobes can be eliminated. We can show this by an example. We shall assume that the current density is distributed according to Gauss's error law, falling off as e^{-ad^2}, where a is a constant and d is the distance from a central point. Then we shall find that the radiation pattern follows the same law, also falling off from its center according to Gauss's law, only of course with dimensions that vary inversely as the dimensions of the actual antenna system.

In Eq. (35.3), we must first set up the quantity ψ representing the current distribution in the xy plane, with the constant of proportionality so chosen that the integral over the plane equals unity. Such a function is

$$\psi = \frac{a}{\pi} e^{-a(x^2+y^2)} \tag{35.26}$$

where a is an arbitrary constant. To see its meaning, we note that if the current were distributed uniformly over a finite area, with the constant value equal to the value of the function (35.26) at the origin, it would cover the area π/a. Thus $1/\sqrt{a}$ might be considered an equivalent radius for the current distribution. We now insert (35.26) into (35.3) and integrate with respect to x and y from $-\infty$ to ∞. The integrals can be carried out easily, and the result is

$$F = \sin \theta e^{-\frac{k^2}{4a}(\cos^2 \theta + \sin^2 \theta \sin^2 \phi)} \tag{35.27}$$

The quantity $\cos^2 \theta + \sin^2 \theta \sin^2 \phi$ represents simply the square of the angular displacement from the center of the radiation pattern, so long as the angles are small. Thus we find that in this case the radiation pattern is given by a Gauss error curve, just as the current distribution is. The coefficient $k^2/4a$ in the exponent of the Gauss curve is, as we should expect, inversely proportional to the coefficient a in the exponent of (35.26), which gives the current distribution. Thus we verify our statement of the preceding paragraph that the radiation pattern follows the Gauss law, with dimensions varying inversely as the dimensions of the antenna system. Since the pattern follows the Gauss law, there are no side lobes, the intensity falling smoothly to zero.

Examination of other examples shows that what we have found in the case of the Gauss law is true in general: if the intensity of the current distribution in the xy plane falls smoothly to zero, instead of discontinuously, the side lobes in the radiation pattern will be absent. In a practical case, of course the Gauss current distribution cannot be used, for at least theoretically this implies a distribution of current out to infinity. However, it is possible to approximate it in a finite region. If one is to use a current distribution through a finite region, as for instance, a distribution within a circle, the side lobes may be diminished by decreasing the intensity of the current as the edge of the circle is approached, instead of using a uniform current density throughout the circle. There are compensating disadvantages, however. If only the central part of the circle is strongly covered with current, which falls off as the edges are approached, the effective area of the current distribution is smaller than the area of the circle, and the gain will be diminished. In practical cases, in other words, one must make a compromise between high gain and absence of side lobes; and one must note that if the distribution fades off toward the edge of the circle, so that only part of it contributes to the effective area, the gain may be a good deal less than that given in (35.21), which was based on the assumption of uniform current distribution.

From the examples that have been given, one can get a good idea of the type of patterns to be expected from a distribution of current in a plane. Many other problems can be reduced to equivalent plane current distributions; we shall see examples in later sections, for instance, in considering radiation from a parabolic reflector. There is one important respect, however, in which a plane current distribution is inadequate to represent many real systems, and that is in the problem of one-sided radiation. There are two beams emitted from a plane current distribution: beams emitted along the normal to the surface in both positive and negative directions, or along $\pm z$, if the current is in the xy plane. We have not stressed this fact in the derivations we have given so far; in fact, in the calculation of gain, in (35.8) and (35.21), we have neglected it entirely; if we had taken it into account, we should have found a value of the gain only half as great as we did. Our reason for this was the practical one that actual radiating systems are usually one-sided ones, the beam along $-z$ being cut out, so that the formulas we derived represented this practical case more closely. But we must now consider what characteristics a current distribution must have so that it will radiate in only one direction, say along the $+z$ direction, and so that the other beam, in the $-z$ direction, will be eliminated. We shall answer this question by a qualitative discussion, rather than by quantitative calculations.

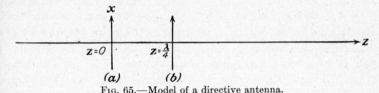

Fig. 65.—Model of a directive antenna.

Suppose that, as in Fig. 65, we had two identical current distributions, one located in the plane $z = 0$, the other in the plane $z = \lambda/4$. These distributions are assumed to be identical as far as their dependence on x and y is concerned, but to be in different phases. In particular, we can have the distribution (a) at $z = 0$ a quarter cycle ahead of that (b) at $z = \lambda/4$. Then first let us consider the beam along $+z$. The radiation from the distribution (a) leads that from the other distribution by a quarter cycle, but it takes a quarter cycle to catch up with the radiation from (b), on account of the path difference. Thus at any point along the $+z$ axis the two beams will be in phase and will reinforce each other. On the other hand, along the $-z$ axis the situation will be reversed. The radiation from (a) will lead that from (b) by one quarter cycle on account of their difference in phase, and by another quarter cycle on account of their path difference, making a phase difference of half a cycle in all, so that they will exactly cancel each other. Thus this combination of currents will give a beam directed along $+z$, with no corresponding beam along $-z$.

We have so far considered the situation only exactly along the axes. If we consider radiation making a slight angle with the z axis, the path difference between the radiation from (a) and (b) will no longer be just a half wave length but will be slightly longer. Thus the reinforcement along the positive direction will not be quite so strong as before, and the cancellation along the negative direction will not be quite complete. Without making calculations, we cannot see exactly what will result, but the result is qualitatively clear. There will be a slight backward beam along the negative axis, with no intensity at the center but with intensity building up slightly as we go away from the center. The forward beam will not have quite twice the amplitude of the beam from a single current distribution but will have less in proportion as we go from the center of the pattern. Clearly if the beam is very narrow, its intensity will have fallen practically to zero by the time this situation comes about, and the backward beam will be almost exactly canceled. On the other hand, if the beam is broad, coming from a current distribution of the same order of magnitude as the wave length, there will be considerable backward radiation, except in the exact negative x direction. Thus two short dipole antennas, arranged as in Fig. 65, will throw more of their radiation in the $+z$ direction than in the backward direction, but by no means will throw all their energy along the positive direction.

The particular arrangement of phases that we have shown in Fig. 65 is one way, but by no means the only way, of securing one-sided radiation. Many other more complicated antennas would do the same thing. They all agree, however, in having current distributions at different points along the z axis, in different phases. For instance, it is obvious that if we have an infinite metallic surface of finite but high conductivity and allow currents to flow on one face of this metal, radiation will be emitted along the normal pointing out from that face, but not from the opposite face of the metal. The radiation must have been emitted from the currents actually flowing and could be computed from those currents by the methods of the present chapter. Now we know from Sec. 12 that a current flowing on the surface of a good conductor really is a rapidly damped wave, attenuated exponentially, and at the same time changing its phase, as we penetrate into the conductor for distances of the order of magnitude of the skin depth. The attenuation is so strong that the intensity of the current has fallen to zero by the time we have penetrated a wave length or so. This is a complicated variation of amplitude and phase of the current with z. We can be sure, however, that if we were to calculate the radiation pattern of such a distribution, taking proper account of phases and amplitudes, we should find that it represented radiation traveling in one direction, outside the metal, but with no corresponding pattern on the opposite side of the metal, where our physical intuition tells us that the radiation will be cut off by the opacity of the metal.

36. Reflection and Scattering from Mirrors and Dummy Antennas.—In the preceding section we have found the radiation patterns from various typical current distributions. Now we must ask how these current distributions could be set up. Of course, one possible method, which is sometimes used with fairly long waves, is to build up an array of dipole antennas, essentially filling a two- or a three-dimensional region, and to feed each dipole from a separate line, with suitable amplitude and phase. This is a straightforward but clumsy way to build up a distribution and is one that is hardly practicable on the small scale required for microwave work. The more convenient and usual method in small-scale work is to feed power into only one part of the system, as for instance a single dipole antenna, but to arrange various reflecting or scattering conductors around this antenna, so that the currents induced in these conductors will set up the directional pattern that we desire. In the present section we shall consider some examples of such conductors, finding what sort of current distributions would be set up in them and what kind of radiation patterns we should expect in consequence.

As a first example, we shall take up the simple case of an infinite plane conductor, with a dipole antenna on one side of it. From either of two legitimate arguments we should expect this conductor to act like a mirror. We might argue that the problem was like one in optics, or we might argue that it resembled an electrostatic problem. In either of these, we could replace the conductor by an image of the dipole, located as far behind the conductor as the actual dipole is in front of it, and we should find that the field of the real dipole and of its image was exactly equivalent to what we really have from the dipole and the mirror. We shall find that in the present case, at least if the mirror has perfect conductivity, so that it is a perfect reflector, we can perfectly legitimately make up the field from that of the real dipole and its image. We can see immediately what we must do to prove this: we must set up the field of the dipole and its image and show that it satisfies the correct boundary conditions on the surface of the conductor, namely that the tangential component of electric field and normal component of magnetic field should be zero on the surface. Let us proceed to see how this can be carried out.

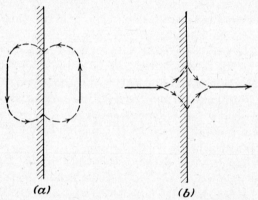

(a)   (b)

Fig. 66.—Image of a dipole in a perfect conductor.

Two cases are clearly possible: the dipole can be parallel to the mirror or perpendicular to it. These two cases are shown in Fig. 66, where the phase of the dipole is indicated by the direction of the arrow. It is clear in both cases that the phases are so chosen that the tangential component of electric field vanishes on the conducting surface. In other words, to satisfy this boundary condition, the electric image must have a phase 180° from what we should have if we just formed an optical mirror image of the arrow representing the real dipole. The field to the right of the conducting surface can then be taken to be the sum of the fields of the real dipole and of its image; inside the conductor, the field of course is zero. The discontinuity of normal component of electric field as usual measures the surface density of charge, and the discontinuity of tangential component of magnetic field the surface density of current, on the surface of the metal. It is not hard to see that the fields of source and image have equal tangential components of magnetic field, and equal normal components of electric field, on the reflecting surface, and have equal and opposite normal components of magnetic field and equal and opposite tangential components of electric field. Thus while the total tangential electric field and the normal magnetic field vanish, the tangential magnetic field and the normal electric field are just twice the values resulting from the source alone. Using the field of the source, then, as we have learned how to find it in earlier sections, we can at once set up the surface densities of charge and current necessary to produce the reflection and satisfy the boundary conditions. This surface current distribution must have the same field, to the right of the conducting surface, that the image dipole would have. It is a rather complicated current distribution. It consists of circular zones in alternating phase, each zone formed by the intersection of a sphere of radius equal to a given number of half wave lengths and centered at the real dipole, with the conducting surface. It is hardly worth while to investigate the current distribution further, since we can equally well find the field from the electric image dipole.

The two dipoles, one real and the other virtual, of Fig. 66, can naturally show similar interference effects to those which we have described in the preceding section, in the discussion of Fig. 65. First let us consider case (a), where the dipole is parallel to the surface. The two dipoles are a half cycle apart in phase. If then their distance apart is a half wave length, the radiation from the virtual dipole will reach a point to the right of both dipoles in phase with the radiation from the real dipole, so that there will be a double amplitude and large intensity. On the other hand, if their distance apart is a whole wave length, the radiations from the two dipoles will cancel directly to the right, though not in other directions. In this case, the radiated intensity will be relatively small. As the real dipole is moved away from the surface, there will clearly be a periodicity in the radiated intensity, so that when the dipole is a quarter wave length, three quarters, five quarters, etc., from the reflector, there will be excess intensity, while halfway between, at a half wave length, whole wave length, etc., from the surface, there will be deficient intensity. In the other case, (b) of Fig. 66, the situation is reversed. There, if the dipole is a quarter wave length, three quarters, etc., from the surface, so that it is an odd number of half wave lengths from the image, the fields of the two will cancel directly to the right; if the dipole is an even number of quarter wave lengths from the surface, the two fields will reinforce each other. This situation is complicated, however, by the fact that a single dipole has no radiation intensity directly along its axis, so that it is only at an angle to the normal to the surface that we have any intensity at all, and in these directions the interference effect is not complete. It would not be hard to compute actual radiation patterns in these various cases, simply by combining the fields of the two dipoles, but we shall not carry this through.

Now that we have considered reflection by a plane mirror, we can take up the much more difficult but much more interesting problem of reflection by a parabolic mirror, since this type of mirror is capable of forming a narrow, concentrated beam, just as in an optical searchlight, and forms one of the easiest methods of directing a beam of microwaves. We shall consider only the simple case where the source is an infinitesimal dipole at the focus of the mirror; if the source is located away from the focus, we run into complications similar to the aberrations of geometrical optics. Just as with the plane mirror, there will be a distribution of charge and current in the surface of the parabolic mirror, just sufficient to cancel the field of the dipole at points behind the mirror but producing the reflected wave in front of the mirror. We shall assume that a small area of the mirror can be treated as if it were plane, so that the charge and current density can be found as they would be for a plane mirror. That is, we find the field of the source at this point of the mirror and assume that the total field at this point has a tangential magnetic field and normal electric field, which are twice the values for the source alone, while the tangential electric field and normal magnetic field are zero, to satisfy the boundary conditions. From the tangential magnetic field and normal electric field we can find the current and charge densities on the surface of the mirror, and we can then find the field at distant points of these current and charge densities. Thus we can investigate the reflected radiation.

Two features of the surface current and charge densities are of interest: its phase, and its direction and magnitude. First we shall consider the phase.   If r is the distance from the source (at the focus) to a given point of the parabola, the disturbance at this point will contain a factor $e^{-i\beta r}$, where β is the propagation constant, determining the phase.   At a point P where we are finding the field of the charge, there will be an additional retardation factor $e^{-i\beta r_1}$, where r_1 is the distance from the current distribution to P, as shown in Fig. 67.   Thus at P the contribution to the field from the particular element of current under discussion contains the factor $e^{-i\beta(r+r_1)}$.   But if P is far enough away so that the vectors reaching it from all points of the mirror are approximately parallel, $r + r_1$ is the sum of the distance from the focus to a given point of the parabola, plus the distance from that point

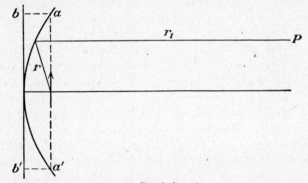

Fig. 67.—Parabolic mirror.

to a plane normal to the axis of the parabola, and by the fundamental geometrical property of the parabola this sum is constant, independent of which point of the parabola we choose.   In other words, the contributions of all current elements on the surface of the parabola will be in phase at P.   This is really the origin of the focusing property of the parabolic mirror; by a fundamental principle of optics, the optical paths from one conjugate focus to another must be equal, no matter which optical path is considered.   As a result of our property, we can imagine a plane surface tangent to the paraboloid at its apex, as shown in Fig. 67, and can assume a distribution of surface charge and current on the surface of this plane, all in the same phase, which will produce the same field at P, and at neighboring points, that the actual distribution on the parabolic surface would produce.   At a given point of the plane, we need only assume a charge and current that can be found by projecting the actual distributions along the normal to the plane, as we shall see in the next paragraph.

Consider a small element of area of the paraboloidal surface. The charge and current on this element will form a small dipole. The dipole moment will have one component along the axis of the paraboloid, another component at right angles to this axis. The component along the axis will emit no radiation along the axis and hence will not contribute to the field at P. This leaves only the component normal to the axis. It is this component

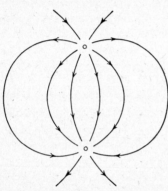

FIG. 68.—Schematic diagram of lines of current flow in paraboloidal reflector.

that we may imagine located in the plane surface instead of the paraboloidal surface, as we have mentioned in the preceding paragraph, in such a way that all current elements in this plane will be in the same phase. It is now a complicated problem in solid geometry to find the lines of current flow of these current elements in the plane, and to compute the radiation at P emitted by them. We shall not carry this through. We can however, give a good idea graphically of the results. In Fig. 68 we show a diagram (from unpublished calculations of E. U. Condon) giving the direction of the lines of current flow in the equivalent current distribution on the plane surface. We notice that there are two poles, at which there is no current flow; lines of flow point into one of these poles, out of the other. These poles are found as follows. First we consider the actual dipole located at the focus and producing the primary radiation. We consider the axis of this dipole and find the two points at which this axis intersects the paraboloid (points a, a' in Fig. 67). Since the dipole emits no radiation along its axis, there is no electromagnetic field at a and a', and hence no surface current. Thus there will be no surface current at the points b, b' of the plane, the projections of a and a' onto the plane. These points b, b', then, are the poles shown in Fig. 68.

The problem of finding the radiation at P and at neighboring points is now that of finding the radiation from a distribution of dipoles in a plane like that of Fig. 68, out to a certain circle representing the size of the mirror. This radiation can be found as in Sec. 35, only of course the problem is more compli- cated on account of the complicated current distribution of Fig. 68. We naturally ask the question how the pattern will depend on the size of the paraboloid; that is, on the area of the illu- minated region of Fig. 68, in comparison with the distance out to the poles. From the figure it is obvious that the current ele- ments above the upper pole and below the lower one are in opposite directions to the rest of the current elements. Thus if the paraboloid is made too large so as to include too many of these current elements, they will tend to cancel the others and reduce the total radiation, rather than increase it. On the other hand, if the paraboloid is made too small, then by the principles of Sec. 35 diffraction will make the pattern too broad. A compromise must be made, depending on the type of pattern desired. Clearly the pattern will be different in a vertical and in a horizontal plane. Looking up and down in Fig. 68, we see that the region contributing to the radiation is not essentially higher than the distance between the poles; even if the paraboloid is larger than this distance, the current density beyond the poles will be in the wrong phase to contribute to the radiation, as we have seen. Looking to the left and right in Fig. 68, however, we see that the illuminated region can be considerably greater than the distance between poles. Since by the principles of diffraction the pattern is narrower where the illuminated region is wider, we see that the pattern will tend to be narrower hori- zontally than it is vertically. On the other hand, vertically the illumination falls off gradually in intensity as the poles are approached. This gradual falling off of intensity, as we saw in the discussion of Eq. (35.27), tends to make the pattern also fall off gradually, without side bands. This is to be expected in the vertical plane. In the horizontal plane, on the contrary, the illumination will stay roughly constant out to the edge of the paraboloid, so that, although the pattern is narrower in that plane, side bands will be more pronounced. It is to be noted that in this discussion we have assumed the dipole antenna to be vertical; if it is horizontal, the situation will naturally be rotated through a right angle. As a matter of notation, it is common practice to denote the plane that we have called vertical as the electric plane (since the electric lines of force in the radiation pattern of the source dipole are in this plane), and the one we have called horizontal as the magnetic plane.   Then our conclusion is that the pattern in the magnetic plane is narrower than in the electric plane, but with greater side lobes.

The actual pattern of radiation emitted from a paraboloidal mirror with an antenna near its focus is more complicated than this ideal situation for several reasons.   In the first place, the real antenna is never infinitesimal and never a simple dipole.   This means that its radiation pattern is more complicated than that of a dipole, so that there is a more complicated current distribution than that of Fig. 68, and furthermore that some parts of the antenna are too close, others too far away, from the mirror, so that all parts of the current distribution on the equivalent plane are not really exactly in phase.   Then we have neglected the fact that the radiation pattern at P is not only that produced by the reflection, but also that coming directly from the source. These two patterns can interfere with each other, something as the source and image interfered in the case of reflection from a plane mirror, and can produce periodic effects, depending on the number of quarter wave lengths between antenna and mirror. These periodic effects will not be nearly so pronounced as with the plane mirror, for in the direction of P the reflected wave has a large gain, which the direct wave does not, so that the two interfering waves are not of the same intensity, but one is much weaker than the other.   We may expect, then, relatively small periodic fluctuations of intensity at P as the dimensions are altered so as to change the focal length by a definite number of quarter wave lengths.   These periodic effects can naturally be made weaker by using some form of reflector to catch the radiation traveling from the source directly toward P and to direct this radiation back on the mirror, so that it will form part of the reflected wave.

Although a parabolic mirror is one of the most obvious directive devices for microwaves, there are other types of devices that should be considered.   One such device is the dummy antenna, a scheme often used at longer wave lengths and applicable at microwave frequencies as well.   Near a dipole antenna and parallel to it can be placed another similar, insulated antenna, not fed directly by any source of power.   The radiation from the driven antenna, falling on the dummy, will naturally set it into oscillation, according to the same principles that we have described in Sec. 33.   The dummy in turn will become a source of radiation, which will interfere with the direct radiation from the driven antenna, and the resulting pattern can have directional effects that a single antenna by itself cannot produce. Thus in Fig. 65 we have seen how two dipoles a quarter wave length apart, with phases a quarter cycle apart, will radiate most of their energy in one direction, with very small radiation in the opposite direction.   Such a situation can be accomplished by a suitable dummy antenna.   To do this, it is necessary to control the phase of the current in the dummy.   This can be done, according to the principles of Sec. 33, by adjusting the length of the dummy.   If the dummy is just the right length for resonance at the frequency being used, the current flowing in it will be in phase with the voltage acting on it from the driven antenna.   If the dummy is shorter than this, however, it will correspond to a capacitive reactance; if it is longer, it will correspond to an inductive reactance.   Thus by suitable choice of length we can make the current in the dummy lead or follow the voltage by any desired amount and can arrange it so that the radiation field either tends to flow from the driven antenna away from the dummy (which then acts as a reflector) or toward the dummy (which acts as a director).   Calculations of patterns for different lengths and positions of dummies have been made by Carter[1] and Brown.[2]   These calculations are made on the same basis as the most elementary calculations of radiation resistance, based on the assumption of a sinusoidal current distribution in the antenna, and for that reason are not to be trusted in detail.   Nevertheless they are undoubtedly correct in a qualitative way.   They are hardly accurate enough to serve as a guide for microwave work, however; the proper design of dummy antennas is still a subject that must be largely determined by experiment rather than theory.

There is one point connected with reflectors, dummy antennas, and all types of directive devices, which is of importance in antenna design.   This is the fact that any directive device changes the input impedance of the antenna.   One way to see

[1] *Proc. I.R.E.*, **20**, 1004 (1932).
[2] *Proc. I.R.E.*, **25**, 78 (1937).

this is to notice that any directive device is bound to reflect
some of the radiation back to the antenna, so that it will be
absorbed again and will set up standing waves in the antenna
itself and in the transmission line feeding it.   This produces, then,
the same net effect as if the impedance of the antenna changed.
As an extreme case, we may note that if the antenna were
enclosed in a completely reflecting box, instead of being in empty
space, the intensity of the reflected wave would equal that of the
radiated wave, no power could be dissipated in the antenna, and
the radiation resistance of the antenna would be reduced to zero
(though its reactance would not).   The calculation of the change
of impedance with a complicated directive device is so difficult
as to be practically out of the question.   In practice an antenna
must be matched to its line with all directive devices in place.
In the simple case of the dummy antenna, however, calculations
of change of impedance are made in the same papers mentioned
in the preceding paragraph, in which radiation patterns are
computed.   These calculations are made by the following simple
method, treating the two antennas as two coupled circuits.   Let
V_1, i_1 be the voltage impressed on the driven antenna and the
current in this antenna, and let V_2, i_2 be the voltage and current
in the second antenna.   (In case the second is a dummy, V_2 is
zero, but we can consider the general case where it is also driven.)
Then we can set up equations

$$V_1 = Z_{11}i_1 + Z_{12}i_2$$
$$V_2 = Z_{21}i_1 + Z_{22}i_2 \qquad (36.1)$$

where Z_{11}, Z_{12}, Z_{21}, Z_{22} are coefficients of impedance and where
by the reciprocity theorem

$$Z_{12} = Z_{21} \qquad (36.2)$$

In the papers mentioned, the coefficients Z_{11}, Z_{12}, Z_{22} are tabulated, as a result of numerical calculation, for different relative
lengths and different positions of the two antennas.   The
quantities Z_{11}, Z_{22} of course reduce to the ordinary input impedances of the two antennas in case they are too far apart to affect
each other, and Z_{12} is of the nature of a mutual impedance
between them, which can be of the form either of a mutual
inductance or a capacity term, depending on circumstances.
For the case where the second antenna is a dummy, $V_2 = 0$

and we have

$$V_1 = \left(Z_{11} - \frac{Z_{12}^2}{Z_{22}}\right) i_1 \qquad (36.3)$$

so that the driven antenna has an apparent input impedance of

$$Z_{11} - \frac{Z_{12}^2}{Z_{22}} \qquad (36.4)$$

The results of the calculation for this apparent input impedance are too complicated to summarize in a few words; the reader is referred to the original papers if he wishes to make calculations. Here as with the question of radiation patterns, however, the calculations cannot be trusted in detail.

CHAPTER VII

COUPLING OF COAXIAL LINES AND WAVE GUIDES

In Chap. IV we have considered composite lines, in which the properties change discontinuously at a given point, and we have considered to what extent they can be approximated by simple transmission lines with a discontinuity in properties. Certain problems were omitted in the discussion of that chapter. In particular, we did not consider the case in which one part of the line is a coaxial line, the other part a hollow pipe. The reason was that in those problems the input from the coaxial into the pipe is of the general nature of an antenna, and the problem is closely related to that of radiation from antennas, taken up in the two preceding chapters. Now that we understand the nature of antennas, we are ready to take up these problems of the excitation of wave guides. As in the antenna problem, there is a simple and fundamental case which we shall take up first, building the rest of our discussion around it. With antennas, this was the radiation from a dipole in free space, and the absorption of energy by such a dipole. Here we consider the corresponding problem, the radiation and absorption from a dipole inside a rectangular wave guide. This problem can be solved exactly, and by means of it we can get qualitative results for the radiation and absorption of real antennas in rectangular wave guides. The corresponding problem for circular wave guides is more involved, and we shall not take it up.

37. Radiation Field of a Dipole in a Rectangular Wave Guide. Suppose we have a rectangular hollow pipe, infinitely long (or of finite length and terminated by an impedance equal to its characteristic impedance, which amounts to the same thing) and containing an oscillating electric dipole of moment $Me^{j\omega t}$, at a specified point. Our present problem is to compute the radiation field of this dipole inside the pipe. The field will have complicated values close to the dipole but will approach a simple value at large distances. It is this limiting value at large distance which we shall compute. Having found it, we can find the

280

power radiated by the dipole and hence its radiation resistance. As with a dipole in empty space, the reactance, unlike the resistance, depends on the field close to the dipole. Consequently we shall not try to compute it, though we can get some qualitative information regarding it.

Before starting with the actual calculation, we shall describe in words the methods used and the results achieved. The method which we use is the method of images. By the method discussed in Sec. 36 and illustrated in Fig. 66, a dipole within a rectangular pipe will have four images, one in each of the four walls of the pipe. Each of these images in turn will form images, and as the process is continued the net result is a two-dimensional array or lattice of images, extending to infinity in both directions in a plane normal to the axis of the pipe. The radiation from this doubly infinite array of images will automatically satisfy the boundary conditions at the faces of the pipe and hence will furnish the solution of our problem. The problem of finding the field of such an array of dipoles is analogous to the optical problem of a diffraction grating. As in that problem, there is interference between the radiation sent out by the various dipoles, which almost completely cancels the total radiation in most directions. Only in a finite number of directions does the interference result in building up the intensity of the radiation. These are the directions in which radiation from different dipoles differs in phase by a whole number of wave lengths. Corresponding to each of these directions, there is a plane wave emitted by the array of dipoles. The radiation at a large distance consists of a superposition of these plane waves. It now turns out that these waves are just those which, by superposition, result in the various waves that can be propagated down the pipe, according to the principles of Chap. III. From our calculation we find the amplitude of each of these waves. For instance, if we are in the range of wave lengths where only one mode can be propagated down the pipe, the only plane waves emitted by the dipoles will be the two that combine to form that mode. By finding the intensity of this wave and setting it equal to the radiation emitted by the dipole, we find the radiation resistance of the dipole. The field near the dipole, in contrast to this, is formed of the waves that are not propagated down the pipe but are exponentially damped. We must use an infinite series of such waves to represent the field, and the convergence is not rapid. The net result of adding these waves is to give the reactance of the dipole, consisting of capacitive and inductive reactance. We shall not try to make this calculation but shall simply point out that the reactance is not greatly affected by the fact that the dipole is in a hollow pipe and is similar to that of a corresponding dipole in empty space.

Let us now proceed with our calculation. (We shall follow the general lines used in an unpublished note by J. L. Synge; the same problem has also been discussed in an unpublished memo-

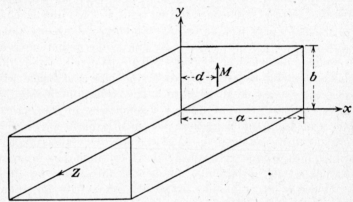

Fig. 69.—Dipole in xy plane, normal to wave guide extending indefinitely along $\pm z$.

randum by S. A. Schelkunoff.) We take coordinates as in Fig. 69. We shall assume that the pipe is of such a size that only the $TE_{1,0}$ wave can be propagated down the pipe. We choose the dipole to have its axis along the y axis, which is the direction of the electric field in the pipe, and can see intuitively that the other cases, in which the dipole has its axis along x or z, will not radiate down the pipe; if the axis is along x, the orientation would be right to produce a wave with its electric field along x, which cannot be propagated down the pipe; if the axis is along z, the dipole could produce only a transverse magnetic wave, and these waves cannot be propagated, by hypothesis. We assume the dipole to lie in the xy plane, at a distance d from the y axis. The vertical distance, from the x axis, as we shall find, is imma-terial, and we shall not specify it.

We next set up our images, following the pattern of Fig. 66. When we do this, the array of dipoles in the xy plane is as shown in Fig. 70.   As we see, there are linear arrays of dipoles following lines parallel to the y axis, spaced with a distance $2a$ along the x axis.   There are two such arrays, one at $x = d + 2na$, the

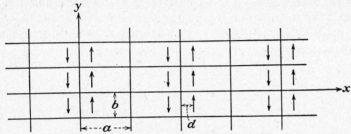

Fig. 70.—Array of image dipoles in xy plane.

other at $x = -d + 2na$, where n is an arbitrary integer.   We shall first find the field of a single linear array of dipoles and then combine them to form the two-dimensional lattice.   For a linear array, it is legitimate to replace the discrete dipoles by a continuous distribution of dipole moment, of amount $(M/b)e^{j\omega t}$ per unit distance along y.   By (30.2), this corresponds to a current

$$ie^{j\omega t} = j\omega \frac{M}{b} e^{j\omega t} \qquad (37.1)$$

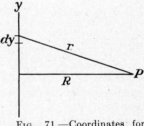

Fig. 71.—Coordinates for finding field of a linear current.

flowing along the array.   We could find the field of such a linear current in terms of Bessel's and Neumann's functions, following the methods of Sec. 20.   Rather than do this, however, we shall find the field directly by integration, so as to illustrate the method which we shall later use to sum the fields of the various linear arrays.   In Fig. 71 we show a linear array, with a set of coordinates appropriate to the problem. We shall treat the current element in dy as a dipole, use the expression (29.8) for its field, and integrate over all elements of length. In this integration, the essential contributions will come from small values of y, for which r approximately equals the perpendicular distance R, the quantity $\sin \theta$ in (29.8) is approximately unity, and E_θ is approximately in the direction of $-y$.   Keeping only the term important at the largest distances, in (29.8), we then have

$$dE_y = \frac{M}{b} \, dy \, \frac{k^2}{4\pi\epsilon R} \, e^{j(\omega t - kr)} \qquad (37.2)$$

as the contribution to the field from dy. In the quantity r appearing in the exponent, the phase is of essential significance, so that we cannot replace this quantity by R. Instead we expand as follows:

$$\begin{aligned}
r &= \sqrt{R^2 + y^2} \\
&= R \left(1 + \frac{y^2}{R^2} \right)^{\frac{1}{2}} \\
&= R \left(1 + \frac{1}{2} \frac{y^2}{R^2} + \cdots \right) \\
&= R + \frac{1}{2} \frac{y^2}{R} + \cdots
\end{aligned} \qquad (37.3)$$

Using this approximate value, we have

$$E_y = \int_{-\infty}^{\infty} \frac{M}{b} \frac{k^2}{4\pi\epsilon R} \, e^{j(\omega t - kR)} e^{-jky^2/2R} \, dy \qquad (37.4)$$

Using the result

$$\int_0^\infty \cos x^2 \, dx = \int_0^\infty \sin x^2 \, dx = \frac{1}{2} \sqrt{\frac{\pi}{2}} \qquad (37.5)$$

we find

$$E_y = \frac{M}{b} \frac{k^{\frac{3}{2}}(1-j)}{4 \sqrt{\pi} \, \epsilon \, \sqrt{R}} \, e^{j(\omega t - kR)} \qquad (37.6)$$

as the limiting value of the field of our linear current, at large distances. This is the same value that we should have obtained from Bessel's and Neumann's functions, if we had used the asymptotic expansion of these functions for large R [similar to the expansions of (27.26)].

Now that we have found the field of a linear current, let us combine the current elements at $x = d + 2na$ to find the field of an infinite lattice. In Fig. 72 we show that such a lattice produces radiation only in certain definite directions. Thus at the point P there is a beam coming normally to the x axis, in which the radiation from each lattice element has traveled approximately the same distance in reaching P, and so is in the same phase. There is another beam coming in the direction θ, in which each lattice element is one wave length farther from P than the next, so that again the waves reinforce each other. Similarly there could be beams in directions such that each element was two wave lengths farther than the next, and so on. In the corresponding problem of a diffraction grating, these are called first-order beams, second-order beams, and so on. We shall now show that in our case, where only the $TE_{1,0}$ wave can be propagated down our pipe, only the first-order beams exist.

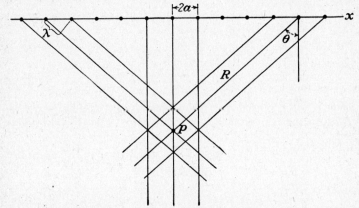

FIG. 72.—Diffraction field of a lattice.

To show this, let us find the condition on θ for the mth order beam. From Fig. 72 it is clear that this condition is that

$$m\lambda = 2a \sin \theta \qquad (37.7)$$

The maximum possible value of m is given by setting $\sin \theta$ equal to 1. In this case we have

$$\frac{2}{\lambda} = \frac{m}{a} \qquad (37.8)$$

for the longest wave length at which the mth order diffracted beam exists. But from (15.17) we see that this is just the condition of cutoff for the $TE_{m,0}$ mode in the pipe. Thus in our case, where only the $TE_{1,0}$ wave can be propagated, only the first-order diffracted beams exist. Not only this, the two first-order beams, shown in Fig. 72, are just the ones which, by interference, produce the $TE_{1,0}$ type of wave in the pipe, as we can see from Eq. (14.8), which is identical with (37.7) (except that in (14.8) the roles of the x and y axes were interchanged) and which gives us the angle with the z axis at which two plane waves must be propagated, to give the $TE_{1,0}$ wave by interference.

Now that we understand the physical side of our problem, we can proceed with the mathematical steps of summing the fields E_y from all linear currents, as shown in Fig. 72. We can handle separately each diffracted beam. We must sum quantities (37.6) for all current elements. In this expression, the quantity R is the distance from the current element to the point P where we are finding the field. If this point has coordinates x, z, $(y = 0)$, and if the current element is at $x = d + 2na$, $z = 0$, then,

$$R = \sqrt{(d + 2na - x)^2 + z^2} \qquad (37.9)$$

Let

$$d + 2na - x = z \tan \theta + \xi \qquad (37.10)$$

so that $\xi = 0$ corresponds to the point from which radiation falls on P satisfying exactly the condition (37.7). Then (37.9) becomes

$$
\begin{aligned}
R &= \sqrt{z^2 + z^2 \tan^2 \theta + 2\xi z \tan \theta + \xi^2} \\
&= z \sec \theta \left(1 + \frac{2\xi}{z} \frac{\sin \theta}{\sec \theta} + \frac{\xi^2}{z^2} \cos^2 \theta \right)^{\frac{1}{2}} \\
&= z \sec \theta \left(1 + \frac{\xi}{z} \frac{\sin \theta}{\sec \theta} + \frac{1}{2} \frac{\xi^2}{z^2} \cos^2 \theta - \frac{1}{2} \frac{\xi^2}{z^2} \sin^2 \theta \cos^2 \theta \cdots \right) \\
&= z \sec \theta + \xi \sin \theta + \frac{1}{2} \frac{\xi^2}{z} \cos^3 \theta \cdots \qquad (37.11)
\end{aligned}
$$

We now substitute the value (37.11) in (37.6), finding for the exponential

$$e^{-jkR} = e^{-jk\left[z \sec \theta + (d+2na-x-z \tan \theta) \sin \theta + \frac{\xi^2 \cos^3 \theta}{2z} \right]}$$

$$= e^{-jk[z \cos \theta + (d-x) \sin \theta]} e^{-jk2na \sin \theta} e^{-\frac{jk\xi^2 \cos^3 \theta}{2z}} \qquad (37.12)$$

where we have used (37.10) and a little trigonometry. Now from (37.7)

$$k2na \sin \theta = \frac{2\pi}{\lambda} 2na \sin \theta = 2\pi n \qquad (37.13)$$

where we remember that n is an integer. Thus the exponential $e^{-jk2na \sin \theta}$ equals unity. It is this fact which distinguishes our diffraction beam from other directions and allows us to integrate (37.12), since n cancels out of the expression.

Having found the expression (37.12) for our exponential, we should sum over all values of n. We have just seen, however, that n appears in (37.12) only through the quantity ξ^2, in a term that varies only slightly from one value of n to the next, so that we can replace the sum by an integral. Since the interval between successive current elements is $2a$, the sum of the E_y's of Eq. (37.6) is

$$\text{Total } E_y = \int_{-\infty}^{\infty} \frac{M}{b} \frac{k^{3/2}(1-j)}{4\sqrt{\pi}\,\epsilon\,\sqrt{z\sec\theta}}\, e^{-jk[z\cos\theta + (d-x)\sin\theta]}e^{j\omega t}$$
$$e^{-\frac{jk\xi^2\cos^3\theta}{2z}}\frac{d\xi}{2a} \quad (37.14)$$

where in the denominator we have replaced R by its leading term, from (37.11). Integrating, using (37.5), we have

$$\text{Total } E_y = \frac{jkM}{4ab\epsilon\cos\theta}\, e^{j[\omega t - kz\cos\theta - k(d-x)\sin\theta]} \quad (37.15)$$

The expression (37.15) represents the total field of the array of current elements at $d + 2na$, arising from the diffracted beam in the direction θ. There will also be a corresponding beam in the direction $-\theta$, however, and in addition to these there will be two beams, of opposite sign, coming from the oppositely directed array of elements at $-d + 2na$. When we add the fields of the four beams, we find from (37.15)

$$E_y = -\frac{jkM}{ab\epsilon\cos\theta}\sin(kd\sin\theta)\sin(kx\sin\theta)e^{j(\omega t - kz\cos\theta)} \quad (37.16)$$

In deriving (37.16), we have considered only the first-order diffracted beams, not the beams traveling along the z axis. The reason is that these last beams cancel, the two arrays of current elements, with opposite signs, exactly balancing in their effect.

When we compare (37.16) with (14.1), we see that the solution that we have found is of the correct form for a $TE_{1,0}$ wave in the pipe. (We note that the roles of x and y are reversed, in comparison with (14.1).) We can then use the comparison with (14.1) to find H_x and H_z, the other nonvanishing field components. We could find these components by direct integration of the field of elementary dipoles, as we have found E_y, but we should come to the same answer that we can find by comparison with (14.1).   We then find

$$E_y = - \frac{j\omega M}{ab} \sqrt{\frac{\mu}{\epsilon}} \frac{\sin (\pi d/a)}{\sqrt{1 - (\pi/ka)^2}} \sin \frac{\pi x}{a} e^{j[\omega t - kz\sqrt{1 - (\pi/ka)^2}]}$$

$$H_x = \frac{j\omega M}{ab} \sin \frac{\pi d}{a} \sin \frac{\pi x}{a} e^{j[\omega t - kz\sqrt{1 - (\pi/ka)^2}]}$$

$$H_z = \frac{j\omega M}{ab} \sin \frac{\pi d}{a} \frac{\pi}{a} \frac{\cos (\pi x/a)}{jk \sqrt{1 - (\pi/ka)^2}} e^{j[\omega t - kz\sqrt{1 - (\pi/ka)^2}]} \quad (37.17)$$

where we have used (37.7) to substitute for θ.   This is the field
at large distances from the dipole, propagated along the $+z$
direction through the wave guide.   We note that at large distances in the negative direction there will of course also be a
wave, propagated along $-z$.   The problem of finding this wave
proceeds in the same way, and the final field can be obtained from
(37.17) by the following changes: change the sign of z, and of H_x,
keeping other quantities unchanged.

**38. Radiation Resistance, Absorption, and Scattering for a
Dipole in a Rectangular Wave Guide.**—In the preceding section
we have found, in (37.17), the radiation field, at large distances,
of a dipole of moment $Me^{j\omega t}$, located in a wave guide of larger
dimension a, smaller dimension b, for the case where the dimensions of the guide are such that only the $TE_{1,0}$ wave can be
propagated.   The quantity d is the distance of the dipole from
the plane $x = 0$, which forms one wall of the guide.   The dipole
is assumed to be parallel to the y direction.   We can now proceed
as in Sec. 30 to find the radiation resistance of this dipole.
To do this, we find the power radiated by the dipole and set this
equal to $\frac{1}{2}I^2R$, where I is the current in the dipole and R is the
resistance.   First let us find the radiated power.   This is
the integral of Poynting's vector, which is $\frac{1}{2} \mathrm{Re} \, (-E_y \bar{H}_x)$.   For
the wave traveling along $+z$, we have

$$- \frac{1}{2} E_y \bar{H}_x = \frac{1}{2} \frac{\omega^2 M^2}{a^2 b^2} \sqrt{\frac{\mu}{\epsilon}} \frac{\sin^2 (\pi d/a)}{\sqrt{1 - (\pi/ka)^2}} \sin^2 \frac{\pi x}{a} \quad (38.1)$$

To integrate, we may replace $\sin^2 (\pi x/a)$ by its average value $\frac{1}{2}$,
and multiply by the area ab of the pipe.   For the wave traveling
along $-z$ we find an equal value for the radiated power.   Adding
the two, we have

$$\text{Radiated power} = \frac{1}{2} \frac{\omega^2 M^2}{ab} \sqrt{\frac{\mu}{\epsilon}} \frac{\sin^2 (\pi d/a)}{\sqrt{1 - (\pi/ka)^2}} \quad (38.2)$$

To set this equal to $\frac{1}{2}I^2R$, we must know the current I in the dipole. Let us assume that the length of the dipole is l. Then by analogy with Eq. (30.2) we have

$$j\omega M = Il \qquad (38.3)$$

Using this value, we then have

$$R_r = \frac{l^2}{ab}\sqrt{\frac{\mu}{\epsilon}}\,\frac{\sin^2\,(\pi d/a)}{\sqrt{1-(\pi/ka)^2}} \qquad (38.4)$$

In (38.4) we have our desired formula for the radiation resistance of a dipole of length l, in a wave guide of dimensions a and b. By comparison with (30.24), we may find the ratio of R to the radiation resistance of the same dipole in empty space. We find that it is

$$\frac{R_r}{R_0} = \frac{3\pi}{2}\left(\frac{\lambda}{2a}\right)\left(\frac{\lambda}{2b}\right)\frac{\sin^2\,(\pi d/a)}{\sqrt{1-(\pi/ka)^2}}. \qquad (38.5)$$

This ratio is of the order of magnitude of unity. For our assumption about the size of the pipe, using (37.7), we see that $\lambda/2a$ must be less than unity but $\lambda/2b$ is greater than unity, so that these factors roughly cancel and the other factors are of the order of magnitude of unity.

We shall next consider the dipole in the wave guide, not as an emitter of energy, but as an absorber or scatterer, following the pattern of Sec. 33. First, as in that section, we shall consider the superposition of two wave fields, the emitted wave field of the dipole, which is given by (37.17), and a plane wave traveling along the z direction through the pipe. For this plane wave, following (14.1), we may write the field components

$$E_y = E_0 \sin\frac{\pi x}{a}\,e^{j[\omega t - kz\sqrt{1-(\pi/ka)^2}]}$$

$$H_x = -E_0\sqrt{\frac{\epsilon}{\mu}}\sqrt{1-\left(\frac{\pi}{ka}\right)^2}\,\sin\frac{\pi x}{a}\,e^{j[\omega t - kz\sqrt{1-(\pi/ka)^2}]}$$

$$H_z = -E_0\frac{\pi}{ajk}\sqrt{\frac{\epsilon}{\mu}}\cos\frac{\pi x}{a}\,e^{j[\omega t - kz\sqrt{1-(\pi/ka)^2}]} \qquad (38.6)$$

We superpose this field and the field (37.17). In finding Poynting's vector, there are now three terms: terms coming from the radiated wave only, which give the value already found in (38.2); terms coming from the plane wave only, which give no net flow of energy into or out of the dipole; and interference terms between

the two. The interference effect will be felt only behind the
dipole, as far as the incident wave is concerned (that is, for $+z$,
since the wave is coming from $-z$, traveling in the $+z$ direction),
for it is only here that the incident and radiated waves travel
in the same direction.   To get the mutual term in Poynting's vector, we must multiply the E of the incident wave by the H of the
radiated wave, and vice versa, and add the two results.   When
we do this and integrate over the area of the pipe as in deriving
(38.2), we find

Radiated power on account of interference

$$= -\frac{1}{2} I l E_0 \sin \frac{\pi d}{a} \quad (38.7)$$

We may now define a voltage acting on the dipole as the value
of the field E_y, of (38.6), acting on the dipole, computed at the
point $x = d$ where the dipole is, multiplied by the length l of the
dipole.   When we define the voltage V in this way, we find

Radiated power on account of interference $= -\frac{1}{2} \operatorname{Re} V \bar{I}$ (38.8)

This result is exactly analogous to (33.14), obtained for the corresponding problem in free space.

We shall now assume that the dipole has a certain impedance,
or ratio of voltage V to current I, as just defined.   This assumption is the same one made in Sec. 33, in particular in Eq. (33.18),
about a dipole in free space.   As in that section, the total
impedance will be the sum of what we might call the intrinsic
impedance and the radiation terms.   Let us be more precise
about this.   The dipole will have a certain reactance, which
should be computed from the attenuated waves in the wave guide.
The result will be similar to the reactance of a similar dipole
in empty space, consisting of a capacitative reactance if the dipole
is short, with inductive terms coming in for longer dipoles.
The reactance will be affected by the walls; for really we have not
a single dipole but an infinite set of images, each of which will
affect the reactance of the real dipole, just as if they were dummy
antennas, acting according to the principles mentioned in Sec.
36.   It is rather hard to estimate the changes in reactance
produced in this way by the walls of the pipe, and we shall not
try to do it.   The dipole will also have a resistance: not only the
radiation resistance but also the resistance due to its finite con-

ductivity.   Finally it may be that the dipole is really connected
to a coaxial line or other transmission line, as was the antenna of
Fig. 54.   In this case the impedance of the line, looking into it
from the dipole, is effectively in series with the dipole, so that its
resistance and reactance are added to the resistance and reactance
of the dipole.   We shall now adopt a somewhat different convention from that of Sec. 33: we shall assume that Z, the impedance of the dipole, includes its whole reactance, its resistance
as arising from finite conductivity, and the resistance and
reactance in series with the dipole, but not the radiation resistance.   That is, the total impedance, the ratio of V to I, is
assumed to be $Z + R_r$:

$$V = I(Z + R_r) = I(R_r + R + jX) \qquad (38.9)$$

We can now understand the situation when radiation traveling
down the pipe falls on the dipole.   Let us suppose that the
incident wave is given by (38.6).   The voltage V acting on the
dipole is

$$V = E_0 l \sin \frac{\pi d}{a} e^{j\omega t} \qquad (38.10)$$

The current induced in the dipole can be at once found from
(38.9), and its dipole moment from the relation

$$M = \frac{Il}{j\omega} \qquad (38.11)$$

By (37.17), the scattered field is then

$$E_y = -\frac{E_0 l^2}{(Z + R_r)ab} \sqrt{\frac{\mu}{\epsilon}} \frac{\sin^2 (\pi d/a)}{\sqrt{1 - (\pi/ka)^2}} \sin \frac{\pi x}{a} e^{j(\omega t - \beta z)} \qquad (38.12)$$

where

$$\beta = k \sqrt{1 - \left(\frac{\pi}{ka}\right)^2} \qquad (38.13)$$

This is the field for large positive z's; for large negative z's,
there is a similar value but with the opposite sign for the term βz
in the exponent.   Combining scattered and incident waves, the
total disturbance for large positive values of z (that is, to the
right of the dipole, or beyond it, in the direction of travel of
the incident wave) is

$$E_y = C \sin \frac{\pi x}{a} e^{i(\omega t - \beta z)}, \qquad H_x = -\frac{E_y}{Z_0} \qquad (38.14)$$

where

$$C = E_0 \left[1 - \frac{l^2}{(Z + R_r)ab} \sqrt{\frac{\mu}{\epsilon}} \frac{\sin^2 (\pi d/a)}{\sqrt{1 - (\pi/ka)^2}} \right]$$

$$Z_0 = \sqrt{\frac{\mu}{\epsilon}} \frac{1}{\sqrt{1 - (\pi/ka)^2}} \qquad (38.15)$$

Similarly for negative z's we have

$$E_y = (A e^{-i\beta z} + B e^{i\beta z}) \sin \frac{\pi x}{a} e^{i\omega t}$$

$$H_x = \left(\frac{-A e^{-i\beta z} + B e^{i\beta z}}{Z_0} \right) \sin \frac{\pi x}{a} e^{j\omega t} \qquad (38.16)$$

where

$$A = E_0$$

$$B = \frac{-E_0 l^2}{(Z + R_r)ab} \sqrt{\frac{\mu}{\epsilon}} \frac{\sin^2 (\pi d/a)}{\sqrt{1 - (\pi/ka)^2}} \qquad (38.17)$$

The results we have just written down remind us of the sort of reflected waves that we should find if a uniform transmission line were shunted by an impedance at $z = 0$. We can in fact set up such an equivalent transmission line problem, which proves to be of great advantage in discussing further problems of a dipole in a wave guide, such as the question of what happens when one end of the guide is closed, or for instance when the dipole contains a source of power, acting like a radiating antenna. We shall find that the problem is not quite so simple as we might suppose. At first sight, it would seem plausible that the equivalent circuit might be a uniform transmission line of characteristic impedance Z_0 (as defined in (38.15), which agrees with the definition of (14.11)), shunted by the impedance Z at $z = 0$. This however does not give the right answer. We must instead use a different value for the characteristic impedance of the transmission line, or else a different value for Z. This is not unreasonable; we have seen in Sec. 24 that the definition (38.15) for the impedance of a wave guide is not a very reasonable value, and that an equivalent impedance equal to b/a times (38.15) (we note that the meanings of a and b are here reversed from the values in (24.2)) is more reasonable. Even that equivalent impedance is not the one that must be used in the present case, however. Let us set up the problem and find the correct value to assume.

Suppose we have a line of characteristic impedance Z_c, shunted by an impedance Z_s. Looking to the right from the terminals aa, in Fig. 73, we see an impedance

$$Z = \frac{1}{1/Z_s + 1/Z_c} = \frac{Z_s Z_c}{Z_s + Z_c} \quad (38.18)$$

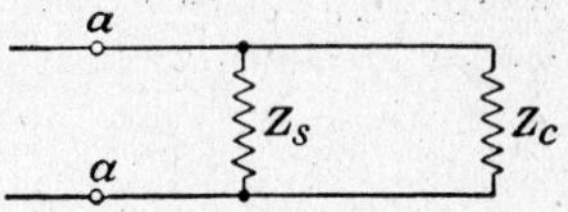

FIG. 73.—Uniform line with shunt impedance.

Using Eq. (3.9), then, the ratio B/A of reflected to incident voltage (the negative of the ratio of currents, which is given in (3.9)) should be

$$\frac{B}{A} = \frac{\dfrac{Z_s Z_c}{Z_s + Z_c} - Z_c}{\dfrac{Z_s Z_c}{Z_s + Z_c} + Z_c} = \frac{-Z_c}{Z_c + 2Z_s} \quad (38.19)$$

Let us set this equal to the ratio B/A from (38.17) and find values of Z_s and Z_c so that this relation will be satisfied, so that the equivalent circuit will lead to the same reflected amplitude as the real wave guide. We can rewrite the ratio from (38.17) by using the value of the radiation resistance R_r from (38.4). When we do this we have

$$\frac{B}{A} = -\frac{R_r}{Z + R_r} \quad (38.20)$$

Equating (38.19) and (38.20) (or, more easily, by equating their reciprocals), we have

$$\frac{2Z_s}{Z_c} = \frac{Z}{R_r}, \qquad \frac{Z_s}{Z} = \frac{Z_c}{2R_r} \quad (38.21)$$

Having found the relation (38.21), there are two possible choices for Z_s and Z_c that are natural; since (38.21) determines only their ratio, the exact choice is a matter of convenience, not of necessity. First, we may choose the shunt impedance Z_s equal to the actual impedance Z of the dipole. Then we have

$$\begin{aligned}
Z_c = 2R_r &= \frac{2l^2}{ab} \sqrt{\frac{\mu}{a}} \frac{\sin^2 (\pi d/a)}{\sqrt{1 - (\pi k/a)^2}} \\
&= \frac{2l^2}{ab} \sin^2 \frac{\pi d}{a} Z_0 \quad (38.22)
\end{aligned}$$

where Z_0 is given in (38.15), or

$$Z_c = \frac{2l^2}{b^2} \sin^2 \frac{\pi d}{a} Z_{eq} \qquad (38.23)$$

where Z_{eq} is the equivalent impedance of (24.2). Or secondly we may choose Z_c to be the equivalent impedance

$$Z_{eq} = \frac{b}{a} Z_0 \qquad (38.24)$$

in which case we have

$$Z_s = \frac{b^2}{2l^2} \frac{Z}{\sin^2 (\pi d/a)} \qquad (38.25)$$

and the shunt admittance of the dipole, $1/Z_s$, is

$$Y_s = \frac{1}{Z} \frac{2l^2}{b^2} \sin^2 \frac{\pi d}{a} \qquad (38.26)$$

Suppose we define a coefficient α, which we may call a coupling coefficient, by the formula

$$\alpha = \frac{2l^2}{b^2} \sin^2 \frac{\pi d}{a} \qquad (38.27)$$

Then the first of our two assumptions, (38.23), gives

$$Z_s = Z, \qquad Z_c = \alpha Z_{eq} \qquad (38.28)$$

The second, (38.25), gives

$$Z_s = \frac{Z}{\alpha}, \qquad Z_c = Z_{eq} \qquad (38.29)$$

The coupling coefficient α, which we have introduced, measures the effectiveness of the dipole in inducing a field in the wave guide. It is proportional to the square of the ratio (l/b) of the length of the dipole to the width of the wave guide and proportional to the quantity $\sin^2 (\pi d/a)$, which for small values of d is proportional to the square of the ratio d/a of the distance of the dipole from the wall, to the other dimension of the wave guide. If the length of the dipole equals b, so that it stretches clear across the guide, and if it is placed in the middle of the guide, so that the sine equals unity, we have $\alpha = 2$, its largest possible value; a small dipole near the edge of the guide, on the other hand, corresponds to a very small value of α. We may now ask under what conditions we wish to use either the assumption (38.28) or (38.29). In the first place, we may be interested in looking into the wave guide from the dipole. Suppose the dipole forms the termination of a coaxial transmission line, and we want to know what the impedance is which terminates this line. In this case we naturally use (38.28). We find then, as in Fig. 74, that the dipole of impedance Z is in series with two parallel impedances, each of $Z_c = \alpha Z_{eq}$, one of these impedances representing the line to the left of the dipole, the other the line to the right. That is, the dipole is in series with $Z_c/2$, which by (38.22) is R_r, the radiation resistance. It is only natural that Z_c in this case should depend on α, for obviously the smaller the dipole is, the less it will radiate, and the less the radiation resistance will be.

Looking in from the input of the dipole, then, the wave guide looks like a transmission line of characteristic impedance αZ_{eq}, a quantity varying all the way from $2Z_{eq}$ to zero, depending on the closeness of coupling between the dipole and the guide, or on the coefficient α.

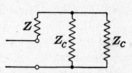

FIG. 74.—Equivalent circuit for dipole in wave guide.

The second assumption (38.29) is the more natural one to use when we are primarily interested in the wave guide. From this standpoint, the definition Z_{eq} is the most natural one for the impedance of the wave guide. Then a dipole in the guide acts as far as the equivalent circuit is concerned like an impedance Z/α shunted across the line, where Z is the actual impedance of the dipole. This impedance Z/α varies, then, from $Z/2$ in the case of closest coupling, to infinity with no coupling, or the admittance varies from twice the admittance of the dipole with close coupling to zero with no coupling. We are to remember in this that Z, the impedance of the dipole, includes its reactance (as affected by the walls of the guide), its intrinsic resistance arising from its finite conductivity, and the resistance and reactance of the line which feeds it, if any, but does not include its radiation resistance, which in this method of equivalent circuits is taken care of by the guide. A particularly interesting case is that in which the dipole is not connected to an outside line but is merely a small metallic element introduced into the guide as a scatterer. If we can neglect energy dissipation in the ohmic resistance of the dipole, Z will then be a pure reactance. We then have the result that a metallic scattering element in a wave guide acts, as far as the equivalent circuit is concerned, like a reactance shunted across the line, the magnitude of the reactance being $1/\alpha$ times the actual reactance of the scatterer.

39. Properties of a Dipole in a Wave Guide Closed at One End.—In the preceding sections we have considered the behavior of a dipole in a wave guide open at both ends, as an emitter, absorber, and scatterer of energy. Now we shall take up the practically more interesting case in which the guide is closed at one or both ends. First we consider the case of a guide closed with a perfectly reflecting wall at one end, open at the other. This approaches the arrangements practically used for generating waves in wave guides, by means of antennas inserted into them. As before, let us first find the radiation emitted by the dipole, far down the pipe toward the end that is not closed. Then we shall consider a wave approaching the dipole, being absorbed and scattered by it.

By the principles discussed in Fig. 66, the closed end of the wave guide will form an image of the dipole, in opposite phase, and the complete field far to the right along the guide will be the sum of the fields of the dipole and of its image. If the dipole is located at $z = 0$ and the end of the guide at $z = -c$, the image will be at $z = -2c$. Using the expression (37.17) for the field far to the right of a dipole and combining two such terms, one for the dipole and the other for the image, we see that the electric field at large distances to the right will be

$$E_y = -\frac{j\omega M}{ab}\sqrt{\frac{\mu}{\epsilon}}\frac{\sin{(\pi d/a)}}{\sqrt{1 - (\pi/ka)^2}}\sin{\frac{\pi x}{a}}\,e^{i\omega t}[e^{-j\beta z} - e^{-j\beta(z+2c)}]$$

$$= -\frac{j\omega M}{ab}\sqrt{\frac{\mu}{\epsilon}}\frac{\sin{(\pi d/a)}}{\sqrt{1 - (\pi/ka)^2}}\sin{\frac{\pi x}{a}}\,e^{j[\omega t-\beta(z+c)]}\,2j\sin\beta c \quad (39.1)$$

This field, except for the change of phase involved in the appearance of $(z + c)$ instead of z in the exponent, is $2j \sin \beta c$ times the field that would be present if the guide were open at both ends. Thus the radiation down the pipe to the right will be $4\sin^2 \beta c$ times as great as without the closed end of the pipe. We can now follow the derivation of (38.4) and find the radiation resistance in the present case. The radiated power down the pipe to the right is $4\sin^2 \beta c$ times as great as that in the same direction in the open pipe, but there is no radiation to the left, so that the total radiated power is only $2 \sin^2 \beta c$ times as great as for the open pipe, and the radiation resistance is then

$$R_r = 2 \sin^2 \beta c \, \frac{l^2}{ab} \sqrt{\frac{\mu}{\epsilon}} \, \frac{\sin^2 (\pi d/a)}{\sqrt{1 - (\pi/ka)^2}} \qquad (39.2)$$

This varies from zero, when for instance the dipole is a half wave length from the end of the pipe, so that the image cancels the dipole in its effect, to twice the radiation resistance in the open pipe, when for instance the dipole is a quarter wave length from the end of the pipe.

We should expect that this same result could be obtained from the type of equivalent circuit used in Sec. 38, and this is in fact the case. In Fig. 75 we show the circuit in this case. To the left of the shunt impedance Z is a length c of transmission line, which by Eq. (38.28) may be assumed to have a characteristic impedance αZ_{eq}. To the right is an open-circuited line of characteristic impedance αZ_{eq}. Thus

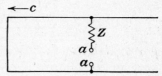

Fig. 75.—Equivalent circuit for wave guide closed at one end.

by fundamental principles the line to the left has an impedance $\alpha Z_{eq} \tanh \beta c = \alpha Z_{eq} j \tan \beta c$, assuming its attenuation is negligible, and the line to the right has an impedance αZ_{eq}. As in Fig. 74, these two impedances are in parallel with each other and in series with Z. A combination of impedances $\alpha Z_{eq} j \tan \beta c$ and αZ_{eq} in parallel with each other is easily shown to be

$$\alpha Z_{eq}(\sin^2 \beta c + j \sin \beta c \cos \beta c) \qquad (39.3)$$

Using Eqs. (38.15), (38.24), (38.27), we see that the resistive component of (39.3) is the same as the radiation resistance (39.2). The reactive component gives the correction to the reactance of the dipole on account of its image in the end wall of the guide, in case the transmission line analogy is applicable. This will be the case if the field of the image, at the dipole, is essentially the same as the field at large distances, which is the case if the dipole is far enough from the end of the guide.

The arrangement we have just described can be made the basis for a matched input from a coaxial line into a wave guide, as shown in Fig. 76. Here the dipole antenna is a section of the inner conductor of the coaxial line. This line extends through the wave guide to the opposite side, where it is terminated by an adjustable plunger b. By moving this plunger, the impedance across the coaxial line at the point where it leaves the wave guide can be given any purely reactive value. This is effectively in series with the antenna, so that we can adjust the reactance of the antenna to any desired value and in particular can tune it to have zero reactance, to match an external circuit that is a pure resistance. Then by adjusting the plunger a in the wave guide we can adjust the radiation resistance of the antenna, which is given by (39.2), within limits, thus matching it to an external line if the resistance of that line lies within the required limits. These limits are zero and a maximum resistance αZ_{eq},

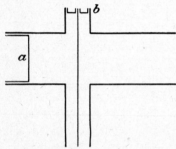

where Z_{eq} is the equivalent characteristic impedance of the guide. We have seen that the maximum possible value of α is 2, attained when the length of the antenna equals b (as it does in this case), and when it is in the middle of the wave guide, as we should normally have it in this arrangement. Thus by such a device we can match the wave guide to any input whose resistance is

FIG. 76.—Schematic diagram of input from coaxial line to wave guide.

less than twice the characteristic impedance of the wave guide, when that characteristic impedance is defined as in (38.24), (38.15). When this match is secured, the power flowing in from the coaxial line will all reappear as power flowing down the guide, and none will be reflected in the coaxial line.

We have now considered the dipole in the wave guide closed at one end, as a radiator. Let us next consider it as an absorber and scatterer of radiation. The physical situation is simple. A wave comes down the pipe from the right, toward the closed end. Since the closed end is a perfect reflector, there would in the absence of the d pole be a reflected wave traveling back to the right, equal in intensity to the direct wave, so that no power would be lost in the reflection (neglecting attenuation on account of skin effect). This combined field of the incident and reflected waves, however, will fall on the dipole and will set it into oscillation. The dipole in consequence of this oscillation will send out a scattered wave of its own, which as we have just seen will travel down the pipe to the right.   This scattered wave will interfere with the wave reflected by the closed end of the pipe, so that the net reflected wave to the right will have different intensity from the incident wave; in general it will have smaller intensity. The loss of energy represents the energy that has flowed into the resistive component of the impedance of the dipole.   If the dipole has no resistance, the reflected intensity will equal the incident intensity, the only effect of the dipole being to change its phase in comparison with what there would have been in the absence of the dipole.   If there is a resistance, however, as for instance if the dipole is in series with a resistive load, for instance a coaxial line terminated by its characteristic impedance, then power will flow into the dipole, and the reflected wave in the pipe will be weaker than the incident wave.   For maximum power flow into the dipole, the situation is as we have found in Sec. 33: the reactance of the dipole must be zero, and its resistance must equal the radiation resistance.   Now, however, in computing the reactance we must make correction for the effect of the end wall, and the radiation resistance we use must also be corrected for the wall, so that we use the values given in (39.3).   When we match the dipole in this way, we now find that we achieve something that cannot be done with a dipole in empty space: all the power flowing to the dipole is absorbed, and none is reflected back. This was impossible in empty space, because the incident wave was a plane wave, the scattered wave a spherical wave, and these two could not possibly cancel everywhere by interference; they canceled only in a shadow behind the dipole.   Here however the scattered wave, like the incident wave, is a plane wave traveling down the pipe, and it can exactly cancel the wave reflected from the end of the pipe, resulting in no reflected wave at all and a perfect match.   We should expect that this would be accomplished when the impedance of the dipole was the conjugate of the value (39.3).   For in this case the sum of the reactance of the dipole and the correction to the reactance given in (39.3) will add to zero, and the resistance of the dipole will equal the radiation resistance.   This proves in fact to be the case.

Rather than analyze this problem of absorption and scattering by setting up each of the waves in the pipe, we shall content ourselves with a treatment in terms of the equivalent transmission line. Looking to the left at the point where the dipole is located, we see the dipole shunted across the terminated line. Neglecting the attenuation in the line, the terminated line has an impedance $Z_{eq}j \tan \beta c$, if we use the formulas (38.29) for impedance, and the dipole is effectively an impedance Z/α shunted across the line. The impedance of this parallel combination is

$$\frac{Z(Z_{eq}j \tan \beta c)}{Z + \alpha Z_{eq}j \tan \beta c} \quad . \tag{39.4}$$

For an impedance match, this should equal the characteristic impedance Z_{eq} of the wave guide. Equating (39.4) to Z_{eq}, the resulting equation leads easily to the relation

$$Z = \alpha Z_{eq}(\sin^2 \beta c - j\alpha \sin \beta c \cos \beta c) \tag{39.5}$$

which is the conjugate of (39.3), as we saw it should be. In Eq. (39.5) we have the value to which the impedance of the dipole must be tuned, so that it will be matched to the wave guide. From what we have seen earlier, this matching will work both ways: a wave striking the dipole from the coaxial will be transmitted without reflection into the wave guide, and a wave striking it from the wave guide will likewise be transmitted without reflection into the coaxial. Thus practically both these results can be obtained by the sort of tuning indicated in Fig. 76.

40. A Dipole in a Wave Guide Closed at Both Ends.—If a dipole is located in a wave guide closed at both ends, the situation is very different from the ones that we have so far taken up. No radiation can now escape from the system; unless we consider attenuation in the walls of the wave guide, or other forms of resistance, there is no way for energy to be lost at all. The dipole then cannot radiate energy, and the radiation resistance must be zero. A dipole in a hollow cavity, then, can have a radiation resistance only if there is some sort of resistance loading of the cavity, and the radiation resistance depends on this loading. Furthermore, a hollow cavity, such as a wave guide closed at both ends, has resonance effects. For certain frequencies, oscillations of extremely high amplitude are set up, compared to the amplitudes at other frequencies. This subject of the resonances of hollow cavities is an extremely large one and is very important in some applications of microwave work. It can, in fact, be made the basis of the whole theory of microwave transmission.

We have preferred rather to reverse the order, handling transmission lines as the fundamental feature and keeping resonant cavities in the background. In the present section, we shall not in any sense go into the whole theory of the modes of resonant cavities but shall merely show how one runs into such things in wave guides closed at both ends, using the transmission line analogy to handle the dipole that excites the radiation in the wave guide.

Suppose we consider the following simple problem: a closed wave guide of length L, running from a short-circuited end at $z = -c$ to another closed end at $z = L - c$. So as to have some loading in the guide and a possibility of a finite radiation resistance for the dipole feeding it, we assume the closed end at $z = L - c$ to have a finite, real resistance R. Aside from this, we assume the walls of the guide to have no resistance. At $z = 0$ we have a dipole of impedance Z, coupling coefficient α. The characteristic impedance of the guide is Z_{eq}. We shall now ask what is the input impedance of the whole combination, as we look into the dipole. For definiteness, we may assume the dipole to be fed by a coaxial, as in Fig. 76; our problem differs from that only in having another plunger, of finite resistance, closing the right-hand end of the pipe. The circuit is now like Fig. 75, with a resistance R closing the right end; and we wish the total impedance across the terminals aa. The left-hand shunt branch of the circuit will have an impedance Z_1, equal to

$$Z_1 = jX_1 = \alpha Z_{eq} j \tan \beta c \qquad (40.1)$$

where we use Eq. (38.28) for the impedances, since we are concentrating our attention on the dipole. The right-hand shunt branch will have an impedance Z_2, equal to

$$Z_2 = R_2 + jX_2 = \alpha Z_{eq} \frac{Z_{eq} j \sin \beta(L - c) + R \cos \beta(L - c)}{Z_{eq} \cos \beta(L - c) + Rj \sin \beta(L - c)} \qquad (40.2)$$

We can rewrite this as

$$R_2 + jX_2 = \alpha Z_{eq} j \tan \beta(L - c) \frac{1 - jR/Z_{eq} \cot \beta(L - c)}{1 + jR/Z_{eq} \tan \beta(L - c)} \qquad (40.3)$$

The case we shall particularly consider is that in which R is small compared to Z_{eq}; that is, a resonant cavity with small resistance. In that case the denominator in (40.3) can be raised to the -1

power and placed in the numerator, expanded in series, and only the first term retained, so that the fraction becomes

$$1 - \frac{jR}{Z_{eq}} \left[\cot \beta(L - c) + \tan \beta(L - c) \right]$$

$$= 1 - \frac{jR}{Z_{eq}} \cot \beta(L - c) \sec^2 \beta(L - c) \quad (40.4)$$

Inserting in (40.3), we then have for small R

$$R_2 + jX_2 = \alpha R \sec^2 \beta(L - c) + \alpha Z_{eq} j \tan \beta(L - c)$$
$$R_2 = \alpha R \sec^2 \beta(L - c), \qquad X_2 = \alpha Z_{eq} \tan \beta(L - c) \quad (40.5)$$

In the circuit of Fig. 75, the total impedance across the terminals aa is now the sum of Z and of the impedance of Z_1 and Z_2 in parallel. This latter value is

$$\frac{Z_1 Z_2}{Z_1 + Z_2} = \frac{jX_1(R_2 + jX_2)}{R_2 + j(X_1 + X_2)} \quad (40.6)$$

where X_1 is given in (40.1), R_2 and X_2 in (40.5). The denominator of (40.6) shows the characteristic behavior of a resonance term: when $X_1 + X_2$ is zero, the impedance (40.6) becomes very large, as in the ordinary case of antiresonance of a parallel tuned circuit. In other words, at this point, for a given current flowing through the terminals aa in Fig. 75, there is an extremely high voltage across the tuned circuit, indicating extremely high currents flowing in the two branches in opposite directions, or a very large circulating current in the tuned circuit or, in this case, in the wave guide. That is, the wave guide is set into violent oscillation at these particular frequencies. We can easily find the values of the length of the wave guide which lead to resonance: they are simply integral numbers of half wave lengths. For suppose

$$L = \frac{n\lambda}{2}, \qquad \beta L = n\pi \quad (40.7)$$

where n is an integer. Then

$$\tan \beta(L - c) = \tan (n\pi - \beta c) = - \tan \beta c \quad (40.8)$$

so that X_2 is the negative of X_1, and the total reactance vanishes. The oscillations occurring at these lengths are called the normal modes of the resonant cavity. For each of these normal modes, there is a voltage node (that is, the voltage is zero) at the short-circuited end of the wave guide, and the voltage is approximately zero at the other end of the guide, so long as the resistance is small, as we have assumed; if the resistance is large, then our approximations are no longer valid, and the resonant length of the cavity is different from an integral number of half wave lengths.

For our case of small R, the resonance peak described by (40.6) is very sharp. Let us describe this peak by two quantities: the impedance at resonance and the value of Q, or the ratio of the frequency difference between the two points where the square of the impedance has half maximum value, to the whole frequency. In the numerator of (40.6), we may neglect R_2 compared to jX_2. Then at resonance the value of the impedance (40.6) will become

$$\frac{(\alpha Z_{eq}j \tan \beta c)[\alpha Z_{eq}j(-\tan \beta c)]}{\alpha R \sec^2 \beta(L-c)} = \alpha \frac{Z_{eq}^2}{R} \frac{\tan^2 \beta c}{\sec^2 \beta c}$$

$$= \alpha \frac{Z_{eq}^2}{R} \sin^2 \beta c \quad (40.9)$$

This is a pure resistance, and we see that it is greater the smaller the loading resistance R is, and greater the longer the dipole is (from the definition of α), and the more nearly the dipole is located at a point of large voltage in the wave guide (from the factor $\sin^2 (\pi d/a)$ in α, and the factor $\sin^2 \beta c$ in (40.9)). Next let us find Q. As we see from (40.6), the square of the impedance will have half maximum value when $X_1 + X_2$ equals R_2. Let us suppose

$$\beta L = n\pi + \delta \quad (40.10)$$

where δ is a small quantity. Then

$$\tan \beta(L-c) = -\tan (\beta c + \delta)$$
$$= -\frac{\tan \beta c + \delta}{1 - \delta \tan \beta c} = -(\tan \beta c + \delta)(1 + \delta \tan \beta c)$$
$$= -\tan \beta c + \delta(1 + \tan^2 \beta c)$$
$$= -\tan \beta c - \delta \sec^2 \beta c \quad (40.11)$$

to the first order of small quantities. The total reactance is then

$$X_1 + X_2 = -\alpha Z_{eq}\delta \sec^2 \beta c \quad (40.12)$$

and for this to equal the resistance (40.5) we must have

$$\alpha R = \alpha Z_{eq}\delta, \qquad \delta = \frac{R}{Z_{eq}} \quad (40.13)$$

Since the frequency is proportional to β, and hence by (40.10) to the quantity $n\pi + \delta$, we see that Q, which is equal to the frequency divided by the frequency difference between the two points of half maximum power, must equal $n\pi/2\delta$. That is, we have

$$Q = \frac{n\pi}{2} \frac{Z_{eq}}{R} \qquad (40.14)$$

The smaller the resistance, in other words, the greater is Q. Increasing the length of the resonant cavity, or increasing n, also increases Q. This result is different from that of Chap. I, where we considered the Q of a resonant length of attenuating short-circuited line, for here the resistance is confined to the end and is independent of length, whereas in that case resistance was distributed along the length of the cavity and was proportional to length, so that n canceled out. In either case, however, a decrease of resistance increases the Q of the cavity.

INDEX

A

Absorption, 235–256, 289–293, 298–304

Acceleration, 89

Admittance, 34–36, 40, 96
  shunt, 17, 96, 294

Alpha (α), 13–15, 19–20, 25–42

Ampere, 88–90

Antenna, 195–279
  dummy, 239, 269–279
  half wave, 200–216

Antinode, 28

Attenuation, 15, 20, 28, 52, 138–150, 161–162, 170–173

B

Barnes, R. B., 255

Barrow, W. L., 124, 137, 149, 188

Beads, dielectric, 63

Bessel's function, 78, 163–168, 189–190, 197–202, 261–262, 283–284

Beta (β), 13–15, 19–20, 25–42

Biconical horn, 201–205, 225–232

Binomial coefficients, 60

Biot-Savart law, 206

Black-body radiation, 252–255

Boltzmann's constant, 253–255

Boundary conditions, 87, 98, 120, 129, 219, 271

Brown, 277

C

c, velocity of light, 89, 94–95

Capacitance, shunt, 19–20, 96–100, 157, 160

Carson, J. R., 124, 251

Carter, 277

Characteristic impedance, 16, 19–42, 94–100

Charge density, 84–90
  electric, 80–96

Chu, L. J., 124, 137, 149, 188, 205, 221–232

Circle diagram, 30–33, 51, 68

Circular wave guide, 162–168

Coaxial line, 155, 158–168, 220

Coefficient, reflection, 21, 25

Composite line, 42–69, 168–178, 280–304

Condon, E. U., 274

Conductance, shunt, 19–20, 96

Conductivity, electrical, 85–87, 111–112

Constitutive equations, 87

Continuity, equation of, 84–85, 90

Copper, 111–112, 114, 116

Coulomb, 88–90

Coupling coefficient, 294–304

Coupling loop, 233

Cross section, effective, 244–245, 263–265

Crystalline media, 84

Curl, 86, 91–93

Current, 9–12, 16, 18, 21–24, 28, 41, 44–46, 70–88, 96–100, 160, 181–184, 203, 246
  density, 84–90, 246
  displacement, 82

Cutoff, in wave guides, 127–130, 136–137, 159, 165, 167, 285–286

Cylindrical coordinates, 188–190

D

Damped waves, 111–123,

Decibel, 149

Detailed balancing, 256

305